Wheelbarrow in action in Northern Ireland, alongside a Pig. The eventual target cannot be seen here but could be up to about 100 metres away—note the reels of cable ready for use (Army PR HQ NI). See page 148 for details.

Encyclopaedia of the
MODERN
BRITISH ARMY

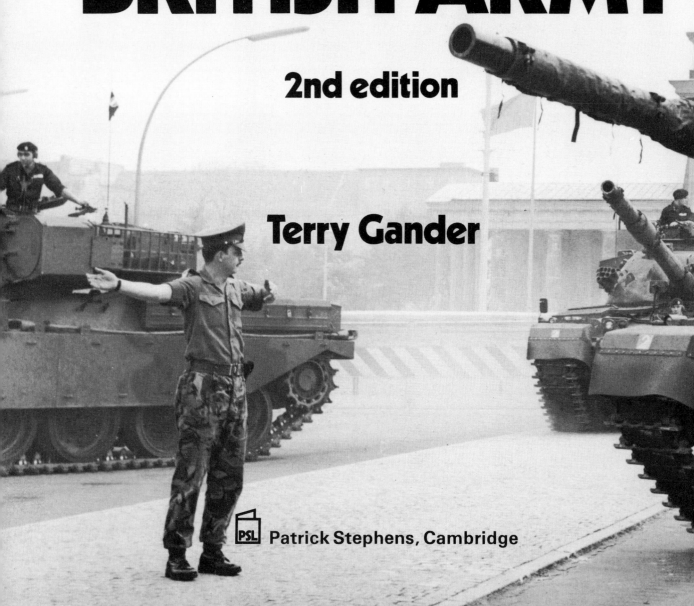

Encyclopaedia of the
MODERN
BRITISH ARMY

2nd edition

Terry Gander

PSL Patrick Stephens, Cambridge

First published October 1980
Reprinted March 1981
Second edition October 1982
Reprinted February 1983

British Library Cataloguing in Publication Data

Gander, Terry
    Encyclopaedia of the modern British army—
    2nd ed.
    1. Great Britain. *Army*—History—1945-
    I. Title
    355'.00941   UA649

    ISBN 0-85059-577-0

*Then it's Tommy this, an' Tommy that,
an' Tommy, 'ow's yer soul?'*

*But it's 'Thin red line of 'eroes'
when the drums begin to roll.*
                                    Kipling.

Text photoset in 10 on 10 pt Baskerville by
Manuset Limited, Baldock, Herts. Printed in Great
Britain on 115 gsm Fineblade coated cartridge,
and bound, by The Garden City Press, Letchworth,
Herts, for the publishers Patrick Stephens Limited, Bar
Hill, Cambridge, CB3 8EL, England.

Title pages *An MP sorts out a traffic jam in
front of the Brandenburg gate for Chieftains of the
4th RTR* (Karl Tietz).

Contents

Introduction 6

The British Army since 1945 9

Organisation 17

Weapons and equipment 93

Uniforms and insignia 259

Index 275

Introduction

The first edition of this book was written only a few years ago but already much has changed in the British Army. The Army is now, in 1982, once more in a state of transition and reorganisation although the recent defence spending cuts have touched the Army relatively lightly compared with the other Services. A few projects have been curtailed or terminated and training has been generally restricted by the need for fuel and cash savings, but the decision to move a divisional head-quarters from Germany to the United Kingdom has produced results out of all proportion to the manpower and other costs involved. As this intro-duction is being written, the Army is still settling down from an upheaval that has, in a few short months, changed its tidy working surroundings into a new and as yet unfamiliar shape.

The general outlines of this new structure are described in this book in the same general terms that were used in the first edition, for the reasons that prompted the writing of the book are even more valid than when I first put pen to paper back in 1979. The British Army still exists in a social structure in which a sizeable proportion of the population would, for wholly understandable reasons, like to see the Army and the other Services cut down to a miniscule size or even done away with. The general run-down of the United Kingdom's international role has brought with it a gradual corresponding run-down in the nation's wealth to the extent that a nation used to all the fruits engendered by an expanding economy, now has to face a general cut-back in living standards. In such an atmosphere, the Army presents a convenient scapegoat as its expensive equipment and public spectacles seem to indicate that they corner too large a slice of the nation's wealth.

The other armed services suffer from the same public strictures but the Army tends to endure more, generally due to the rather poor image it has

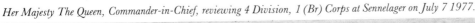

Her Majesty The Queen, Commander-in-Chief, reviewing 4 Division, 1 (Br) Corps at Sennelager on July 7 1977.

presented in the past. Past mistakes and blunders, excessive spending and the memories of National Service, have all combined to give the Army a bad press. But it is now all in the past and we have never been in need of a powerful Army more than we are at present. On the Continent and elsewhere the huge forces of the Warsaw Pact and its allies are still growing at an alarming rate out of all proportion to what they might construe as threats to their way of life. At home the signs of internal disruptiion to our own way of life are annually making themselves more apparent, and every year the general tone of life becomes more violent and unsettled. Under such circumstances, the Army becomes an essential bastion of all that the civilised world holds dear. It is an established, unpolitical force that acts as the tool of a democratically elected executive, and that executive has decided that the Army will act as a purely defensive force. In combination with the other NATO nations, the British Army is a purely defensive force—it cannot act in an offensive role in Europe or elsewhere, either alone or in concert with any ally.

With this in mind, the British Army still needs a book of this nature to explain how it is organised, how it would fight, and the equipment that it uses. The old National Service Army has long since gone, and the modern Army is a vastly better and more publicly-orientated organisation than it ever was. It is well-equipped, but it still has many omissions from its armoury, some of them the result of wrong planning but some of them, it must be said, the result of clinging to traditions established over centuries. The regimental tradition is still as strong as ever it was with all its inherent strengths and weaknesses. Other restrictions are imposed from outside the Army, especially in the amount of money the Army can spend on such essential items as an adequate anti-aircraft defence system for the front-line soldier.

Taking account of this, the following pages contain an attempt to describe what is still one of the best-trained, best-led and best-equipped armies in existence. Such a statement must be kept in proportion by a comparison of its numbers as opposed to the far more populated armies in existence elsewhere. Another proviso must also be made before these pages are read. As this book is published the Army is in a state of transition—this is nothing new as even a cursory glance at the history of the Army will reveal that it always has been. Thus some of the organisations mentioned may well have been changed, even in the short time period that takes place between writing and publishing. Some equipment changes or performance improvements may also have taken place.

Needless to say, a book such as this just cannot be written by an individual in isolation from assistance, and this book in particular is no exception. During its assembly and production I have been aided and guided by a large number of individuals, organisations and concerns. Top of this list must come the officers, men and women of the Army itself. Throughout all my dealings with the Army, I have constantly been afforded courtesy, forebearance and assistance of all kinds. The list of individuals is too long to give here but many will no doubt recognise their words or opinions on these pages. My thanks are due to them all.

One individual who has helped at all stages is Mr Derrick Knight of MoD(Army)PR. He has been a constant source of guidance, assistance and material from the very first day of production and he, and his colleagues, deserve more appreciation than these mere words. Other individuals who must be mentioned are Digby Smith and Bob Marrion who contributed the uniform section, Ken Musgrave who has produced the excellent four-view scale drawings in a dauntingly short time-scale, Chris Foss who has been so free with his advice and guidance, and Peter Guiver who has been a considerable source of assistance. To them, and all the many others, my thanks are due.

One last individual must be mentioned and that is Bruce Quarrie, for it was he who unwittingly planted the seed of this book on a Canadian prairie—in time he has helped to make that seed into a considerable tree.

Terry Gander
Billingshurst, 1982

Acknowledgements

The following concerns have contributed to the production of this book both in the provision of illustrations and information. To all my thanks are given. Bedford Commercial Vehicles, British Aerospace Dynamics Group, Carawagon Coachbuilders, Crane Fruehauf Limited, Hunting Engineering Limited, Ferranti Limited, Marconi Space and Defence Systems Limited, Morfax Precision Engineering Limited, Liner Limited, Racal, Scammell Motors, United Scientific Instruments Limited. All photographs in this book which are not otherwise credited are by the author.

The British Army since 1945

There is an old maxim that states 'History always repeats itself'. Whether it is true in a general sense is a matter for debate, but for the British Army it has a very ominous ring. Twice in this century the Army has been through a cycle of general neglect and lack of appreciation of its proper role and worth, and twice it has had to suffer appalling losses and experiences as a result of that neglect. Twice it has had to expand its numbers and powers to unheard-of limits, and twice it has emerged victorious from the worst historical and social upheavals the world has known. But for the Army the worst that history has had to show is that twice it has been relegated to its former state of acceptability in a nation reluctant to accept the true cost of defending all they profess to hold dear.

As these words are written the British Army is still a major component of the fabric of the British nation but in numbers and capabilities it is a mere shadow of its former self. Thus in a number of senses history has repeated itself, for the years since 1945 have seen a gradual and insidious decline in numbers and roles of the Army. It is true that in equipment, striking power and general expertise the Army has never been stronger but its position in society and national esteem has reverted once again to that which it has occupied for centuries, a role of that of an almost closed society that seemingly devours a larger slice of the national cake than many would wish.

The fallacy of this situation has been disproved so many times that it is one of the major faults of the British character and social make-up, but it is still with us nevertheless. For centuries the Army has been regarded as little more than a necessary evil that was called upon to convert the decisions of the executive body into the physical occupation of foreign soil, while at home it was handy for the suppression of an unruly populace. While the overseas forays were greeted with acclaim and honours,

these symbols of acceptance seldom lasted long and in the (infrequent) periods of peace the numbers in the ranks were slashed to the absolute minimum and elaborate and cheap systems of reserve or volunteer semi-trained civilians were kept in being ready for any future conflict. By the late 1800s the Army system had become a small segment of the expanding British economy but it was starved of funds just the same, despite the fact that it was in a very large part responsible for the huge areas of the globe that were coloured red in the school atlases read by an increasingly literate population.

The Cardwell Reforms of 1860 perpetuated the traditions built up over the years by an Army that was organised and led on a social system little changed from the Middle Ages. Landowners' sons led working class soldiers into battles where initiative and innovation were regarded with suspicion. The tiny British Army of 1914 crossed the Channel to France to fight the invading German hordes but in so doing they were the unwitting vanguard of a new move in British history which reversed the policies of a century by once more bringing the physical evidence of a new British involvement in Europe. The Great War transformed not only Europe, it transformed the United Kingdom and its Army. Between the years 1914 and 1918 the Army ceased to be a closed society by virtue of the sheer weight of human numbers imposed by the seemingly insatiable demands of trench warfare. The Army received an infusion of all that the best of the British nation could provide and despite the efforts of the hidebound high-ranking establishment, it was never to be the same again.

After the massive victories of late 1918 the Army lost little time in reverting to its former social order and its former enclosed self. But the seeds of change had been sown deep by the passage of the masses of 1914 to 1918. It had (grudgingly) accepted the needs of large-scale mechanisation, it had accepted the need for new weapons and equipment and it had

Left *A patrol during the Malayan Emergency* (MoD).

December 1957 and the Malayan Emergency in full swing. This REME workshop gives an excellent idea of the equipment used during that period as it shows Daimler Scout Cars adapted by the addition of 'dustbin' turrets, a Bedford truck altered into an early 'Pig', and early Ferrets altered to accommodate extra turret armour (MoD).

already started to become a fully professional force abreast of technological change. Between 1920 and 1935 the main restrictions on the role of the Army came not from within but from the national purse. The dreadful demands of the Great War on the British economy and nation led to the wishful delusion that the 'War to end all Wars' had been fought and there was no further need for the Army other than to provide imposing garrisons for the numerous colonies. Consequently the 1920s and early 1930s were years of financial starvation and regression as units once more paraded and disported themselves in formations that employed tactical methods proved obsolete by the machine-gun and the aeroplane. Horses wheeled and charged in ranks that ignored the battlefields of France, and infantry trudged on weary route marches made unnecessary by the advent of the motor lorry. But there were many who had learned the lessons so dearly imposed in France and elsewhere, and many high-ranking officers used what little funds there were for experimentation and new equipment.

With the coming to power of Hitler and the

NSDAP in Germany in 1933 the political climate of Europe began once again to change for the worse. After 1919 it had become an unstated British political policy not to become involved in the structure of Europe, as had France, but this reluctance to accept a political role had led to the gradual emergence of Nazi Germany to occupy the power vacuum left by the collapse of Whilhelmine Germany and the old Austro-Hungarian Empire. By 1935 the British attitude to Germany and Europe as a whole was gradually changing, and with the change came reluctant acceptance of the fact that any involvement with Germany would once more include the need to send an armed force over to Europe. But to expand a small well-intentioned garrison Army into an expeditionary force no longer involved the passing of a Bill in Parliament along with the resultant recruiting campaign and the issuing of uniforms. Modern warfare had changed all that into the expensive and time-consuming training and equipping of a new type of Army, an Army that depended on radio and motor traction. New weapons had to be hastily obtained or made, new bases had to be constructed and Home defences contrived and brought into use. The years after 1935 saw a gradual but growing importance of the Army in the United Kingdom establishment, even if it was behind the Admiralty and the Air Ministry in the allocation of what funds a Parliament inclined to appeasing dictators was wont to release. The 1938 Munich fiasco came as a welcome return to reality to the military and political scene in the United Kingdom as a whole, and from then onwards the Army began to prepare for war.

It prepared suprisingly well, in retrospect. The little BEF which crossed to France in September 1939 was the only fully-mechanised contingent in *any* of the warring European armies and its equipment levels were high. It suffered from the fatal weakness of being emotionally and practically equipped for the Great War and not for the fast-moving onslaught it had to face. It also suffered from not having any practical reserve, for after the Battle of France virtually all its mobile and heavy equipment and weapons were lost. Overseas, enemy pressure was everywhere desperate but weapons and equipment came from America and the old Empire provided men. These were insufficient to prevent the loss of many colonies in the Far East when Japan entered the war in late 1941. By that date the British Army and the Allies were out of Europe and everywhere the Axis forces seemed triumphant. The Army had suffered overwhelming defeat, or so it seemed, and a great deal of criticism was directed at the Army and its leaders from all quarters. The truth was that the

Army was taking the brunt of the blame that should
have been directed to the British nation as a whole
for their years of failing to accept that nationhood
imposes responsibilities as well as benefits. The
failure of the United Kingdom to assume a
European role after 1918 was a direct cause of the
holocaust of 1939 to 1945 with its costs, not only in
lives but in the bankruptcy of the British nation
after about 1941. The Army took the blame for all this
in 1941 as it was the instrument that had to convert
years of financial and social neglect into practical
terms on the battlefield. Not suprisingly it often
failed. What is surprising is that in many ways it
managed to do so well. The build-up of a new effective Army in the years after 1940 was an
achievement of major magnitude.

After 1941 the worst was over. But the Great War
still cast its long shadow by the reluctance of the
General Staff to become involved in the types of
campaign epitomised by the messy slogging mat-
ches of Flanders and the Somme. The Army had to
be built up into an instrument capable of crossing
the Channel to take the war into Europe once again.
In the meantime trained formations were sent to
North Africa to take part in the Western Desert
campaign, a venture that has now grown into a
major part of British legend. In truth, the campaign
provided an excellent forming and training ground
but its eventual conclusion aided the general Allied
war effort but little. For all its dramatic to-ing and
fro-ing it was a sideshow in the overall framework of
the eventual defeat of Nazi Germany.

After 1941 the United Kingdom was no longer
fighting alone. In the United States and the USSR it
had two allies who ensured the eventual victory, a
victory that was considerably aided by the most
extreme example of German military tactical
excellence taking precedence over strategic sense.
That example was provided by Hitler's decision
to invade the Soviet Union, a campaign that came
to overshadow all the others that took place later. It
was in the Soviet Union that the attrition of the
Great War trenches was replaced by the sheer scale
and enormity of total war to the death between
nations. The affluence of the USA provided equipment, money and men to all, including the British
Army, but after 1942 the British took less and less
part in the overall conduct of the conflict. The Army
took part in the type of slogging combat to which it
was best suited along the mountainous length of the
Italian peninsula, and it provided about one third of
the formations used in the Invasion of Normandy in
1944 and the subsequent operations that led to the
eventual defeat of Nazi Germany in May 1945. In
the Far East units of the British Army joined with
the old Indian Army to fight the long, bitter and

A patrol in the Aden hinterland (MoD).

seemingly forgotten war against the Japanese in
Burma, while the American forces island-hopped
across the Pacific Ocean. But to this day the British
people are reluctant to acknowledge that by 1945
they had become a secondary power among the
Allies. The war effort had bled the British economy
white and the British nation no longer held effective
sway over large tracts of its former overseas colonial
(and wealth-making) territories.

At the end, the British forces were everywhere
victorious. In Europe the Army was deep within
Germany and in Italy the long slog through the
mountains was over and the Army was on the
Austrian borders. In Burma the Japanese were
driven from their last strongholds, and a new force
was being formed for the invasion of Japan itself.
The dropping of the first operational atomic bomb
on Hiroshima ended that project, and for the first
time for six years the Army was able to take stock of
itself and its achievements. It had much to be proud
of. From a small nucleus the Army had grown into a
huge citizens' army that had mastered the arts of
battle in the desert, the jungle and the mountains. It
had developed new forms of transport into battle
and had learned how to fight from the sky itself. It
had also relearned the art of amphibious warfare
and in so doing had raised the state of the art to new
heights. It had also learned to harness modern tech-

nology and science for its overall aims, and it had played its part in transforming a peaceable population into a highly disciplined and skilled fighting force. In 1945 the Army was at the very peak of its powers and at the height of its achievements, but within a very few months nearly all of that had been swept away.

With the coming of victory the massive machine that the Army had become was soon in the process of being dismantled. The citizens' Army returned to its homes in large drafts but the post-war task of the Army was far from over. All over the world societies and peoples were in turmoil and chaos as the wake of war subsided. Nations overthrew their former governors and many others went through the painful and costly process of insurrection. Wherever the British Army was based it, often alone and unaided, had to bear the brunt of keeping an often fragile peace, and in many places (such as Greece) it often found itself taking up arms against people who only a few short months before had been allies. In the turmoil of post-war events this keeping of the peace passed almost unrecognised but it marked a major reversion of the Army's role from that of a fighting field force to that of 'action in support of a civil power'. The major field forces were kept in being and trained constantly for major war but after 1945 the Army more and more became an international policeman.

In the years following 1945 the gradual run-down of the Army's numbers continued apace, but the international situation for once prevented a general reversion to the pre-war strengths as had taken place so swiftly in 1919. In Europe the clash of ideology between the wartime Allies proved too strong for the alliance to survive more than a few months and the Cold War set in with the Churchillian 'Iron Curtain' dividing the continent into its mutually suspicious halves. The political and military threat provided by the presence of massive Soviet forces deep within Europe ensured that at last the Army had a European task imposed upon it and that task was accepted and carried out to the limit. It has been carried out so effectively that today the Army is not only still well installed on the European continent but its major forces have now been subordinated to an overall European ideal, that of a component in a European Army. The NATO Treaty was signed in Washington on April 4 1949 and as a direct result the United Kingdom provides a component of the NATO forces guarding the borders between themselves and those of their Eastern counterparts, the armies of the Warsaw Pact.

Outside Europe, the Army had a thankless role to carry out in the gradual dismantling of the old British Empire. The war years had accelerated the pace of withdrawal from Empire, and in many cases had initiated it, but it was a process that took place nevertheless. For the first time in history a major nation voluntarily handed over autonomy of its often hard-won possessions to their inhabitants. Often the hand-over did not run smoothly, or at a rapid-enough pace to suit all concerned, but it took place all the same and in nearly every country concerned the British Army had to bear the brunt of the difficult work. But nowhere was the task more deeply felt by the Army than in the withdrawal from India in 1947.

The old British Army had two homes. One, the smaller, had been in Ireland, but that had finally been lost in 1922 so that left only one, and that was the finest of all; it was India. India, the 'jewel in the crown' of the Victorian Empire, was the Army's spiritual home where it had drilled, fought and lived for over two centuries. The Home Army supplied it with men and equipment but it was in India that the old Army planted its roots, formed its traditions and kept its active skills finely honed by the endless skirmishes on the North-West Frontier. A whole string of colonial stations were established along the routes to India to keep the country supplied and, even more important, to guard the trade routes to and from the United Kingdom. But India was the heart, not only of the old Empire but also of its Army. When the Army left India it left not only its heart but a large piece of its very soul. The Army was never the same again after 1947—it had to find a new heart, a new reason for its existence, and much of the turmoil and evolution that has taken place within the Army since then can be traced directly to this cause. By the late 1970s the new home had been recognised at last, reluctantly by many, as being in Europe.

The withdrawal from India also led to a gradual withdrawal from the many stations on the route to India. After 1947 there was little reason or purpose in keeping them under British control, and the body politic retained them only for reasons that were understandable but historically invalid. The United Kingdom after 1945 was a nation reluctant to accept the true cost of victory. It was eager to return to the affluence and comforts of the pre-war years and at a loss to accept that the sources of cheap imports had vanished and that the long-term markets for Britain's staple industries were dwindling. We clung to the trappings of Empire in an attempt to turn back the historical clock but it was to no avail. Between 1947 and 1967 the bulk of the old Empire changed hands. Burma was one of the first nations to go, followed by Palestine, the Nile Delta and eventually by Aden, Cyprus and Malta. Even the hallowed Canal Zone in Egypt was handed over in

1954. In Africa the old colonies passed to their native political leaders one after the other; Kenya, Uganda, Tanganyika, the Gold Coast, Nigeria and many others changed from colonial rule to independence. The Army was involved in every hand-over and it alone often had to bear the burden of the transfer of power. In many cases the transfer did not take place rapidly enough to suit all and in many countries the hand-over of power was to the wrong political bodies or groupings, at least as far as political activists were concerned. Thus the Army took the brunt of the disruptions which often resulted. Political dissidents often took to the bomb or gun to accelerate the leaving rate of British government or to express their dissatisfaction at the planned methods of hand-over. The Army tried to keep the peace as its troops were attacked by terrorists or struggled to keep fighting factions apart. It was the common soldier who had to bear the constant threat of ambush or the stealthily lobbed grenade, and it was he who had to carry out the onerous and unwelcome searches, the tiresome roadblocking and the constant patrolling. When it finally left the Army was all too often the only organised body that stood for law and order during the last desperate days of hand-over. In many of the old colonies there were often many who mourned the Army's leaving as the first heady days of independence turned into power struggles, civil war and dictatorships.

Among all the post-war withdrawal from Empire the Army was able to claim one major achievement. That was the successful campaign carried out against the communist-inspired rebel forces in Malaya. To this day it is still the only such campaign to have been won by an established Army and government against the practitioners of revolutionary warfare, and it took place between 1948 and 1960. The Army took once more to the jungle and sought out and destroyed the communist guerrillas on their own ground and on their own terms. They fought a corresponding 'hearts and minds' campaign among the civil population to prevent the guerrillas finding their traditional refuges among the static settlements, towns and cities. When the Army left Malaya it was able to hand over the government to a democratically established nation.

Apart from the role of the colonial gendarme, the Army fought a major campaign in Korea. There a British brigade earned the admiration of all by its conduct in battle and the unflagging high spirits of its soldiers under dreadful conditions, not only in the front lines but also in the squalid conditions of the prisoner-of-war camps into which many British soldiers found their way.

But all the time the Army was gradually declining in numbers and the effectiveness of its equipment. The major impact of the Korean War for the Army was not to be found in the campaign itself but in the political realisation that the threat from the Communist Bloc was a real one and that steps would have to be taken to counter it. A re-armament programme was initiated, and steps taken to halt the run-down in numbers that had steadily taken place since 1945. By the mid-1950s the Army in Europe, by then well established as the British Army of the Rhine (BAOR), was ready to fight a defensive battle once again but time was to show that the measures taken were insufficient and too half-hearted to fully carry out the task that the Army was called upon to undertake.

The realisation came with Suez. The Suez campaign of 1956 had origins that are outside the scope of this book but basically the Army was called upon to play its part in an Anglo-French landing at Suez, an action which was called for because of, and created even more, political muddle, unclear objectives, and disorganisation. The Army was already stretched to its limits in Europe and elsewhere and the action took place over an over-extended period in which the rest of the world gradually combined to form a hostile reaction to the Anglo-French activities. Militarily the Suez landings were a disaster, as nearly all the dearly-bought lessons of 1940-1945 had been forgotten, and the supposedly large-scale operation was brought to a rapid halt before the full magnitude of the fiasco was demonstrated to all. While the politicians had to bear the bulk of the blame for Suez, the Army was shown to be overstretched and unable to carry out the type of operation that had once made the United Kingdom a world power.

The truth was finally recognised and out of the economic upheaval that Suez initiated came the realisation that the United Kingdom was no longer a major and independent world power but a secondary nation in need of allies and economic assistance. The Army finally turned its face to Europe and at the same time carried out the last of the major colonial policing operations in Aden. As it no longer had to provide garrisons for the old colonies and stations, the manpower levels could be run down to practical levels. A direct result of this was the ending of conscription in 1960, an event that had not only a social impact on the nation but also on the Army. Since 1945 conscription had ensured a steady flow of recruits for the ranks and the officer corps, and with them came the unwelcome chore of training the constant flow of bodies. But the constant flow also brought with it a healthy flow of ideas, attitudes and intellect that kept the Army more of a part of the mainstream of British society than it had ever

Troops of the Rhodesia-Zimbabwe monitoring force being briefed during December 1979.

been before. The Army, and the other armed services, became a factor of everyday life. Not everyone benefitted from the experience but as a general rule the nation gained from those who had 'done their bit' as they brought back into civilian life an independent outlook and education that often proved to be only slightly less effective than a university education. The Army gained through the understanding of its role, traditions and methods, as well as by the number of technically-minded and educated civilians who left their considerable mark. With the passing away of conscription the Army lost a great deal.

When the burden of conscription was removed, the Army reverted to what soon proved to be very much its former structure. It once more became a highly-trained professional body that rightly or wrongly gradually re-established itself as a closed society. With the withdrawal of a transient population, the long-term soldiers were again able to become more involved members of the family spirit and cameraderie provided by their regiments and corps. Gradually the old social patterns reappeared. The officer corps once more became a group that

drew its carefully selected members from an elite formed by the upper echelons of the British class system, while the rank and file once again drew the bulk of their number from the established working class. Fortunately, the total withdrawal of the Army into its former social shell did not take place—it was not allowed to, and neither did the Army wish it to happen. Many factors combined to keep the Army a greater part of the general mainstream of British life. The Army had learned during World War 2 that public relations were important to ensure a stream of the right sort of recruits and also to put forward its political and financial messages. Perhaps the most important factor in the social change was that the Army became a married Army. In the old days prior to 1939 few soldiers were able to marry and obtain married quarters for their wives and families. But by the mid-1950s, the regular soldier was often a married man with a family. The Army had to provide not only married quarters but schools, shopping centres and all the myriad medical and social services needed by garrisons at home and abroad. The huge civilian population that has gradually attached itself to the Army (not forgetting the thousands of civilians who now carry out jobs and roles once filled by serving soldiers) has ensured the Army has a sensibility to civilian needs.

The new 'civilian' stance of the armed service was to a great extent responsible for the fact that the Army has not reverted to the old 'huntin' and polo' days of the 1920s and 1930s, but it was not the only influence. The Army of the 1960s and 1970s soon showed itself to be far more professional and far more concerned with technical competence than its predecessors. The impact of the growth in general education made this improvement possible but it was a change imposed by the very nature of the role the modern soldier has to execute. He is now a highly-trained and competent technician in many fields, and the days when all he had to learn about were his rifle and foot drill have long since gone. His equipment is now so complex and expensive that he has had to learn many new techniques and skills derived from commerce and industry in order to remain abreast of the many changes in technology and man management that emerge year by year, and both in their turn have formed a bridge between the Army and the rest of the nation.

The main problem for the Army of the 1960s and the 1970s was that the new skills had to be learned in a period of constant turmoil and change, while at the same time the size and format of the Army were diminishing. Year after year, the manpower levels of the Army declined and progressive Defence spending cuts prevented the procurement of new equipment or facilities. Trained manpower gradually left the service and recruiting levels fell to the point where the Army reached its present level of about 160,000 men. For the Army the main problem was that they were still called upon to carry out many roles that had not been foreseen. It was at one time thought that the retreat from Empire had virtually ended after Aden, but it was not so. The Army was constantly being asked to provide formations to police various trouble spots all over the world, and to provide aid and assistance to all manner of bodies. In the Far East the Brunei and Borneo campaigns were typical of many 'Brushfire' conflicts, while on the other side of the globe, Central America was often a potential trouble spot. These constant forays abroad were a drain away from the main task of providing a meaningful presence in Europe and NATO, but to add to it all the events in Northern Ireland from late 1968 onwards necessitated the stationing there of a large permanent force of troops that has at times numbered some 21,000 men. Such numbers could only be achieved by the adoption of four-month tours (now $4\frac{1}{2}$-month) by all manner of combatant and non-combatant units which has greatly added to the problems of training and the establishment of fully-effective units.

To some extent the Army itself has added to its troubles by the retention of a regimental system that is now outmoded and inefficient. The regimental system built up by the British Army over many years has grown into an established form in which nearly every regiment and corps jealously guards its own particular honours, customs and idiosyncrasies. Based on what is very often a territorial recruiting area, each regiment or corps forms a family for its members and fosters a unit spirit that is almost impossible to intrude upon or break. While this system has many advantages in forming pride and a feeling of mutual trust within a formation it has inevitably led to a lack of co-operation between even different formations of the same divisions of the Army, and it has made inter-posting very difficult indeed. While many foreign armies regard the British regimental system highly, it is noticeable that few of them (other than the armies established by the British themselves) have adopted it, and retain a corps establishment with unified training methods and mutual inter-dependability. Within the British Army the regimental system was at its most pronounced with the Infantry, but the rundown in manpower levels enforced the amalgamation of many fiercely independent regiments and the virtual abolition of some. Traditionalists both within and without the Army fought many hard campaigns to prevent the disappearance of famous regimental names, but the

acceptance of the battle group as a combat formation further dictated the changes. In the end the Infantry adopted a typical British compromise. The regimental system stayed, but within a new structure of five administrative divisions. Within each division, the regiments, or such of them that remained recognisable, were regarded as mutually-supporting units, but only within their own particular division. Only the Guards and the Parachute Regiment remained outside the new reorganisation (at the cost of having their numbers attenuated) which took effect initially from 1958 to 1961, and the final touches were added during 1967.

The emergence of the battle group as a tactical formation also took place over an extended period, but it is now the established method of using Infantry and their supporting arms in modern warfare. Like so many innovations that were thrust upon the Army by a combination of tactical experience and financial strictures, the battle group and combat team concept has had a mixed reception, but its adoption has imposed its own command and administration difficulties. The old 'company, battalion, division, corps . . . ' hierarchy could not be adopted to suit the newer and more flexible battle group philosophy, so a new battle command structure was derived and is dealt with elsewhere in these pages. The new organisation was set in motion during the mid-1970s and received its first full test in large scale exercises within BAOR during 1976.

With the new structure came new command, communication and information systems, aimed not only at time-saving but also at savings in precious manpower. The four-armoured-division structure settled down to become the 1 (Br) Corps form, around which grew an established running and administrative routine to which future planning could be fixed. New communication and administration systems were designed and projected around the structure to the extent that when changes were imposed from without during 1981 the results were out of all proportion to those intended. The Thatcher government imposed strict restrictions on all facets of government spending and the defence establishment had to bear its share of the resultant cuts. In the event, the Army came off relatively lightly in cash terms, but it meant that one of the four armoured division headquarters had to be redeployed to the United Kingdom. In the upheaval, the armoured division concerned became an infantry division in the process and the carefully structured four-armoured-division Corps was transformed into three armoured divisions and one infantry division. With it, all future planning for such systems as Bates and Wavell were also put into uproar. The old system, which had been put to the test during the large-scale international 'Crusader' exercises in 1980, was altered into the system described elsewhere in these pages but the time scale after such an upheaval is still short for a book of this nature. The Army is still settling down and re-arranging its surroundings. New organisations will still have to be made and some 'fine-tuning' of existing arrangements still has to be done. Some are doubtless being acted on as these words are written so in a few cases the interval between writing and publication may render some of the enclosed information out of date.

Despite the many strictures imposed by successive governments on Defence spending the Army is now well equipped and is at present more powerful in fighting potential than at any time in its long history. But it is woefully short of the technicians it sorely needs to man and maintain its complex equipment, and via them, its full NATO and national role. One of the main reasons for the shortfall in numbers has been the monetary attractions of civilian life and employment, and recent pay awards will no doubt have made up some leeway, but still the Army is either not attracting the right sort of recruit, or if they have him, they are often unable to retain his services for very long. There are in the ranks of the Army the very examples of what the modern Army needs but there are never enough of them. Thus the modern Army finds itself in a quandary. It is well equipped (but not well enough to suit everyone, and there are some large gaps still unfilled in the armoury) and it is better led and managed than at any time in its history. But 'God is on the side of the big battalions', and considering the size of the potential forces pitted against the units in Germany and their NATO allies, one is inclined to consider if the numbers involved will ever be able to make any real impression. Thus in one sense, the British Army is seeing history repeat itself. The gradual wastage of funds and manpower over the years to below the level of safety is following the ominously familiar parallels of 1914 and 1939. Those two years were the forerunners of years of bitter misery and massive losses of life and resources. In both wars the ultimate victory has tended to disguise exactly how close we came to disaster. Let us hope we do not have to suffer the same cycle again.

The Army in action since 1945

Trieste	1945-1954
Java/Sumatra	1945
Greece	1945-1947
Canal Zone/Egypt	1946-1954
India	1945-1948
Palestine	1945-1948
Aden	1947
Northern Ireland	1947-1948
Gold Coast	1948
British Honduras	1948
Eritrea	1948-1951
Malaya	1948-1960
Somaliland	1949-1951
Aqaba	1949
Singapore	1950
Korea	1950-1953
Aqaba	1951
Kenya	1952-1956
British Guiana	1953
Cyprus	1954-1959
Aden	1955-1958
Singapore	1955-1956
Hong Kong	1956
Bahrein	1956-1957
Suez	1956
Belize	1957
Muscat and Oman	1957-1959
Togoland	1957
Jordan and Lebanon	1958
Gan	1959
Cameroons	1960
Jamaica	1960
Bahamas	1961
Kuwait	1961
British Guiana	1962
Belize	1962
Malaysia/Borneo	1962-1966
Zanzibar	1963
Swaziland	1963-1966
Cyprus	1963-?
British Guiana	1963
Zanzibar	1964
Kenya/Uganda/Tanganyika	1964
Radfan	1964-1967
Mauritius	1965
Oman	1965-1977
Hong Kong	1966
Seychelles	1966
Hong Kong	1967
Libya	1967
Northern Ireland	1969-?
Anguilla	1969-1971
Dhofar	1969-1976
Cyprus	1974
Belize	1976-?
Zimbabwe-Rhodesia	1979-1980
Falkland Islands	1982-?

NB The above list is not complete as the Army has frequently been asked to assist various governments at times of crisis and it has often had to be called in to help after natural disasters when the efforts needed were often greater than those involved in a military campaign.

Organisation

One of the primary things to realise when thinking of the modern British Army is that it is no longer a national British Army concerned with the United Kingdom alone. Today, the Army is a part of a much larger European Army organised under the auspices of NATO. The bulk of the British Army is stationed in Europe, it is intended for use in Europe and operates, not on its own instructions but as part of a multi-national force. The United Kingdom acts as a manpower and training base (to say nothing of the all-important supply function) for the NATO units and only a small proportion of Army manpower will be earmarked for Home Defence. The strategy behind this thinking is that the United Kingdom can best be defended in Europe with the Army acting as part of the NATO forces.

In Europe the Army has been assigned only a small portion of the long border between the Warsaw Pact forces and the NATO nations. The area it has been assigned to defend is on the North German Plain, but even this task is undertaken only in conjunction with other NATO allies. The Army forces involved come under the command of 1 (Br) Corps, who in their turn come under the command of the NATO Northern Army Group, or NORTHAG. The headquarters of NORTHAG are at Mönchengladbach and this headquarters controls the following forces: 1st Belgian Corps, Headquarters, Cologne-Junkersdorf; 1st British Corps, Headquarters, Bielefeld; 1st German Corps, no fixed headquarters; and 1st Netherland Corps, Headquarters, Apeldoorn.

NORTHAG boundaries run north of a line drawn westward from (roughly) Hersfeld in West Germany to the North and Baltic Seas. Of this area, the 1st (British) Corps is assigned an area of the North German Plain which can roughly be defined as that from the border on a line westward through Kassel to a line westward from the border and drawn through the area north of Hannover. (These boundaries are only approximate.)

1 (Br) Corps is the main combat echelon of the British Army of the Rhine, or BAOR. In all the BAOR consists of some 55,000 men distributed back from the expected battle zone to the main supply port of Antwerp. In this area are the main BAOR garrisons with all their attendant service and accommodation areas, and it is in the BAOR area that the bulk of the front-line modern Army has its present 'home'.

The 1st (British) Corps, or 1 (Br) Corps, consists of four major combat formations. Three of these are armoured divisions, each with three brigades, and the other an infantry division with three infantry brigades. As they are the main striking force of 1 (Br) Corps, the armoured divisions will be considered first.

Before the recent Nott-inspired defence reorganisation, there were four armoured divisions, each with two armoured regiments which combined with other arms to form two brigades, with support from the 5th Field Force. With the reorganisation, one of the armoured divisions went, along with the 5th Field Force. Each of the three armoured divisions now has a basis of two armoured brigades with a general reserve of two armoured brigades and an infantry brigade. For administrative purposes each armoured division is considered as having three brigades.

The three armoured divisions are : 1st Armoured Division with Headquarters at Verden and consisting of the 7th and 22nd Armoured Brigades; 3rd Armoured Division with Headquarters at Soest and formed of the 6th and 33rd Armoured Brigades; and 4th Armoured Division with Headquarters at Hereford comprising the 11th and 20th Armoured Brigades. The two 'reserve' units are 4 and 12 Armoured Brigades, which would normally be deployed with two of the forward armoured divisions. The third armoured division would be deployed in the rear as a general reserve together with the other reserve formation, 19 Infantry Brigade.

The infantry division is the 2nd Infantry

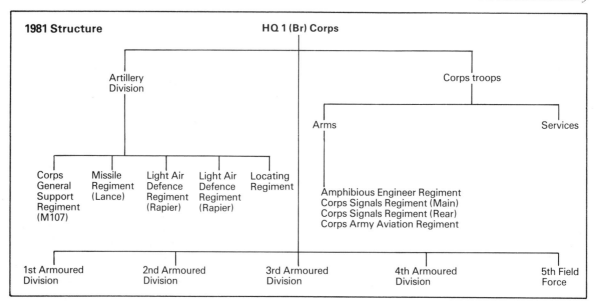

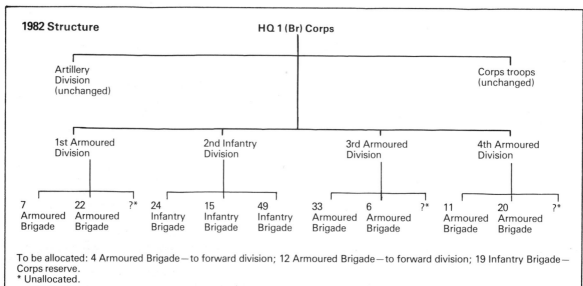

Division. The divisional headquarters is amalgamated with that of the North East District at York, in the United Kingdom. One of the 2nd Infantry Division's three infantry brigades is based in West Germany—this is 24 Infantry Brigade. The other two are 15 and 49 Infantry Brigades, both TA formations and drawn from areas in the north-east of England. 15 Infantry Brigade has its Headquarters at Topcliffe, and 49 Infantry Brigade at Chilwell. Thus 2nd Infantry Division is formed from 15, 24 and 49 Infantry Brigades.

There is no precise tidy way to describe how these four divisions would be deployed in war, other than the general outline given above. Two of the armoured divisions would be deployed in the forward area, each with three of the armoured brigades. The third division would be used as a general rear area reserve and would consist of two armoured brigades and one infantry brigade. The infantry division would be deployed among the armoured divisions.

Each of the three armoured divisions will be

organised into two (or three) 'brigades', although the more generally understood and used term is task force. The task force is sub-divided into battle groups, which in turn consist of a number of combat teams. Each of these fighting formations consists of a balanced arrangement of infantry, artillery, cavalry, engineer and other arms to provide what are virtually independent combat units. The main thing to understand about these fighting formations is that there is no precise establishment for any of them. They are formed and armed according to their role, the terrain over which they have to fight, and their objectives. For example, forward units might be heavy in armour and anti-armour weaponry, while rear units might have a preponderance of infantry. Likewise, the number of battle groups of a division might vary. One might have as few as eight, while another might have 12. The same applies to their deployment. Some battle groups might be deployed in depth while in another area they might well be deployed in line. Their size, composition and weapon mix will rely entirely on the local commanders.

The task force, battle group and combat team system is a flexible method of organising combat formations, and normally certain task forces and battle groups would work and train with certain other similar units. In combat the system is so organised that there can be the almost inevitable switching and transfer of formations from one command to another.

One of the main problems for 1 (Br) Corps is that the Corps is reliant upon reinforcement units arriving from the United Kingdom in an emergency. These units are provided by United Kingdom Land Forces (or UKLF). UKLF is organised to act as a training and personnel base for the whole of BAOR and is organised into three main echelons. The first of these is 19 Infantry Brigade, based at Colchester; the second is 1 Infantry Brigade, based at Aldershot; and the third is 5 Infantry Brigade. 19 Infantry Brigade is the general 1 (Br) Corps reinforcement brigade. It is not assigned to any particular division and will be used as a general Corps reserve together with the reserve armoured brigades. (These reserve armoured brigades are 4 and 12 Armoured Brigades.)

1 Infantry Brigade has a more complex role. It is earmarked for the direct command of the Commander Allied Command Europe (ACE) who has his headquarters at SHAPE, near Mons. In this form 1 Infantry Brigade acts as a central reserve for NATO but it also forms the basis of the United Kingdom Mobile Force (Land) or AMF(L). Based at Seckenheim, the AMF(L) is a multi-national force designed for the rapid reinforcement of the NATO flanks in Turkey and Norway. 1 Infantry Brigade consists of three Regular and two TA Infantry battalions, plus their supporting arms, and a logistic support group (the latter is primarily intended for AMF(L)). With ACE, 1 Infantry Brigade becomes part of the SACEUR Strategic Reserve, or SSR (SSR will also be allotted three SAS squadrons).

5 Infantry Brigade is intended for the defence of the United Kingdom. It is based on three Regular and two TA Infantry battalions plus whatever can be assembled from the various depots and training establishments in the UK. Supporting arms such as cavalry and artillery will have to be found from whatever is left once all the various BAOR and 1 (Br) Corps units have been sent to West Germany.

There will be three other infantry brigades based in the United Kingdom, but all have mainly administrative control and command functions. In South East District is Headquarters 2 Infantry Brigade at Shorncliffe. In Scotland there are Headquarters 51 Highland Brigade and 52 Lowland Brigade.

Apart from the forces assigned to BAOR there is in Germany the Berlin Brigade. This force is not part of NATO and is present in Berlin only as the United Kingdom contingent required to support the 1945 Berlin Treaty. It numbers some 3,000 men formed from three Infantry battalions and an armoured squadron plus the usual supporting arms.

Elsewhere around the globe, the British Army still retains some garrisons and other formations. A single Infantry battalion is stationed at Gibraltar together with an Engineer force. In Cyprus there is an augmented Infantry battalion plus their supporting units, including Engineer and AAC units. Across the Atlantic in Belize are two more Infantry battalions (one of them with only two companies) together with a full range of supporting units including an armoured reconnaissance unit, Artillery, AAC and a logistic support force.

In the Far East the bulk of the manpower is drawn from a Brigade of Gurkhas who supply one battalion in Brunei (maintained by the Brunei government until 1983) and three battalions in Hong Kong. Also in Hong Kong is a further 'British' Infantry battalion together with an AAC squadron and a Gurkha Engineer squadron.

Army training establishments are maintained at Suffield in Alberta and in Kenya. Further training is carried out all over Europe and on occasion in the USA and various African nations.

There remains one further location to mention and that is Northern Ireland. For over a decade a large proportion of the Army's resources has been diverted to keeping the Queen's Peace in that troubled province. At any one time so many units are based in Northern Ireland that they have had to be organised into three brigades. There is a permanent garrison of five Infantry battalions and at any one time a further seven equivalent formations are also acting in an Infantry role. To support these units there is the full panoply of Army support including REME workshops, AAC squadrons, Signals, armoured reconnaissance squadrons and Engineers. There is even a SAS presence. To form the seven extra 'Infantry' formations many operational units from BAOR have to take their turn on 4½-month 'roulement' tours and the withdrawal and training of these units makes a considerable inroad into the operational readiness of the Army as a whole. In the event of an emergency, it has been stated that the NATO-assigned units in Northern Ireland could be returned to Germany 'within 72 hours'.

The United Kingdom-based Army units come under the administrative control of one Army Command, namely the UKLF. The headquarters for UKLF is at Wilton, near Salisbury, and this administers ten Districts which are located as follows: NW District—Preston; NE District—York; Wales—Brecon; Midland District—Shrewsbury; Eastern District—Colchester; SW District—Taunton; SE District—Aldershot; London District—Horse Guards; Scotland—Edinburgh; Northern Ireland—Lisburn.

While these Districts are used for administrative purposes, in an emergency they would also act as the combat commands for 5 Infantry Brigade and other units in their individual areas.

Strength of the Army—by unit

	Regular				TA
	BAOR	Berlin	UK	Other	UK
Headquarters					
Corps Headquarters	1				
Armoured Division Headquarters	3				
Artillery Division Headquarters	1				
Infantry Division Headquarters			1		
Brigade Headquarters	1	1	3	1	
Armour					
Armoured Regiments	8		2		
Armoured Recce Regiments	5		4		2
Artillery					
Field Regiments	9		4		
Medium Regiments			1		2
Heavy Regiments	1				
Missile Regiments	1				
Guided Weapons Regiments			1		
Anti-tank Regiments	1				
Air Defence Regiments	2		1		3
Locating Regiments	1				
Engineers					
Armoured Division Engineer Regiments	4				
Engineer Regiments			4		7
Amphibious Engineer Regiments	1				
Infantry					
Battalions	15	3	29	3	38
Gurkha Battalions			1	4	
SAS					
Regiments			1		2
AAC					
Regiments	5		1		
HAC					
Regiments					1

The Cavalry

The Cavalry elements of the Army can be divided into three main groupings. Two are the Household Cavalry and the Royal Armoured Corps. The third, and by far the smallest grouping, consists of the Yeomanry, of which there are now only two regiments. Within each grouping the Cavalry regiments concerned are as follows:

The Household Cavalry: The Life Guards and The Blues and Royals;

The Royal Armoured Corps: 1st The Queen's Dragoon Guards, The Royal Scots Dragoon Guards (Carabiniers and Greys), 4th/7th Royal Dragoon Guards, 5th Royal Inniskilling Dragoon Guards, The Queen's Own Hussars, The Queen's Royal Irish Hussars, 9th/12th Royal Lancers (Prince of Wales's), The Royal Hussars (Prince of Wales's Own), 13th/18th Royal Hussars (Queen Mary's Own), 14th/20th King's Hussars, 15th/19th The King's Royal Hussars, 16th/5th The Queen's Royal Lancers, 17th/21st Lancers, 1st Royal Tank Regiment, 2nd Royal Tank Regiment, 3rd Royal Tank Regiment and 4th Royal Tank Regiment;

The Yeomanry: The Royal Yeomanry Regiment and The Queen's Own Yeomanry.

The above resounding array of titles tends to detract from the fact that in the modern Army the role of the Cavalry has changed greatly from the time when it carried out its historic tasks with panache and splendour. The modern Cavalry now has to function within the framework of an

Cavalry badges. 1 *The Life Guards.* **2** *The Blues and Royals.* **3** *1st The Queen's Dragoon Guards.* **4** *The Royal Scots Dragoon Guards.* **5** *4th/7th Royal Dragoon Guards.* **6** *5th Royal Inniskilling Dragoon Guards.* **7** *The Queen's Own Hussars.* **8** *The Queen's Royal Irish Hussars.* **9** *9th/12th Royal Lancers.* **10** *The Royal Hussars.* **11** *13th/18th Royal Hussars.* **12** *14th/20th King's Hussars.* **13** *15th/19th The King's Royal Hussars.* **14** *16th/5th The Queen's Royal Lancers.* **15** *17th/21st Lancers.* **16** *The Royal Tank Regiment.*

organisational arrangement which has more in keeping with the distant past than the grim efficiency of today, but the recent reshuffles and amalgamations of regiments has reduced the situation to more manageable proportions.

Very basically, the Cavalry now has to provide the manpower for two essential battle formations, the armoured regiment and the armoured reconnaissance regiment. The Cavalry regiments themselves are likely to exchange their roles and equipments to fulfil either commitment, so it is not possible in a book of this nature to specify exactly what regiment will be involved in either task at any specific time. For instance, within the Household Cavalry, the regiments are either based in Germany or in the United Kingdom. When in the United Kingdom they carry out their well-known ceremonial duties, but also man an armoured reconnaissance regiment. When they are part of BAOR they form an armoured regiment. As there are variations between the types of armoured formations, they are best dealt with under separate headings.

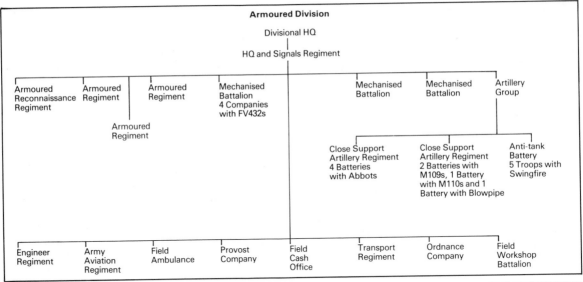

Armoured Division

Divisional HQ

HQ and Signals Regiment

Armoured Reconnaissance Regiment | Armoured Regiment | Armoured Regiment | Mechanised Battalion 4 Companies with FV432s | Mechanised Battalion | Mechanised Battalion | Artillery Group

Armoured Regiment

Close Support Artillery Regiment 4 Batteries with Abbots | Close Support Artillery Regiment 2 Batteries with M109s, 1 Battery with M110s and 1 Battery with Blowpipe | Anti-tank Battery 5 Troops with Swingfire

Engineer Regiment | Army Aviation Regiment | Field Ambulance | Provost Company | Field Cash Office | Transport Regiment | Ordnance Company | Field Workshop Battalion

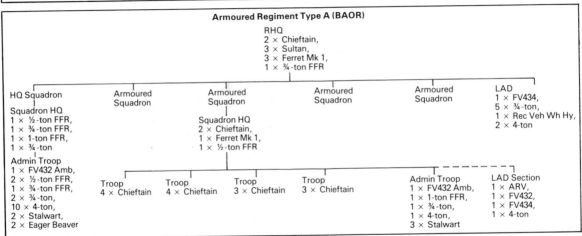

Armoured Regiment Type A (BAOR)

RHQ
2 × Chieftain,
3 × Sultan,
3 × Ferret Mk 1,
1 × ¾-ton FFR

HQ Squadron

Squadron HQ
1 × ½-ton FFR,
1 × ¾-ton FFR,
1 × 1-ton FFR,
1 × ¾-ton

Admin Troop
1 × FV432 Amb,
2 × ½-ton FFR,
1 × ¾-ton FFR,
2 × ¾-ton,
10 × 4-ton,
2 × Stalwart,
2 × Eager Beaver

Armoured Squadron | Armoured Squadron | Armoured Squadron | Armoured Squadron | LAD
1 × FV434,
5 × ¾-ton,
1 × Rec Veh Wh Hy,
2 × 4-ton

Squadron HQ
2 × Chieftain,
1 × Ferret Mk 1,
1 × ½-ton FFR

Troop
4 × Chieftain | Troop
4 × Chieftain | Troop
3 × Chieftain | Troop
3 × Chieftain | Admin Troop
1 × FV432 Amb,
1 × 1-ton FFR,
1 × ¾-ton,
1 × 4-ton,
3 × Stalwart | LAD Section
1 × ARV,
1 × FV432,
1 × FV434,
1 × 4-ton

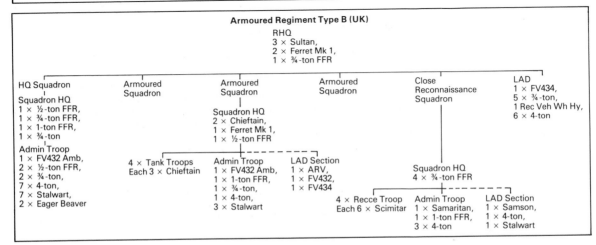

Armoured Regiment Type B (UK)

RHQ
3 × Sultan,
2 × Ferret Mk 1,
1 × ¾-ton FFR

HQ Squadron

Squadron HQ
1 × ½-ton FFR,
1 × ¾-ton FFR,
1 × 1-ton FFR,
1 × ¾-ton

Admin Troop
1 × FV432 Amb,
2 × ½-ton FFR,
2 × ¾-ton,
7 × 4-ton,
7 × Stalwart,
2 × Eager Beaver

Armoured Squadron | Armoured Squadron | Armoured Squadron | Close Reconnaissance Squadron | LAD
1 × FV434,
5 × ¾-ton,
1 Rec Veh Wh Hy,
6 × 4-ton

Squadron HQ
2 × Chieftain,
1 × Ferret Mk 1,
1 × ½-ton FFR

4 × Tank Troops
Each 3 × Chieftain | Admin Troop
1 × FV432 Amb,
1 × 1-ton FFR,
1 × ¾-ton,
1 × 4-ton,
3 × Stalwart | LAD Section
1 × ARV,
1 × FV432,
1 × FV434

Squadron HQ
4 × ¾-ton FFR

4 × Recce Troop
Each 6 × Scimitar | Admin Troop
1 × Samaritan,
1 × 1-ton FFR,
3 × 4-ton | LAD Section
1 × Samson,
1 × 4-ton,
1 × Stalwart

The armoured regiment

There are a total of ten armoured regiments in the British Army, of which eight are based in BAOR. These eight 'teeth' regiments are organised along different lines from the United Kingdom-based regiments and are known as Type A regiments— the United Kingdom equivalent is the Type B. Both types of regiment are equipped with the same fighting vehicle in the shape of the Chieftain tank, one of the finest Main Battle Tanks (MBT) in service anywhere in the world. By the mid-1980s these will be supplemented by the FV4030/4 Challenger.

The eight BAOR armoured regiments are distributed among the three armoured divisions of 1 (Br) Corps, but there is an extra armoured squadron, also equipped with Chieftains, assigned to the Berlin Brigade. (The Berlin squadron, however, is not a part of BAOR as its manpower comes from the training regiment based at Catterick, in the United Kingdom.)

The organisation and equipment levels of the BAOR Type A armoured regiments can be seen in the following table. Each Type A regiment consists of a regimental headquarters and four armoured, or Sabre, squadrons. Within each squadron there is the squadron headquarters with two Chieftain control tanks (both have secure Clansman sets, and one is fitted with a dozer blade), and four troops—two have four tanks and the other two have three. However, this is under peace-time establishments for each squadron also has an extra two Chieftains kept under Driclad wrappings. Thus the tank total for each armoured regiment is 66 in time of peace and 74 in time of war. In addition both at regimental and squadron levels there are administrative and REME light aid troops and sections.

The armoured regiment has three main roles in time of war, as follows: 1) Agressive mobile action to destroy the enemy armour; 2) Close combat in conjunction with the Infantry; and 3) The exploitation of shock action, ie, using to the full the primary tactical characteristics of the tank—firepower, protection, mobility and flexibility.

None of these roles can be fully carried out by the Cavalry alone, so the armoured regiments are distributed, under the control of task force commanders, into battle groups. Within the battle groups are the combat teams, each of which is formed according to its particular role or the type of terrain it has to cover, but the usual combat team consists of an armoured squadron combined with platoons of mechanised infantry. Thus the armoured regiments, within the battle group concept, have the following operational tasks: 1) Defensive operations, in both mobile and static situations; 2) Counter-attack and counter-penetration; 3) Exploitation in support of nuclear warfare; 4) Covering force operations; 5) Advancing in contact with the enemy; 6) The assault and destruction of the enemy; 7) Penetration, exploitation and pursuit; and 8) Direct fire and other support of the Infantry.

The above-mentioned roles and tasks apply also to the United Kingdom-based Type B regiment. There is only one of these based at Tidworth, as the other home-based armoured regiment is the Training Regiment at Catterick. The Type B regiment has no specific NATO role and its function in time of war is not fully determined at the time of writing. It may well be sent across to Germany if the time factor in an emergency situation allows. The Type B regiment has only three armoured squadrons, each with 14 Chieftains. Each squadron has a two-tank squadron headquarters and four three-tank troops. The main change from the Type A organisation is that the Type B armoured regiment incorporates a tracked close reconnaissance squadron equipped with Scimitars. Thus a Type B armoured regiment has 42 Chieftain tanks and 24 Scimitars.

The armoured reconnaissance regiment

While there are two different types of armoured regiment, there are three versions of the armoured reconnaissance regiment. All three are shown in the tables, and although they differ in organisational outline all have the same role in warfare, one which is as old as organised warfare itself.

The role of the armoured reconnaissance regiments is to obtain accurate and useful information regarding the enemy and pass it back to the appropriate command level in as short a time as possible. Any related information, such as that pertaining to terrain, potential obstacles, etc, is dealt with in the same way. With this in mind, the armoured reconnaissance regiments have to rely on field craft, mastery of their equipment and good old-fashioned stealth to obtain their information— the use of firepower will often negate their intentions so firepower is thus a secondary consideration with regards to the vehicles and other equipment employed.

To return to the various types of armoured reconnaissance regiment, there are four of the Type A regiments in Germany. There are also three Type B regiments based in the United Kingdom. That leaves two TA regiments, both of which will be given roles in Germany in the event of an emergency. There is also a composite Training Regiment.

Both the Type A and the Type B regiments have medium and close reconnaissance elements and a word of explanation is needed on the two functions. The medium reconnnaissance squadrons are kept under the direct control of the regiment headquarters. In the 'teeth' Type A regiments they are equipped with the FV101 Scorpion, armed with a 76 mm gun. In the Type B regiments they have a mixture of FV101 Scorpions and FV107 Scimitars. The close reconnaissance squadrons are usually separated from the regimental headquarters control and come under that of battle group commanders. Within each close reconnaissance squadron there are five troops—in the Type A regiment they are equipped with the FV107 Scimitar armed with the 30 mm Rarden cannon, while in the Type B regiment the squadrons are equipped with the FV721, again armed with the 30 mm Rarden. Each of the five close reconnaissance troops is an entity in itself and each troop operates in direct support of each of the five battle groups within the armoured division—thus each battle group has an allocation of eight FV107 Scimitars or FV721 Foxes.

The TA Regiments use only the FV721 Fox and have no separate close or medium elements.

As well as the reconnaissance troops, the medium reconnaissance squadrons also have surveillance troops equipped with the FV103 Spartan carrying ZB298 battlefield surveillance radar—the TA set-up does not have this facility.

Whatever type of organisation each armoured reconnaissance regiment has, it has several tasks in a limited or a general war. They are as follows: 1) Covering defensive positions or withdrawals, usually in conjunction with other arms; 2) Observing obstacles; 3) Protection for the flanks of a formation; 4) Anti-helicopter or anti-airborne forces operations; 5) The advance to contact; 6) Independent raids and deep penetration missions; 7) Disruption in a pursuit situation; 8) Escort tasks for supply echelons and similar formations; 9) Major traffic control; and 10) Nuclear, biological and chemical reconnaissance.

The above are tasks carried out during general warfare but the armoured reconnaissance regiments also have an important role to play during the various types of counter-revolutionary and counter-insurgency operations that now proliferate throughout the world. The light and handy vehicles involved in the reconnaissance role are also useful for a number of tasks in this demanding form of warfare, and in the British Army the FV721 Fox has proved itself to be a particularly valuable vehicle in this role, far more suitable in fact than tracked vehicles. The major tasks involved for the recon-

naissance regiments in these counter-revolutionary operations are: 1) Mobile patrolling, either by foot, vehicle or helicopter; 2) Manning observation points; 3) Road blocks and area cordons; 4) Escorting convoys, VIPs or important traffic; 5) General communications; 6) Crowd control and dispersal; and 7) Fire support for Infantry operations.

There are a few variations from the general Type B organisation, one of which involves the armoured reconnaissance regiment based at Omagh in Northern Ireland. This has its two medium reconnaissance squadrons equipped with the FV721 Fox.

There is an armoured reconnaissance squadron based in Cyprus which differs both in its equipment and organisation from any other Cavalry squadron. The squadron has six troops each equipped with four Ferrets. Four of the troops have a surveillance squadron equipped with Saracens, and in addition the Cyprus squadron is the last operational unit still using the FV601(C) Saladin armoured car.

In addition to all the other variations on the organisational theme, the Royal Armoured Corps has to find one squadron for the ACE Mobile Force Land. This squadron is manned by the RAC Centre Regiment and is normally based at Tidworth. It has four troops, each with two FV101 Scorpions and two FV107 Scimitars. There is also a surveillance troop equipped with five FV103 Spartans.

Although the general organisational outlines of most of the Cavalry formations is now thought to be more or less static for the foreseeable future, the role of the armoured reconnaissance regiments may still be altered in order to improve their general anti-armoured role. At present, as outlined above, their general reconnaissance role is more dependent on stealth than on firepower, and in view of the number of vehicles involved in the role it is felt that they could become more cost-effective in the general battles that will develop in any future conflict. Exactly what form this general improvement will take has not yet been determined.

One important point must be made regarding the personnel forming the manpower for the armoured regiments and the armoured reconnaissance regiments—they are not all drawn from the Cavalry regiments. As will be seen from the organisation charts, the REME has a very important part to play—they are the largest individual component after the RAC regiments themselves. Also involved are the Army Catering Corps, the Royal Army Pay Corps, the Royal Army Medical Corps and a single NCO from the Army Physical Training Corps. The actual establishment varies with each type of regiment.

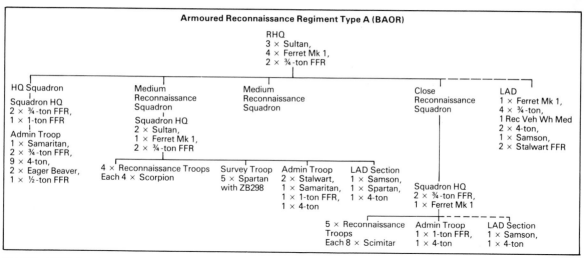

Armoured Reconnaissance Regiment Type A (BAOR)

RHQ
3 × Sultan,
4 × Ferret Mk 1,
2 × ¾-ton FFR

HQ Squadron

Squadron HQ
2 × ¾-ton FFR,
1 × 1-ton FFR

Admin Troop
1 × Samaritan,
2 × ¾-ton FFR,
9 × 4-ton,
2 × Eager Beaver,
1 × ½-ton FFR

Medium
Reconnaissance
Squadron

Squadron HQ
2 × Sultan,
1 × Ferret Mk 1,
2 × ¾-ton FFR

Medium
Reconnaissance
Squadron

4 × Reconnaissance Troops
Each 4 × Scorpion

Survey Troop
5 × Spartan
with ZB298

Admin Troop
2 × Stalwart,
1 × Samaritan,
1 × 1-ton FFR,
1 × 4-ton

LAD Section
1 × Samson,
1 × Spartan,
1 × 4-ton

Close
Reconnaissance
Squadron

Squadron HQ
2 × ¾-ton FFR,
1 × Ferret Mk 1

5 × Reconnaissance
Troops
Each 8 × Scimitar

Admin Troop
1 × 1-ton FFR,
1 × 4-ton

LAD Section
1 × Samson,
1 × 4-ton

LAD
1 × Ferret Mk 1,
4 × ¾-ton,
1 Rec Veh Wh Med
2 × 4-ton,
1 × Samson,
2 × Stalwart FFR

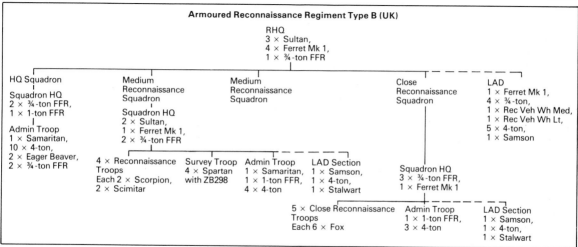

Armoured Reconnaissance Regiment Type B (UK)

RHQ
3 × Sultan,
4 × Ferret Mk 1,
1 × ¾-ton FFR

HQ Squadron

Squadron HQ
2 × ¾-ton FFR,
1 × 1-ton FFR

Admin Troop
1 × Samaritan,
10 × 4-ton,
2 × Eager Beaver,
2 × ¾-ton FFR

Medium
Reconnaissance
Squadron

Squadron HQ
2 × Sultan,
1 × Ferret Mk 1,
2 × ¾-ton FFR

Medium
Reconnaissance
Squadron

4 × Reconnaissance
Troops
Each 2 × Scorpion,
2 × Scimitar

Survey Troop
4 × Spartan
with ZB298

Admin Troop
1 × Samaritan,
1 × 1-ton FFR,
4 × 4-ton

LAD Section
1 × Samson,
1 × 4-ton,
1 × Stalwart

Close
Reconnaissance
Squadron

Squadron HQ
3 × ¾-ton FFR,
1 × Ferret Mk 1

5 × Close Reconnaissance
Troops
Each 6 × Fox

Admin Troop
1 × 1-ton FFR,
3 × 4-ton

LAD Section
1 × Samson,
1 × 4-ton,
1 × Stalwart

LAD
1 × Ferret Mk 1,
4 × ¾-ton,
1 × Rec Veh Wh Med,
1 × Rec Veh Wh Lt,
5 × 4-ton,
1 × Samson

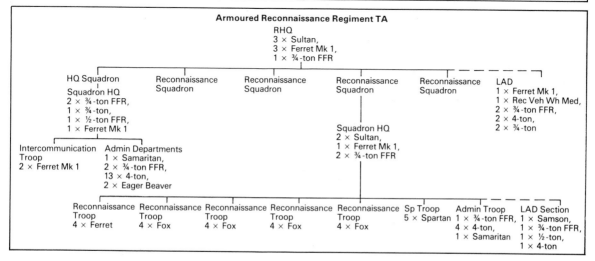

Armoured Reconnaissance Regiment TA

RHQ
3 × Sultan,
3 × Ferret Mk 1,
1 × ¾-ton FFR

HQ Squadron

Squadron HQ
2 × ¾-ton FFR,
1 × ¾-ton,
1 × ½-ton FFR,
1 × Ferret Mk 1

Intercommunication
Troop
2 × Ferret Mk 1

Admin Departments
1 × Samaritan,
2 × ¾-ton FFR,
13 × 4-ton,
2 × Eager Beaver

Reconnaissance
Squadron

Reconnaissance
Squadron

Reconnaissance
Squadron

Squadron HQ
2 × Sultan,
1 × Ferret Mk 1,
2 × ¾-ton FFR

Reconnaissance
Troop
4 × Ferret

Reconnaissance
Troop
4 × Fox

Reconnaissance
Troop
4 × Fox

Reconnaissance
Troop
4 × Fox

Reconnaissance
Troop
4 × Fox

Sp Troop
5 × Spartan

Admin Troop
1 × ¾-ton FFR,
4 × 4-ton,
1 × Samaritan

Reconnaissance
Squadron

LAD
1 × Ferret Mk 1,
1 × Rec Veh Wh Med,
2 × ¾-ton FFR,
2 × 4-ton,
2 × ¾-ton

LAD Section
1 × Samson,
1 × ¾-ton FFR,
1 × ½-ton,
1 × 4-ton

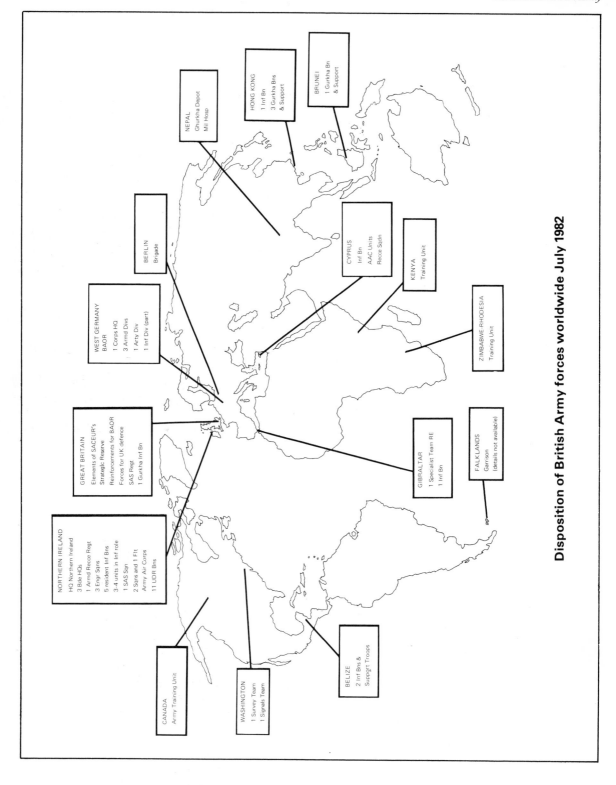

NEPAL
Ghurkha Depot
Mil Hosp

HONG KONG
1 Inf Bn
3 Gurkha Bns
& Support

BRUNEI
1 Gurkha Bn
& Support

BERLIN
Brigade

CYPRUS
Inf Bn
AAC Units
Recce Sqdn

KENYA
Training Unit

WEST GERMANY
BAOR
1 Corps HQ
3 Armd Divs
1 Arty Div
1 Inf Div (part)

ZIMBABWE RHODESIA
Training Unit

GREAT BRITAIN
Elements of SACEUR's
Strategic Reserve
Reinforcements for BAOR
Forces for UK defence
SAS Regt
1 Gurkha Inf Bn

GIBRALTAR
1 Specialist Team RE
1 Inf Bn

FALKLANDS
Garrison
(details not available)

NORTHERN IRELAND
HQ Northern Ireland
3 Bde HQs
1 Armd Recce Regt
3 Engr Sqns
5 resident Inf Bns
3–4 units in Inf role
1 SAS Sqn
2 Sqns and 1 Flt
Army Air Corps
11 UDR Bns

CANADA
Army Training Unit

WASHINGTON
1 Survey Team
1 Signals Team

BELIZE
2 Inf Bns &
Support Troops

Disposition of British Army forces worldwide July 1982

The Infantry

'(physical occupation being ten points of the law in war, and infantry the bailiff's men)'

John Keegan, *The Face of Battle.*

Today, as always, the main strength of the Army still rests in its Infantry battalions. The Army currently has 55 battalions of Infantry, all of them front-line units. They are organised into six divisions plus three other separate formations. Of these six divisions one, the Guards Division, holds the same placing as the Household Cavalry does to the rest of the Cavalry units. To the lay public the Guards Division means only the well-known ceremonial and red tunics of the London-based battalions, but like the Household Cavalry again, it operates on a ceremonial/combat basis with battalions in the United Kingdom carrying out their ceremonial functions, while other battalions are on a combat standing in Germany and elsewhere.

The battalions that make up the separate divisions are as follows:

The Guards Division: 1st Battalion Grenadier Guards, 2nd Battalion Grenadier Guards, 1st Battalion Coldstream Guards, 2nd Battalion Coldstream Guards, 1st Battalion Scots Guards, 2nd Battalion Scots Guards, 1st Battalion Irish Guards and 1st Battalion Welsh Guards.

The Scottish Division: 1st Battalion The Royal Scots (The Royal Regiment), 1st Battalion The Royal Highland Fusiliers (Princess Margaret's Own Glasgow and Ayrshire Regiment), 1st Battalion The King's Own Scottish Borderers, 1st Battalion The Black Watch (Royal Highland Regiment), 1st Battalion The Queen's Own Highlanders (Seaforth and Camerons), 1st Battalion The Gordon Highlanders and 1st Battalion The Argyll and Sutherland Highlanders (Princess Louise's).

The Queen's Division: 1st Battalion The Queen's Regiment, 2nd Battalion The Queen's Regiment, 3rd Battalion The Queen's Regiment, 4th Battalion The Queen's Regiment Albuera Company, 1st Battalion The Royal Regiment of Fusiliers, 2nd Battalion The Royal Regiment of Fusiliers, 3rd Battalion The Royal Regiment of Fusiliers, 1st Battalion The Royal Anglian Regiment, 2nd Battalion The Royal Anglian Regiment, 3rd Battalion The Royal Anglian Regiment and 4th Battalion The Royal Anglian Regiment.

The King's Division: 1st Battalion The King's Own Royal Border Regiment, 1st Battalion The King's Regiment, 1st Battalion The Prince of Wales's Own Regiment of Yorkshire, 1st Battalion

Above *Men of the Light Infantry in Belfast* (MoD). **Below** *The author's projection of the Infantry section of the 1980s.*

Infantry badges. 1 *The Grenadier Guards.* **2** *The Coldstream Guards.* **3** *The Scots Guards.* **4** *The Irish Guards.* **5** *The Welsh Guards.* **6** *The Royal Scots.* **7** *The Royal Highland Fusiliers.* **8** *The King's Own Scottish Borderers.* **9** *The Black Watch.* **10** *The Queen's Own Highlanders.* **11** *The Gordon Highlanders.* **12** *The Argyll and Sutherland Highlanders.* **13** *The Queen's Regiment.* **14** *The Royal Regiment of Fusiliers.* **15** *The Royal Anglian Regiment.* **16** *The King's Own Royal Border Regiment.* **17** *The King's Regiment.* **18** *The Prince of Wales's Own Regiment of Yorkshire.* **19** *The Green Howards.* **20** *The Royal Irish Rangers.* **21** *The Queen's Lancashire Regiment.* **22** *The Duke of Wellington's Regiment.* **23** *The Devonshire and Dorset Regiment.* **24** *The Cheshire Regiment.* **25** *The Royal Welch Fusiliers.* **26** *The Royal Regiment of Wales.* **27** *The Gloucestershire Regiment.* **28** *The Worcestershire and Sherwood Foresters Regiment.* **29** *The Royal Hampshire Regiment.* **30** *The Staffordshire Regiment.* **31** *The Duke of Edinburgh's Royal Regiment.* **32** *The Light Infantry.* **33** *The Royal Green Jackets.* **34** *The Parachute Regiment.* **35** *The Brigade of Gurkhas.* **36** *2nd King Edward VII's Own Gurkha Rifles.* **37** *6th Queen Elizabeth's Own Gurkha Rifles.* **38** *7th Duke of Edinburgh's Own Gurkha Rifles.* **39** *10th Princess Mary's Own Gurkha Rifles.*

The Green Howards (Alexandra, Princess of Wales's Own Yorkshire Regiment), 1st Battalion The Royal Irish Rangers, 2nd Battalion The Royal Irish Rangers, 1st Battalion The Queen's Lancashire Regiment and 1st Battalion The Duke of Wellington's Regiment.

The Prince of Wales's Division: 1st Battalion The Devonshire and Dorset Regiment, 1st Battalion The Cheshire Regiment, 1st Battalion The Royal Welch Fusiliers, 1st Battalion The Royal Regiment of Wales (24th/41st Foot), 1st Battalion The Gloucestershire Regiment, 1st Battalion The Worcestershire and Sherwood Foresters Regiment (29th/45th Foot), 1st Battalion The Royal Hampshire Regiment, 1st Battalion The Staffordshire Regiment (The Prince of Wales's) and 1st Battalion The Duke of Edinburgh's Royal Regiment (Berkshire and Wiltshire).

The Light Division: 1st Battalion The Light Infantry, 2nd Battalion The Light Infantry, 3rd Battalion The Light Infantry, 1st Battalion The Royal Green Jackets, 2nd Battalion The Royal Green Jackets and 3rd Battalion The Royal Green Jackets.

Following on from the above Divisions is the Parachute Regiment, comprising 1st Battalion The Parachute Regiment, 2nd Battalion The Parachute Regiment and 3rd Battalion The Parachute Regiment.

Very much a part of the British Army but, in a way, separate from it, are the five battalions of the Brigade of Gurkhas. The five battalions are the 2nd King Edward VII's Own Gurkha Rifles (The Sirmoor Rifles)—two battalions, 6th Queen Elizabeth's Own Gurkha Rifles, 7th Duke of Edinburgh's Own Gurkha Rifles and 10th Princess Mary's Own Gurkha Rifles.

In addition to the above, there are the 38 Infantry battalions of the TA, some 60 per cent of which will be assigned to BAOR in an emergency. The Regular battalions are distributed with 15 in BAOR, three as part of the Berlin garrison, 31 in the United Kingdom and a further seven based elsewhere. Thus, on paper at least, the British Army has a grand total of 94 battalions of Infantry, including the TA battalions.

With so many Infantry battalions, it should come as no surprise that there are many different organisational structures for the various types of unit. Unfortunately, at the time of writing all the different types of organisation were under review to the extent that the future Infantry organisation may be very different from what it is now. Therefore, by the time these words are read, a new Infantry structure may well have emerged rendering the following outlines at best obsolescent.

At present there are two basic Infantry organisations, both of them based on the battalion. In BAOR the Infantry is organised into mechanised infantry battalions, while the bulk of the United Kingdom-based units are wheeled infantry battalions. There are, currently, several variations on the themes, but both are made up from the same basis, namely a combination of numbers of Infantry sections.

The basic Infantry section consists of from six to eight soldiers who work together as a more or less permanent team. A typical section in a mechanised battalion comprises eight soldiers who travel together in their own FV432. The section is usually under the command of a Corporal or Sergeant and one of the section is the driver who remains with the FV432 at most times. The rest of the section is made up of five riflemen, armed with the L1A1 rifle, one soldier who fires the section GPMG, and another who is armed with the 84 mm L14A1 'Carl Gustav' anti-tank gun. The second-in-command of the section usually controls the fire of the GPMG which is used in the LMG role. The soldier with the L14A1 gun also carries his own rifle and one of the section also carries the ammunition for this gun. One man further carries the section radio set. So all in all the Infantry section is well loaded. Three such sections combine to form a platoon and three or four platoons combine to form a company. Each company has its own headquarters section with extra radios, the company fire support section which includes an extra GPMG and the company mortar section which may eventually have the 51 mm Light Mortar. Mechanised battalions have four Infantry companies with a further headquarters company which includes the battalion headquarters, and two support weapons platoons. One of these platoons has four sections armed with two 81 mm mortars each, and the other being the anti-tank platoon with another four sections each equipped with either four Milan anti-tank missile launchers or two Wombats.

As the name implies, wheeled battalions rely on the truck for transport (or the Land Rover) while mechanised battalions are based on the FV432. Each Infantry battalion also has sections from other arms. At company level there is an RAMC ambulance section, and at battalion level there is the REME LAD.

The Parachute Regiment is included here in the Infantry section as, despite its adventurous method of reaching the combat area, once on the ground it functions as Infantry. The parachute battalions of the Army (there are three Regular and three TA battalions) are almost alone among NATO airborne forces in being equipped with normal Infantry weapons and equipment, only a small proportion of their kit being adapted to their airborne role. In any

Section briefing on the Suffield Ranges.

future combat the Paras are not likely to be used in any formation above company level as their training of late has rarely been carried out above that level, mainly due to restrictions on the numbers of RAF aircraft available. The normal Para transport is the RAF C-130 Hercules C.1, each of which can carry up to 64 men ready to jump. Another potential problem for the Paras is that there are now only enough aircraft available for their prolonged training to enable one of the three Para battalions to be maintained in the paradrop role at any one time (this may well be increased to two battalions by the time these words are read). The other two Para battalions are at present serving as conventional Infantry. To aggravate the lack of a modern role for the Paras other than that of behind-the-lines disruption and penetration of rear areas, there are now no airborne Artillery or Cavalry units as the last of them were disbanded some years ago. The Parachute Regiment depot is at Aldershot.

The vanguard of the Infantry, as in the past, is still the Guards Division. As always, the Guards combine ceremonial and combat roles, usually on a three-year tour basis, but their long-established function is that of the Sovereign's personal escort, a function long overtaken by circumstances but cherished as a tradition. The function can still be seen with the ceremonial appearances so beloved by the tourist, and by the positioning of the main Guards depots at Birdcage Walk, Chelsea, Windsor, Caterham and Pirbright.

The Brigade of Ghurkas is included in this Infan-try section despite the fact that the brigade also includes Gurkha Signal, Engineer and Transport formations. The Infantry component of the brigade comprises five battalions, all of them recruited in Nepal. Apart from the small Nepal base staff, all the Gurkhas serve far away from home. Four of the battalions are stationed in the Far East, three of them in Hong Kong and one in Brunei where it is maintained at the request and expense of the local government. The other battalion is based in the United Kingdom, at Church Crookham. Officers for the brigade are no longer all-British, but the formation is still an integral part of the British Army and the friendships and traditions forged between the Army and the men from Nepal are still treasured and maintained on both sides. The brigade depot is at Pokhara, Nepal.

The Light Division contains the old Light Infantry battalions in some form or another and, despite the fact that the Light Infantry no longer have any modern tactical task, the battalions of the Light Division are noticeable by their retention of all the old Light Infantry traditions. Their drill is still carried out at the old 180 paces to the minute (the norm is 120 to the minute), their uniforms retain the old field green shades, their leatherwork is black, and orders are still passed on by bugle. For all this, the Light Division on the battlefield will still be used as conventional Infantry and will travel into battle in FV432s, as will the rest.

The 'rest' is really the backbone of the British Army. The battalions of the King's, Queen's, Scottish and Prince of Wales's Divisions contain all the old Regiments of the Line that have served the

Army and the nation so well for many centuries. The solid fighting qualities of the British soldier have long been epitomised by the old soldiers of the Line and their modern equivalents still maintain their traditions to produce a unit loyalty that is almost without parallel in any other army. These traditions are maintained in the face of reorganisations, contractions and amalgamations, and the upheavals of the last years would have been far more disruptive without this bond with the past. But tradition is only one part of the make-up of the Line battalions. They are well-trained and well-led, and if the occasion comes when they have to be tried in action (as they have been in Northern Ireland and the Falklands) they respond in the same dour and reliable manner as have past generations.

No matter in which form the modern Infantry battalion is organised, it can be argued that the present four-company structure has its strengths and its weaknesses. The use of the combat team will often mean that it is very probable that many battalions will not fight as a unit but will be split up, rendering the carefully structured fire support function rather weaker than it should be. The basic section, at the other extreme, is also rather overloaded as far as weight is concerned, and rather weak in firepower. Although the GPMG in the LMG role is the basic section weapon, the individual rifleman can contribute but little and in an eight-man section there are often only four riflemen capable of opening fire. (If the FV432 driver stays with the vehicle, the L14A1 is kept at the ready, the section NCO is in communication with the platoon or company HQ, and one man is supplying the GPMG with ammunition, there are only four rifles ready to fire.) From this it may well emerge that any future Infantry reorganisation will start at section level. Future Infantry weapon developments would seem to point to a smaller section structure with four soldiers armed with the 5.56 mm IW and LSW on a ratio of 3:1. This smaller section should have the equivalent firepower of the present eight-man section, and the advent of the LAW should give almost every soldier an anti-tank defence capability while at the same time not impairing the rifle function. It would also seem very likely that at company HQ level the fire support section will be enlarged, making the company rather than the battalion the Infantry component in the combat team structure. Such a revision should lead back to the old three-company battalion for administrative purposes.

The Royal Regiment of Artillery & The Royal Horse Artillery

'The Infantry don't understand their orders, the Cavalry ignore them . . . the Artillery make their own arrangements.'

(Anon).

The Artillery component of the British Army is made up from two elements. By far the largest part of the Royal Regiment of Artillery is more commonly known as the Royal Artillery, the other element being the Royal Horse Artillery. In practical terms on the battlefield the two carry out the same functions and operate in the same manner, but the Royal Horse Artillery is constituted as an elite force and works and acts accordingly. Officers for the RHA are carefully selected from the regiment as a whole; once they have been 'given their jacket' they spend a term with the RHA and then return to the Royal Artillery. As the RHA standards are so high this procedure has the overall effect of raising the working and operating standards of the Artillery.

The modern Artillery is a powerful and complex branch of the Army. It is the only branch of the Army to employ nuclear weapons, the very weapons that are now 'Queen of the battlefield', and far outweigh any other single weapon type in destructive and disruptive impact. Thus when the functions of the modern Artillery are examined, the nuclear role must be afforded the overall priority, but the other functions of indirect fire, long-range anti-tank defence and air defence must not be overlooked.

The functions of the Artillery are: 1) Nuclear warfare—to provide the capability of engaging selected targets with nuclear weapons at the appropriate stage of the battle; 2) Indirect fire—to a) Provide depth fire designed to disrupt, delay and destroy enemy forces before they can come into contact, and in particular to destroy or suppress enemy artillery (the same application can be made against enemy forces not committed to battle); and to b) provide close support to battle groups in the destruction or neutralisation of enemy forces in the close contact battle; 3) Long range anti-tank—to operate the Army's Long-Range Anti-Tank Guided Weapon (LRATGW—Swingfire); and 4) Air defence—to provide the low-level air defence of the Field Army.

The control of Artillery as it is now practised is the outcome of a very long period of practical experience combined with pragmatic necessity. Artillery commanders now have to control many powerful weapons that range from devastating nuclear weapons down to one-man air defence missiles, and the present command system is one that attempts to combine close control with the looseness that the modern battle will require. The control system is based on a flexible signal network combined with close personal contact at every command level. This can be seen in the BAOR Artillery command network where at every level the Artillery commanders liaise and work alongside the formation commanders. At HQ 1 (Br) Corps level, the corps commander has immediate and close access to the officer commanding all the artillery in the corps. This officer, a Major General (MGRA), acts as the corps commander's artillery advisor while at the same time commanding the Artillery division. At a lower level, each armoured division commander has his own artillery advisor who also acts as the commander for all the Artillery formations within the division. This officer, a Brigadier, is the Commander Royal Artillery (CRA) who commands his own HQRA and the two field regiments under his command, along with the LRATGW battery. Each field regiment has its own Tactical Headquarters (TacHQ) with two Fire Direction Centres (FDCs), each of which is connected by radio not only to the TacHQ, but also to the HQRA in each division. In this manner flexibility is built into the system to enable fire to be switched from one target to another so that one formation can provide fire for another, and fire concentrations can be rapidly switched from target to target. Normally one FDC controls the artillery fire for one task force or battle group, but the Artillery control system enables the FDCs to switch their fire to support other formations than their own. The whole network is devised to support the precept that artillery fire must always be used *en masse,* and never in dribs and drabs—one massed salvo from many guns has a far more destructive and disruptive impact than the same number of projectiles delivered by a single gun.

At corps level the Artillery Division comes directly under the control of the MGRA, and has five components. In 1 (Br) Corps these are: 5th Heavy Regiment—Equipped with the long range 175 mm M107 gun, this regiment has four batteries and is responsible for the counter-battery role; 50 Missile Regiment—This unit has four batteries, each equipped with the Lance missile, and is kept in reserve until its nuclear capability is required; 94 Locating Regiment—The three batteries of this regiment provide survey, meteorological information, sound ranging and general intelligence via their Midge drones for all the Artillery units in 1 (Br) Corps; and 12 and 22 Air Defence Regiments— Each of these is equipped with Rapier missiles, each

Swingfire launch from an FV102 Striker (British Aerospace).

regiment being organised into three batteries. Both regiments carry out the Area air defence role.

The Artillery Division retains the flexibility associated with the other Artillery units within 1 (Br) Corps. Normally most of its regiments are divided up among the armoured divisions and in action certain batteries would expect to be working with certain divisions. However, as any situation develops the various batteries can be easily switched from one grouping to any other, as and when battle circumstances dictate. There are two exceptions to this—the missile regiment which is always under the command of the MGRA for obvious reasons, and the air defence regiments which could, on occasion, be given specific areas to defend.

The divisional Artillery Group comprises three components—two close support regiments and a LRATGW battery. Each close support regiment is a field regiment and they are assigned at the rate of one field regiment to a task force. One of the field regiments has a fairly straightforward organisation as it is based on the 105 mm Abbot. The Abbot unit has three batteries with eight guns in two troops per battery. Each Abbot field regiment also contains a troop of four Cymbeline mortar locating radar equipments in the HQ battery.

The other type of field regiment is based on the 155 mm M109A1 or M109A2. It has three batteries, each with eight guns, and will be all M109A1 or M109A2. The 155 mm field regiment

The main punch of the Royal Artillery—the nuclear Lance missile.

also has a Blowpipe battery for unit air defence. The M110 howitzers that were formerly part of the 155 mm field regiment have now been grouped into a single Heavy Regiment of three batteries, and this Heavy Regiment will allocate its batteries and troops among the various divisions.

The organisation of the close support field regiment stems from the 1981 Defence review. In practice the organisation works, mainly due to the flexible control system already mentioned above. The close support batteries can switch their fire very rapidly from targets within the area of their own task forces to areas occupied by other task forces. It may well emerge that in some areas tactical situations will require the concentration of all the divisional artillery behind one specific task force or battle group—the permutations and possibilities are legion.

In addition to the two close support field regiments within each armoured division there is one Swingfire battery to provide the LRATGW defence. These batteries (all four of those in 1 (Br) Corps are RHA batteries) may be deployed to suit the tactical or local situation but are usually used at task force level. For administrative purposes each of the Swingfire batteries is attached to one of the field regiments in each armoured division.

Normally, particular field regiments would work with specific divisions. It is known that 45 and 49 Field Regiments, RA, combine to provide the 1st

Armoured Division Artillery Group, the first of the BAOR artillery groups to form into the new eight-gun batteries. Due to the recent reorganisation of BAOR involving the introduction of the 2nd Infantry Division, it is still uncertain at the time of writing exactly what will happen to 27 and 40 Field Regiments, RA, which were part of the old 2nd Armoured Division. 19 and 26 Field Regiments, RA, continue to provide support for the 3rd Armoured Division and 25 and 39 Field Regiments, RA, for the 4th Armoured Division.

The Artillery field regiments in BAOR are completed by 7 RHA equipped with the 155 mm FH70. This regiment has three batteries.

In the United Kingdom, 1 Infantry Brigade has been assigned 4 Field Regiment. This regiment has three batteries, all equipped with the 105 mm Light Gun plus three towed Cymbeline mortar locating radars.

40 Field Regiment is based at Colchester and is a 155 mm FH70 regiment. It is assigned to 19 Infantry Brigade, and has three batteries.

The other regiments resident in the United Kingdom are headed by a medium regiment, 1 RHA, which has three batteries, now equipped with the 105 mm Abbot and based at Topcliffe. Bulford is the home of 32 Guided Weapons Regiment, a composite formation having three Swingfire batteries and one Blowpipe battery. Another guided weapon unit is 16 Air Defence Regiment equipped with Rapiers. It is another three-battery regiment, and is based at Kirton-in-Lindsay. Plymouth is the home base for 29 Commando Regiment which is equipped with the 105 mm Light Gun, and organised into three batteries with three towed Cymbeline radars.

There are two more Regular Field Artillery units to mention, both of them based in the United Kingdom. One is the 2nd Field Regiment which, until very recently, was the support regiment for the Royal School of Artillery at Larkhill, although at the time of writing this regiment was due to move to Munster. 32 Guided Weapons Regiment will now provide support to the AMF(L) in its place and a new support regiment will be assigned to Larkhill. The Royal School of Artillery is further supported by the independent 22 Locating Battery which will provide support for 1 Infantry Brigade when necessary.

In addition to the operational units mentioned above, there is still one more Regular Artillery unit to mention, and that is the King's Troop, RHA, based at St Johns Wood in London. The King's Troop performs ceremonial and display duties only and their Great War 13 pr guns have not had an offensive function since they were last put back on to the 'active list' during the desperate days of 1940. Without a doubt, the King's Troop puts on one of the finest military displays to be seen anywhere, and competition to join its ranks is very keen.

There are five major TA Artillery regiments plus a whole host of smaller units. Two of these are Field Regiments RA(V), and both are equipped with the 105 mm Light Gun. The two TA field regiments involved are 100 and 101, and in an emergency they are likely to support 19 and 24 Infantry Brigades. There are three Air Defence Regiments RA(V), namely 102, 103 and 104. All are equipped with Blowpipe and in an emergency will be assigned to BAOR for the defence of VPs (Vital/Vulnerable Points) in rear areas. Other TA Artillery units provide OP (Observation Post) parties for the field regiments in 1 (Br) Corps—the Honourable Artillery Company being one unit that trains and provides these parties.

To back up all these various units, the Artillery training organisation is based at Woowich—the home of the Royal Artillery. Recruits are trained by the Depot Regiment at Woolwich and from there they are posted direct to their regiments. The Junior Leaders for the Royal Artillery are trained at Bramcote. The Royal School of Artillery at Larkhill deals primarily with the training of instructors for Artillery, both officers and NCOs, as well as providing general courses for battle group commanders from all other branches of the Army.

Dealing as it does with so much complicated and expensive equipment, the Royal Artillery is one of the most scientific branches of the Army. The personnel of the Artillery have to deal not only with their guns and missiles but also with computers, signals, meteorology, artillery survey, maintaining and driving their many forms of vehicle, and self defence as well. With such a broad spectrum of skills to be maintained it is not surprising that the Artillery are constantly improving and updating their methods and systems as well as the power of the weapons themselves, with all manner of modern techniques becoming involved. Bearing in mind that the weapon of the Artillery is not the gun or launcher but the projectile, the latest ballistic innovations are always under observation and such warheads as scattered bomblets or minelets are currently under consideration for future employment. Field artillery calibres are now being centred on 155 mm and above, and the long range MLRS rocket is now being prepared for the depth fire role. Laser-guided projectiles (eg, the American Copperhead) are another future possibility. Away from the firing line, the Artillery fire control systems in service will be considerably enhanced by the introduction of BATES, which has been described as the most powerful Artillery firepower multiplier for many generations, enabling the Artillery commanders to carry out their task with far greater flexibility, response and impact than has hitherto been even remotely possible. BATES is at present scheduled for introduction once the Wavell command network has been established and is functioning smoothly.

Royal Artillery survey and observation

For the Artillery, survey has more than one function. Not only does it supply the essential information as to the enemy's position but it also provides the equally valuable information as to the precise location of one's own forces and equipments. To this end, survey is a vitally important part of the Artillery and considerable pains are taken to ensure its accuracy and relevance. Each major Artillery formation has its own survey troop which forms part of the locating battery, and this troop is responsible for the Artillery survey on the battlefield, using maps supplied by the Royal Engineers. The methods used by the troop follow conventional civilian survey practice but their equipment is generally more robust than the commercial equivalents. Numerous different instruments are issued from the basic steel measuring tapes up to the Tellurometer (MRA5), the Gyroscopic Orientor (GS908) and the Surveying Theodolite (Watts Mocroptic No.2 Mark 4). Some of the survey tasks will soon be supplemented by PADS but the survey troops will still be responsible for the important survey points that enable PADS to function.

The Royal Artillery Observation Post (OP) is the home of a number of other specialised instruments which have gradually been evolved into a common 'package'. A Forward Observation Officer (FOO) has to observe and correct the fall of artillery fire and give corrections back to his battery to ensure hits. For this purpose he must know exactly where he is (here PADS or survey once more come into play), but to determine exactly where the target is relative to his position a whole host of aids are ready to be mobile on an FV432 or an FV103 Spartan. All these vehicles can carry a device known as a Head Angulation Sighting Equipment (HASE), which is an instrument table giving survey angle related to its orientation (if used from a static position, the HASE is mounted on a Medium Level Tripod, or MLT). On to the HASE goes a Laser Rangefinder (LRF) and to add to the goes a Laser Rangefinder (LRF) and to add to the bulk, a Night Observation Device (NOD) can be added for night or low visibility use. Very basically the LRF is used to determine the range and angle of the target from the HASE. From these the enemy

The FOO 'Christmas Tree' mounted here on a FV432 (Gunner Magazine).

range and bearing can be assessed accurately and relayed to the battery in a very short space of time. The system, if correctly set up and surveyed, is very accurate and in past exercises opening rounds have landed within 60 metres of the lased target on 80 out of 100 occasions—subsequent corrections can then be made with a minimum of time and projectile wastage.

Lasers have another important function in that they can be used as target designators for ground attack aircraft. In this role a Laser Target Marker (LTM) is aimed at the selected target and a long burst of laser radiation is then 'fired'. The reflected beam can be picked up from up to 10,000 metres away by the attacking aircraft and the marker information is fed directly into the pilot's head-up display. In this manner a strike aircraft can attack a ground target without seeing the target itself.

Artillery fire is not directed by the methods outlined above in isolation. There are many other factors to be taken into account such as the meteorological conditions (data provided by AMETS), and the various ballistic data (individual gun muzzle velocities provided by PACER, charge temperatures, propellant lots, etc). Much of this technical detail these days is calculated by the FACE computer, but a skillful OP will also rely on good old-fashioned experience.

Field Artillery Computer Equipment (FACE)

The fire control of modern field artillery is a complex business which no longer has time for the old, 'fire-for ranging, fire-for-effect' orders. Instead artillery fire has to be capable of ranging on to targets that present themselves for fleeting instances, using artillery with variables such as differing projectiles and ranges, and with differing equipment. Fire orders have to be given to the guns quickly and accurately with any delays cut to an absolute minimum. Thus the days when all the variables involved were laboriously worked out by hand or from massive tables before any fire orders could be given are now over—the computer age is with us, and to the Artillery the computer is now an invaluable aid. The Royal Artillery uses one well-tried and reliable system known as the Field Artillery Computer Equipment, but more generally referred to as FACE.

FACE was first considered as an adjunct to the Artillery in about 1963 when the commercial computer was still in its relative infancy. Several industrial and Ministry agencies were involved but the final contract went to Marconi as their Marconi-Elliott 920B computer formed the heart of the final production model. The first examples were issued to the Army in 1969.

FACE has two main artillery tasks. The first is survey, in which it computes all the variables involved with the meteorological data required by modern artillery, and can even make allowances for the earth rotation effects and differing latitudes. But the main task of FACE is fire control in which role it acts as a rapid processor for the mass of variables involved in firing artillery. The usual issue of FACE is one to a battery, whatever its nature, but when some batteries have to be split into components for various tasks, this issue is increased. A usual arrangement is one FACE to two troops. Normally two men man the computer, one actually operating the console and the other either operating the associated teleprinter/paper punch and the signal equipment—sometimes an extra man is used for this role. The operation of the FACE console is fairly straightforward as the computer is programmed to operate in a set sequence or drill which reduces operator error to a minimum.

To explain FACE operation it is perhaps best to follow a battery into action. Once in position the FACE is switched on using a 24 volt supply. A paper tape outlining all the information relevant to the type of gun (or rocket) in use is fed into the computer, followed by another tape with all the relevant weather and survey data. Once the tapes have been fed in the manual data is then inserted. This includes a pre-set sequence of information such as the centre of the battery position, the siting of the guns from that point, and the temperature of the ammunition charges to be used (such variables as muzzle velocity variations for each gun are already in the computer memory bank). Any meteorological variations are then fed in and the next information is the target data. This comes in the form of the target position (on a grid location), the types of projectile to be used, and the charges selected. The FACE then computes all the fire information needed for each gun, which in turn is displayed ready for voice transmission to the guns via land line or radio or, if it is in use, AWDATS (Artillery Weapon Data Transmission System). AWDATS presents the fire information to each gun on a display console next to the gun layer. Corrections, observed by the Forward Observation Officer (FOO), can be quickly fed into the computer and corrections are then made for each gun.

As well as these 'variable' targets, fire plans can be stored in FACE ready for use—up to 40 pre-planned targets can be stored ready to use, and of these, ten are automatically updated as meteorological variations are fed in. Each FACE can handle fire control orders for up to three batteries at their different locations and each of those batteries can be of up to eight guns.

The normal vehicle in which FACE is installed is the FV432 for service with BAOR batteries, while the towed batteries based in the United Kingdom have their FACE installations in Land Rovers. FACE has also been fitted to a few Bv202 Over-Snow vehicles.

Artillery Meteorological System (AMETS)

Until comparatively recently the art and science of artillery had little need to take the state of the weather into account, other than sometimes noticing the wind strengths in the immediate vicinity of a firing point. As artillery improved in range and power it was gradually noticed that weather phenomena could cause projectiles to deviate from their planned trajectories and the observation of meteorological factors became an important section of artillery studies. By the end of the Second World War the use of balloons and the consulting of meteorological instruments was commonplace and well-established, but the methods employed were often slow and cumbersome. With the advent of the fire control computer in the shape of FACE it became possible to take into account a whole range of factors that were up till then only theoretical niceties. Humidity, air density, air

FACE installation in a Land Rover, as used by the 105 mm Light Gun batteries (Marconi SDS Ltd).

temperatures at the altitudes modern projectiles could achieve, and many other meteorological measurements could be readily assimilated and calculated by a FACE computer, but the problem was how could this information be gathered and distributed in time to be useful to the accuracy of the guns?

The answer was to utilise modern data collecting and process techniques in the shape of data processors, radar, transmitting sensor carriers (or radiosondes), all combined in a new system. The United Kingdom Meteorological Office, Plessey and Marconi Space and Defence Systems Limited combined their resources to develop and produce the Artillery Meteorological System, or AMETS. AMETS has now been in Army service for some years but it is still far in advance of any similar weather data information gathering system in use by any other field army.

AMETS consists of several inter-related components. The heart of the system is contained in a Command Post Vehicle (or CPV) which contains the main data processor. This is the Marconi-Elliott 920B computer as used with FACE. Along with the other CPV equipment the computer is housed in a container body mounted on a 4-tonne truck (the truck also tows the main power generator for the system). Another vehicle tows a trailer carrying the tracking radar—the radar itself is a military version of a civil model known as WF3M. The other component is a specially-designed balloon-borne radiosonde which weighs 0.75 kg.

In action, the AMETS troop is usually situated near the front line and in the centre of the formation (usually a division) it is supplying with information. Every four hours (and sometimes more frequently), a radiosonde and balloon are prepared and launched. As they rise they are optically monitored until the radar picks them up, after which the tracking is automatic. As the radiosonde rises, the wind strengths and direction are automatically computed, and at fixed intervals, temperature and other readings are transmitted and automatically processed. In the CPV all this information is produced by the computer in paper tape form, fed into a teleprinter and transmitted to the customer FACE teleprinter terminals. From them, the information is fed into the FACE processors themselves. In the CPV a printed feed-out may also be used. Although a full radiosonde mission is released every four hours, updates of wind situations are made every hour by balloon tracking alone.

AMETS troops consist of about 20 men, and are part of the Locating Regiment under Corps HQ control. In action they are usually distributed one troop to a division and each troop is equipped to supply meteorological information to all the batteries and other customer units in that division.

The system has been designed to operate over a wide range of climatic conditions, and can be used in temperatures from -32 to +52°C. The radiosondes can supply data from up to 20,000 metres. AMETS is very mobile and easily serviced, and as all its components are well-tried and generally available, its reliability level is high. At present, AMETS is used to feed its data directly into battery FACE terminals. With the advent of BATES other forms of input at different command levels will become necessary, but it does not seem likely that the overall system will need to be altered to any great extent.

Position and Azimuth Determining System (PADS)

In modern warfare, the accuracy of weapon delivery systems is such that it becomes essential to know exactly where a potential target is situated. Just as important is to know exactly where the delivery system itself is located. Consequently there are several different systems currently employed to determine the exact location of a potential firing point, ranging from the time-honoured system of a finger on a map right up to the sophisticated systems associated with space satellites. The latter are very

accurate position indicators in themselves (and are likely to be much used by future location-assessing systems) but at present they are very expensive, and the necessary ground equipment is bulky and too costly to issue on a large scale. As a result the British Army has invested in a self-contained system known as PADS, or the Position and Azimuth Determining System.

PADS is a self-contained unit carried on vehicles or helicopters which is capable of determining the exact location of the vehicle relative to a fixed point. To use PADS the vehicle is positioned on or near an accurately-determined survey point. The co-ordinates are entered into the PADS panel and the vehicle can then move off. As the vehicle moves, the exact amount of movement and bearing shifts from the survey point are registered automatically by the PADS inertial navigation platform. The whole PADS system is self-contained and highly accurate. Up to an hour after the initial input of the survey point data, the PADS system can give the carrying vehicle position with an accuracy of about ten metres for both Eastings and Northings, and to an accuracy of less than one mil in azimuth. The data can then be used for navigation or for entry into FACE or any similar system. The data can also be used to locate minefields accurately, update maps, and for artillery survey.

The Army has invested heavily in PADS and consequently it will be an important part of their inventory in the 1980s. Produced by Ferranti, the PADS

Setting-up a PADS installed in a Bv202 (Ferranti).

system is housed in a single container weighing 35 kg. The dimensions of the container are 0.46 × 0.45 × 0.25 metres and the system runs off a single 28 volt DC power supply.

Battlefield Artillery Target Engagement System (BATES)

At present the overall fire control system of the British Army is still based at battery or regiment level with any overall command being given only in general terms or as part of a pre-set fire plan. Considering the size of the potential artillery threat to be encountered in any future European conflict, the best possible use has to be made of what artillery potential the British Army is likely to possess both now and in the future. This is going to involve a major shake-up of the way in which the artillery arm is organised at present, and a significant re-think in its communication and command equipment needs.

The potential problem was forecast in the mid-1970s, and the initial definite planning began in 1976. Several industrial and Ministry teams are involved in the final definition of what is already known as the Battlefield Artillery Target Engagement System, or BATES. As yet very little concrete evidence has emerged as to exactly what form the final system will take but it will be computerised, and it will have to be very flexible. A brief outline of what BATES will involve is given below.

1) An overall picture and command system which will present to all levels (battery, regiment, division, headquarters) the overall target situation to enable the best use possible to be made of the available resources, and to meet the most pressing needs at any one particular time.

2) The replacement of the existing FACE computers and their associated AWDATS. It may well be that the introduction of BATES will see a lessening of battery-level devices to enable an overall command system to be used.

3) A method of providing input from observation posts or officers, and providing reciprocal outputs. In this way fire orders and data can be fed into the system from the front line without disturbing the overall network, but enabling the central processing computers to issue the eventual fire orders or corrections.

4) The new system must be able to communicate with other command networks such as Wavell, using either the Ptarmigan trunk system or the Clansman combat radio nets, or both. It may well be that some form of intercommunication with other NATO systems will have to be incorporated. (The US Army has been working on a similar fire control system known as Tacfire since well before 1970.)

It is likely that BATES will initially be employed only with 1 (Br) Corps, but its introduction will still mean a major upheaval of existing artillery thinking and working methods even though it will be essential if the Royal Artillery is to be used to its maximum potential in any future major conflict. Modern artillery is a complex weapon but a very powerful one, and if that power is to be used to its full, a greater degree of overall control and co-ordination is necessary. The full introduction into service of the BATES network has been stated to be 'in the mid-1980s'.

As well as being involved in the BATES programme, Marconi Space and Defence Systems and Norden are also involved in the American Battery Computing System for the US Army. Indications have been given that the same model of computer will be used for both the American and British programmes.

The Corps of Royal Engineers & The Queen's Gurkha Engineers

The Royal Engineers have one main task—they provide military engineering support to the Defence Services. As far as the Army alone is concerned this means that they help the Army to fight, to live and to move, while at the same time denying the same functions to an enemy.

The main component of the Royal Engineers is the combat engineer. The modern combat engineer is a capable and skilled tradesman and technician and in a way he epitomises the wide variations in role and versatility that are typical of the Royal Engineers themselves. The combat engineer is first and foremost a trained soldier and well schooled in the basic Infantry and soldiering skills. He is also a trained combat engineer with all the specialist education that such a role involves, but in addition to the two above attributes every member of the Engineers can add a third function, for each man is also an artisan capable of turning his hand to a wide variety of tasks.

These tasks can involve a wide variety of military duties ranging from building a road through virgin country in all parts of the world to painting a sign to hang outside a building. The building itself may well have been built by the Engineers as well, for the Royal Engineers contain within their ranks some of the most widely diversified artisan skills that are to be found in any civil concern concerned in major civil engineering. But where the Royal Engineers differ from the civil concerns is in the fact that they also have to turn their hands to the military engineering tasks of bridging, road building and mending, battlefield constructions, life support constructions such as water supply and shelters and various other fieldworks. They are also concerned in such military functions as mine warfare, anti-tank obstacles and even such relatively peaceful duties as postal services, surveying and diving. Another Royal Engineer role that has both peacetime and wartime functions is bomb disposal.

In times of war, the combat engineer has to carry out a number of tasks and for this purpose they are organised into engineer regiments. In BAOR there are three types of engineer regiment, the armoured division engineer regiment, the Armoured Engineer Regiment and the Amphibious Engineer Regiment. The regiments based in the United Kingdom are known as Field Engineer Regiments. Of these regiments, the armoured division engineer regiment will be considered first.

Each regiment is made up of a regimental head-quarters and three field squadrons, and each is completely self-contained and can move and survive completely under its own resources. Once in action, the regiment has two prime functions. In defence, it has a responsibility to reduce the mobility of an enemy and protect friendly formations. In attack the engineer regiments have to remove obstacles and keep up the momentum of an advance.

The defensive role involves the engineer regiments in a number of tasks, as there are many different ways of placing obstacles in the path of an advancing force. One is mine laying and for this task the Royal Engineers use two main types of mine—the Bar Mine for use against tanks and the Ranger mine system for use against personnel. Other mines in use are the Horizontal Action anti-tank mine and the older Mine Mark 7. Since it is anticipated that any enemy advance would be based on large numbers of tanks and other types of AFV, the Engineers employ other obstacles against tanks, one of which is the time-honoured anti-tank ditch. Despite the simplicity of the ditch, it is still a very effective obstacle which can be crossed only by the use of specialised filling or crossing equipment which has to be employed under fire and with a subsequent loss of time and momentum. Other obstacles can be created by the use of explosives to produce craters and the demolition of bridges or structures to hinder the movement of mobile forces. Defensive positions and fire positions can also be dug, often at short notice. All these measures are carried out by the engineer regiments.

In the attack, the combat engineers have to keep the advance moving and this involves the removal or neutralising of obstacles. Mines can be cleared by the use of such devices as Giant Viper or mine detecting equipment. Ditches and wet gaps can be crossed by bridging equipment, both mobile and constructed, and physical obstacles can be cleared by the use of engineering plant and machinery.

From the precis of the role of the combat engineer given above it can be seen that the role of the armoured division engineer regiment is a very varied one. It will also be seen that the skills and equipment involved are complex too, and the combat engineer is not only trained to carry out all the many jobs involved but he also has to master the many types of equipment issued to the engineer regiments.

Each of the three field squadrons in an armoured division engineer regiment can turn its hand to any of the above-mentioned tasks. To enable this to be achieved the three field squadrons are organised into a squadron headquarters and three field troops. There is also a support troop at squadron level which holds the bulk of the specialised plant other than that held by the troops themselves, and another support squadron at regimental level holds the really heavy plant and such specialised equipment as bridging components. The field support squadron has three troops—a plant troop, a resources troop (which holds the bulk of the regimental stores) and a bridging troop.

As the name implies, the armoured division engineer regiments are based on the armoured FV432s and FV103 Spartans but of necessity they have to include a large wheeled transport element. Some of the plant is armoured, including the CET.

Within 1 (Br) Corps there are two further specialist engineer regiments. One is 32 Armoured Engineer Regiment under the control of HQ 1 (Br) Corps. This unit has the mobile bridging role and also operates the Centurion AVREs. The mobile bridges involved are carried by the FV4205 AVLBs based on the Chieftain chassis. 32 Armoured Engineer Regiment has a regimental HQ and two armoured engineer squadrons. Each squadron has its own squadron HQ troop and four armoured engineer troops.

The other specialist engineer unit is 28 Amphibious Engineer Regiment, also under the direct control of HQ 1 (Br) corps. This formation is equipped with the M2 bridging and ferrying vehicle, and has a regimental HQ and two am-

Above right *A Construction Troop* (MoD). **Right** *The Medium Field Support Crane—the Coles Hydra Husky 150T.* **Far right** *The TEREX TS-8 Motor Scraper.*

phibious engineer squadrons. Each squadron has two troops. A third squadron is a training squadron.

To back up the BAOR Royal Engineer regiments there are a further four field engineer regiments based in the United Kingdom, six TA engineer regiments and a number of independent field squadrons formed into two engineer brigades (29 and 30 Engineer Brigades). All these units are based on wheeled transport alone but they are completely self-contained and self-supporting. The organisation of the four TA regiments is based on three field squadrons whilst the four Regular engineer regiments in the United Kingdom differ in that one of their field squadrons is replaced by an airfield construction squadron. and they are equipped accordingly, but their organisation is similar to that of the field squadrons in that they have a squadron HQ and three construction troops, plus a further support troop. The four Regular field engineer regiments based in the United Kingdom are Nos 22, 36, 38 and 39.

In addition to the above formations, the Royal Engineers also provide two further specialist combat engineer units. These are 9 Parachute Squadron Royal Engineers, a squadron within 36 Engineer Regiment (which itself forms part of 1 Infantry Brigade); and 59 Independent Commando Squadron based at Plymouth. It supports all the Royal Marine Commando forces. This inter-service support function is not confined to the Royal Marines for the Royal Engineers also provide a support function for the Royal Air Force Harrier squadrons.

Inter-service support is also supplied by 42 Survey Engineer Regiment. This unit is based in the United Kingdom with a squadron (14 Topo Squadron) in BAOR, and both are primarily concerned with the supply of land maps to all three Services, even to the extent of providing the special moving map display 'hardware' fitted to most Royal Air Force tactical aircraft. The survey units not only draw, produce and supply the maps but they also provide a service known as TACIPRINT used mainly by the Army itself. TACIPRINT is a mapping system that can provide commanders with a large number of local area maps overprinted with the locations and natures of the units in the area concerned. Up to date maps can be provided in as little as 15 minutes by a self-contained unit based on a 4-tonne truck. It is planned that the use of TACIPRINT will spread to all units within 1 (Br)

Top left *The Heavy Crawler Tractor, a Caterpillar D6C.*
Above left *The new Heavy Crawler Tractor—the TEREX 82-30B.* **Left** *The Light Crawler Tractor.*

Corps by the end of 1981 but initially there was only one unit in BAOR with another based in the United Kingdom. As a result of the activities of the survey units, the Royal Engineers have a comprehensive library of maps of nearly all parts of the globe.

Another well-known Royal Engineer function is that of explosive ordnance disposal or EOD. The Royal Engineers have a precisely prescribed function in this area as they are responsible for EOD clearance above the high water mark but below ground and any devices delivered from the air. (The RAOC deals with above ground and terrorist-type devices, the Royal Air Force with all devices on their own property, and the Royal Navy with devices below the high water mark or underwater.) There is one Royal Engineer regiment for the EOD role, namely 33 Engineer Regiment (EOD) made up of one Regular squadron and two TA squadrons. The Regular squadron is 49 Squadron EOD, based at Lodge Hill Camp, near Rochester, and this unit, in addition to its other responsibilities, also provides support for the Defence EOD School, a tri-service organisation also based at Lodge Hill Camp. 49 Squadron has three troops. 1 Troop is at Felixstowe, 2 Troop at Aldershot and 3 Troop, together with the Squadron Support Troop, is at Lodge Hill Camp itself. All three troops contain civilian elements, especially 1 and 2, but 3 Troop is the one that is still responsible for clearing the old Luftwaffe bombs that continue to reveal themselves after years of concealment beneath the surface of the United Kingdom. The two TA squadrons are 590 and 591 Squadrons, Royal Engineers (Volunteers), both based at Rochester.

Another Royal Engineer function is that of postal and courier communications. The engineers provide post offices wherever the Army travels and at present are responsible for Forces Post Offices in the following locations: West Germany, Berlin, Belgium, Italy, Holland, Norway, Cyprus, Gibraltar, Sardinia, Hong Kong, Canada, Korea, Nepal, Saudi Arabia, Kenya, Belize and Portugal. In addition to these BFPOs the Royal Engineers also provide courier services for sensitive and classified documents, both in battle zones and across international frontiers. To carry out these tasks there are four Royal Engineers (Postal and Courier Communications) Regiments numbered 1 to 4. These regiments vary a great deal in composition and organisation and do not relate to any other

Top right *An armoured Wheeled Tractor fitted with a pallet lifting device, the Muir-Hill A5000 (more commonly used as a Bucket Loader).* **Above right** *The Light Mobile Digger, a trench digger based on a Thornycroft chassis.* **Right** *An Aveling-Barford MT Motor Grader.*

formations but they travel wherever the Army travels, and wherever the other two Services travel as well.

One further specialised RE unit is the 1st Fortress Specialist Unit, RE, which is based at Gibraltar. It provides general support to all the other units based on the Rock and is responsible for the general running and operation of the Ministry of Defence Dockyard (to be relinquished in the near future), the military power station, and the Rock's sea-water distillation plant which provides fresh water, not only for the garrison, but also for public supplies. The unit also provides other services as well.

To back up all the above Royal Engineer functions there are a number of stores depots dealing with Royal Engineer equipment and plant alone. The largest of these is at Long Marston, near

Stratford, but there are several others elsewhere.

With such a wide array of functions and talent at their disposal, all the Royal Engineer departments are much in demand in times of peace for a wide range of duties, often with a civilian leaning. Engineer units frequently find themselves carrying out projects in all parts of the globe building bridges, driving roads through wild country and providing the back-up for amenity programmes such as parks and sports facilities in many places. They are well able to carry out such programmes for as mentioned at the beginning of this section, each combat engineer, in addition to his soldiering and engineer skills, also has an artisan skill. A combat engineer who drives a CET may well be also trained as a signwriter, an AVRE Gunner may well be a sheet metalworker, and a Fitter RE may well double as a driver. In this way field squadrons could find themselves in Nepal building a school in a remote village, an airfield construction squadron could find itself converting a rubbish dump in Gibraltar into a small park and a field squadron may well apply its skills building a bridge in the wilds of Canada.

The Royal Engineers also provide divers for the Army. Within the Royal Engineers these divers are used for the clearing of underwater obstacles and mines in river crossings, and underwater demolition, as well as a number of more peacefully orientated functions. The divers are trained at Marchwood but there is another continuation school at Kiel.

All basic Royal Engineer recruit training is carried out by 1 Training Regiment RE at Hawley, near Cove in Hampshire. At the same location, combat engineering is carried out by 3 Training Regiment RE, but the really advanced engineer studies are carried out at the Royal School of Military Engineering based in the Chatham/Medway area. The RSME has six wings. The largest is the Field Engineer Wing which has an offshoot at the Armoured Engineer Wing at Bovington. Other wings are the Tactics Wing, the Signals Wing, the Plant, Roads and Airfields Wing, the Civil Engineering Wing and the Electrical and Mechanical Wing. There are also Royal Engineer training establishments at Newbury (for survey skills) and Mill Hill in London (for postal and courier operators). The Junior Leaders Regiment Royal Engineers is at Dover while the Army Apprentices College at Chepstow trains the future NCOs and specialist officers of the Royal Engineers. Between them, these last two establishments provide nearly half the

Above left *A Scammell LD55 dump truck, widely used by several units of the Royal Engineers.* **Left** *An armoured Fiat-Allis Medium Wheeled Tractor.*

soldiers for the corps.

The Royal Engineers also sponsor many TA units, and have an Engineer specialist pool of civilians who have skills that would be called upon in an emergency, but most of these specialists would be officers. The sponsored Royal Engineers TA units are as follows: 111 Engineer Regiment (Volunteers), 120 Field Squadron (Volunteers), 130 Field Squadron (Volunteers), 198 Engineer Park Squadron (Volunteers), 501-503 Specialist Teams (Bulk Petroleum) (Volunteers), 504 Specialist Team (Power Station) (Volunteers), 505 Specialist Team (Procurement) (Volunteers), 506 Specialist Team (Public Utilities) (Volunteers), 507 Specialist Team (Railway Construction Team BAOR) (Volunteers) and 525 and 526 Specialist Teams (Construction) (Volunteers).

All the above TA units are committed to either the AMF(L) or BAOR in an emergency and a perusal of their titles will give yet another indication of the wide and varied number of tasks the Royal Engineers are called upon to carry out. They also give another example of the way in which the Royal Engineers enable the Army to fight, live and move. If any further instance of the importance of the Royal Engineers is needed it can perhaps be provided by the fact that at any time the Royal Engineers have a stockpile of equipment worth some £12 million. There are Royal Engineers in Northern Ireland, Belize and Cyprus, while in Hong Kong the Brigade of Gurkhas have their own Gurkha Engineers in the form of the Queen's Gurkha Engineers. This is a regiment consisting of a regimental HQ and two field squadrons. They maintain close affiliations with the Royal Engineers.

Similarly, if any further example of the expertise of the Royal Engineers were needed it can be given by mentioning the Engineer officers who acquire professional qualifications within the corps. Certain officers, when they reach the age of 28 or 29, may decide to specialise in civil or electrical and mechanical engineering, which they can do while still serving within the corps. To achieve the necessary qualifications, these officers attend a two-year course, part of which is spent at the RSME Chatham and part working with civilian concerns. The end of the course brings with it certain civil professional qualifications, and the successful officers are then assigned to specialist teams based at Barton Stacey. There they can become involved with all aspects of engineering from basic design right through to the supervision of the actual construction work in all parts of the world. Much of this

is carried out for both military and civil agencies and ministries such as the Foreign and Commonwealth Office and the Overseas Development Agency. The specialist teams are assisted by Clerks of Works who are highly trained technicians drawn from the Royal Engineer artisan trades. In this low-key and rarely-mentioned manner the Corps of Royal Engineers act as quiet ambassadors in many parts of the globe.

The Army Air Corps

The Army Air Corps is one of the more recent additions to the corps and regiments of the British Army, despite the fact that the Army has long been involved in aviation (the Royal Engineers had a balloon section as early as 1873). The AAC was formed in September 1957 by amalgamating the old Glider Pilot Regiment with the Royal Air Force Air Observation Post squadrons—the latter being manned by Royal Artillery pilots, but the links with the RAF remain in the squadron designations, all of which begin with '6'.

The AAC has five main roles: 1) Observation and reconnaissance; 2) Armed action in the anti-tank role; 3) Direction of fire; 4) Command and control; and 5) Limited movement of men and material.

The modern AAC is an almost entirely helicopter-orientated corps—only a handful of their aircraft

Right *A combination pile driver/boring rig mounted on a Bedford TK chassis and used by Royal Engineer bomb-clearing teams.*

are fixed-wing. In common with the rest of the Army, the AAC is committed or stationed ready for service in Germany, and it is there that the five front-line Army Air Corps Regiments are based. The armoured divisions each have their own AAC Regiment. There is also a further regiment, 9 Regiment, under the control of HQ 1 (Br) Corps.

Each of these AAC Regiments has two squadrons, each with 12 helicopters. Each squadron has its own particular role, in that one squadron is primarily a reconnaissance unit equipped with Gazelles and the other is an anti-tank squadron equipped with the Lynx (at the time of writing the transition from the Scout to the Lynx is still not complete). Each regiment is completed by a REME Light Aid Detachment (LAD) so that a full AAC regiment numbers some 229 all ranks.

The AAC presence in Germany is completed by a flight of four Gazelles based at Wildenrath for the use of HQ BAOR, and there is a further flight of three Gazelles at Gatow for the support of the Berlin Brigade. To coordinate the AAC activity in Germany there is also an AAC HQ based in Germany. Those AAC squadrons based in Germany are Nos 651, 652, 653, 654 and 659, together with 661, 662, 663, 664 and 669.

While the organisation of the AAC in Germany can be seen from the above to be fairly straightforward, the organisation of the rest of the corps is rather more complex, and like that of the rest of the Army at present it is subject to change and amendment.

One of the UK-based AAC units is 7 Regiment located at Netheravon. It has but one squadron, No 658, which is intended for service with 5 Infantry Brigade in an emergency. No 7 Regiment does have a further two flights, one of which (2 Flight) is assigned as the AAC contribution to the AMF(L) and equipped with six Gazelles, while the other, (3 Flight), normally forms part of the Northern Ireland garrison, although from time to time it does travel back to the mainland for odd periods. No 658 Squadron itself has two flights. One is 6 Flight equipped with six Gazelles which, in addition to its other duties, has the responsibility for carrying PSIs (PSI is the current term for what were known as VIPs—a PSI is a Person of Special Importance). The remaining 658 Squadron component is 8 Flight equipped with eight Scouts and they, in addition to their other duties, have the role of supporting the various Arms Schools and Staff Colleges.

No 656 Squadron is based at Farnborough and supports 1 Infantry Brigade. It has two flights, one equipped with six Gazelles and the other with six Scouts, but the latter are due to be replaced by the Lynx by 1983. No 657 Squadron is based at Oakington in support of 19 Infantry Brigade, and 655 Squadron is based at Topcliffe with the role of supporting 24 Infantry Brigade in Germany—both have the same composition as 656 Squadron.

All AAC Squadrons spend some of their operational time on 'roulement' tours in Northern Ireland, but unlike the rest of the Army, they take their operational equipment with them and use their helicopters in the anti-terrorist and liaison roles.

Away from the United Kingdom the AAC has units in Cyprus equipped with the last of the AAC Alouette 2s. There are two separate flights equipped with this helicopter, one of three at Dekhelia and the other, also with three machines, in support of UNFICYP at Nicosia. In the Far East, 660 Squadron is based at Sek Kong in the New Territories of Hong Kong—they have six Scouts with a further three supporting the Gurkhas in Brunei. In Belize there is a section of three Gazelles detached from UKLF, and further north in Canada, BATUS has a Scout and Beaver on its permanent strength. Every year a number of AAC helicopters are sent to BATUS to support the various tactical exercises that take place there, but they are not permanently stationed in Canada.

The only other service unit to mention is the Beaver Flight, whose aircraft are deployed wherever they are needed, including Northern Ireland. This is the last fixed-wing element of the AAC (apart from the training Chipmunks) and its strength is variable.

Middle Wallop is the home of the AAC. It is also its main training base and acts as the home for some of the AAC supporting arms. The three largest non-AAC units at Middle Wallop are the Aircraft Engineering Training Wing REME, 70 (Aircraft) Workshop REME, and 1 Aircraft Support Unit RAOC. Middle Wallop also acts as the Depot AAC and houses the headquarters of the Director AAC.

Perhaps the best way of describing the training functions which are carried out at Middle Wallop would be to follow the career path of a typical AAC soldier. A new recruit to the AAC carries out his basic military training with the RAC at Catterick and then proceeds to driver training with the RCT. From there he goes to the AAC Centre at Middle Wallop for the training to become a groundcrewman. This training involves aircraft training and basic signalling. He is then assigned to a squadron. After a minimum of two years he can apply to become an aircrewman. If he passes the necessary selection process the potential aircrewman will return to Middle Wallop for a ten-week course covering such items as map reading, air OP (the direction of artillery fire), flight servicing, basic tactics and other such skills. He will also be given some

A Gazelle lands to refuel from a Bedford MK equipped with bulk refuelling equipment.

very basic flying training so that he will be able to land a helicopter in an emergency. From this course the aircrewman will be sent as an Aircrewman/Observer to a reconnaissance squadron flying Gazelles, but a further four-week course is necessary to convert the aircrewman into an Air Gunner to fire the TOW missiles carried by the Lynx squadrons, or the SS11s carried by the Scouts.

The aircrewman will then spend at least two years with a squadron before he can apply to become a pilot. Subject to his CO's recommendation he will be sent to the Aircrew Selection Centre at RAF Biggin Hill to assess his basic aptitudes for the task. If he passes the Biggin Hill requirements he will then return to Middle Wallop to go before the AAC Pilot Selection Board to discover whether or not he is really suitable for the role of an AAC pilot. If he manages to meet the AAC board requirements he can then proceed to his pilot training proper.

Before the flying training commences, all NCOs are given a five-week pre-flying training course, but the real flying starts with the Basic Squadron. The Basic Squadron is equipped with the fixed-wing Chipmunk T.10s and all the flying instruction is given by civilian instructors. The basic instruction period involves 60 flying hours which takes 12 weeks. Once qualified as a fixed-wing pilot, the trainee then passes on to the Basic Helicopter Flight. This flight is an all-civilian establishment

equipped with civil Bell 47G-4s and this stage of the training lasts a further 60 hours over a period of ten weeks. Then comes a one-week course away from Middle Wallop at Seafield Park where the trainee is given some aero-medical training and undergoes ditching drills and the like. It is then back to Middle Wallop for a session with the Advanced Rotary-Wing Squadron and the conversion to the Gazelle. This is the longest part of the course and occupies 115 flying hours spread over 16 weeks. From here the pilot can be assigned to a squadron but if he is to be sent to a Scout squadron a further 48 hours' training is necessary, spread over a further seven weeks. At present a newly trained pilot would not convert directly to the Lynx without the minimum of one year with a squadron, but when he does convert the course lasts 40 flying hours over eight weeks.

As can be seen from the above, becoming an AAC pilot is no easy matter but the AAC does accept trainee pilots from all branches of the Army. Volunteers have to undergo the same selection procedure as the AAC personnel but once trained they stay with the AAC for a three-year tour. After that, the officers and NCOs are given the opportunity of staying with the AAC or returning to their parent regiments or corps (subject to there being places for them in the AAC). Officers with a career path to follow often return to their original units and may return to the AAC later during their careers, but some do stay. NCOs usually opt to stay with the AAC.

There is one further path into the ranks of AAC pilots and that is by way of a direct entry. There are very few selected for this path as AAC pilots have to have a considerable amount of Army experience to enable them to carry out their job to the full—the normal AAC path ensures that a potential pilot has at least five years of Army experience, and secondment and transfer from other branches ensures that trained soldiers only are chosen. Therefore the direct entry method is rarely encountered and is usually limited to around six hopefuls a year. If the potential direct entry pilots manage to pass the Biggin Hill and Middle Wallop selection processes, they are sent to Sandhurst for the six month Standard Military Course (they stay there for 12 months if they take the Regular Career Course), and then have to spend six months with an Infantry unit before they can even start their flying training.

As well as training AAC personnel, the AAC Centre at Middle Wallop is responsible for training Royal Marine aircrew, and also training the REME technicians who look after the AAC aircraft. Middle Wallop also houses the WRAC personnel who assist in the handling of the resident aircraft. They, like all the other arms and services not part of the AAC but who are stationed in AAC units, wear the distinctive light blue beret but with their own parent cap badge.

With the field units the Gazelle has established itself as a good sturdy battlefield helicopter with a lively performance. The Scout, now in the process of being gradually replaced by the Lynx, is still assured of a place within the AAC ranks for some while to come as its strong construction and functional basic design combine still to give the airframes a considerable number of flying hours ready to be utilised. With the anti-tank squadrons the Lynx/TOW combination looks like being a real winner. The Lynx itself has a good performance and while it lacks the armament potential of the various American 'gunships', its large fuselage makes it a much more versatile and useful load carrier. No doubt, in time, the TOW misile armament will be replaced by something even more potent against enemy AFVs. Meanwhile, for the foreseeable future the venerable Beaver plods on, and it will be interesting to see what form of fixed-wing aircraft, if any, will replace this versatile aircraft.

The Special Air Service Regiment

Despite the attention directed towards the Special Air Service Regiment by the various forms of the media in recent years, very little can be written regarding this most unusual formation as it does not welcome publicity and, indeed, at the time of writing it is still an offence to even take a photograph of a member of the regiment. Much has been written about the SAS, much of it sheer twaddle, for the regiment by its very nature attracts the romantically minded or the scrutiny of the very people the SAS is currently employed to combat. But despite all this attention it is still difficult to write anything really definite regarding the SAS.

There is only one Regular Special Air Service formation, namely the 22nd SAS, based at Hereford. Formed in 1950, the SAS is the modern equivalent to the various deep penetration and disruption units that sprang up during the Second World War in all theatres and caused so much havoc to their enemies by their unconventional methods and tactics. In time of war the SAS would retain the same role, namely that of penetrating the rear echelons of the enemy and disrupting communications, while at the same time carrying out reconnaissance of rear areas and targets. Exactly how the SAS would go about this operational task it is not possible to mention, or even discover, but the SAS is committed to the Strategic Reserve of the Supreme Allied Commander Europe (SACEUR).

Although the SAS has this war commitment, it has become better known in the public eye for its counter-insurgency role in Northern Ireland and elsewhere. This task was first carried out during the Malayan emergency and has continued ever since—the Ulster campaign is just another job to be carried out for the SAS and is, for them, nothing special. Again, exactly how the SAS conducts its role in Northern Ireland is very difficult to discover, but it has been involved in ambushes, the surveillance of suspected terrorist caches and arms dumps, the establishment of hidden sentry posts in rural and town areas, and the general infiltration of organisations known or suspected of being involved in revolutionary activities. All these tasks have to be carried out in a clandestine manner and as a result the SAS has gained for itself a notoriety out of all proportion to its involvement for even at the busiest periods of the Ulster situation it is doubtful if there are ever more than about 160 SAS members in the province. But the general 'success' rate has been high, even if many of the results of SAS activities seldom become known to the general public. The assault on the Iranian Embassy in London is, of course, an exception to this 'rule'.

From the above, it will become obvious that nothing definite can be written on the organisation of the 22nd Special Air Service Regiment. It is known that the three Regular SAS squadrons are

Corps badges. 1 *General Service Corps.* **2** *The Royal Regiment of Artillery.* **3** *The Royal Horse Artillery.* **4** *The Royal Engineers Regiment.* **5** *The Queen's Gurkha Engineers.* **6** *The Army Air Corps.* **7** *The Special Air Service Regiment.* **8** *The Small Arms School Corps.* **9** *The Royal Corps of Signals.* **10** *The Gurkha Signals.* **11** *The Royal Electrical and Mechanical Engineers.* **12** *The Royal Corps of Transport.* **13** *The Gurkha Transport Regiment.* **14** *The Intelligence Corps.* **15** *The Royal Army Ordnance Corps.* **16** *The Army Catering Corps.*

committed to SACEUR in time of war, and that the squadrons (known as 'Sabre' squadrons—SAS members are 'Troopers') are broken down operationally to what are virtually individual teams which vary in size but are usually limited to four men. Each unit member has a particular specialised skill, and a typical team would consist of a signaller, a weapon specialist, a medical specialist and a linguist. All these skills are supposed to be interchangeable but exactly how they are imparted has not been made public. The size of the team will vary according to the specific task and the theatre of operations, but each member is trained to act independently and consequently each SAS trooper may be given responsibilities out of all proportion to his rank or position when related to other arms of the Forces. The equipment of the SAS is also a matter of conjecture, but it is known that SAS members often have their own choice of individual weapons. It can only be assumed that the operational equip-

ment chosen will suit the role being carried out, but it has been noticeable that the Land Rovers once often seen at various Army displays on SAS display stands, and which were liberally covered in machine-guns redolent of the 'Popski's Private Army' era, are now conspicuous by their absence.

The SAS is now the only unit within the Army which does not recruit direct from the general public. SAS members are all trained soldiers who have spent some time in the Army, and are all volunteers. Admission to the SAS is no easy course of action, for all potential recruits have to undergo a four-week selection course which is held twice a year. The course is a strenuous one involving not only tests of physical stamina (which sometimes hit the headlines when a course member becomes a casualty as a result) but tests of mental ability and determination to carry out assigned tasks with no imposed stimulii. Once past this exacting selection process the SAS member has to undergo what must be very involved training programmes before the operational roles can even be attempted (one important item of note regarding the training is that the SAS Trooper is trained as an individual and is personally responsible for his own follow-on training instigation and implementation), and it must be tempting to think of the SAS troopers as being very much members of an elite formation. The truth is that they do not regard themselves as such. They are selected from what are already regarded as elite formations (most SAS personnel seem to come from either the Guards Division, the Household Cavalry or the Parachute Regiment), and to them the SAS is just a unit with a role to play, albeit an unusual and flexible one. But the SAS does have its own particular distinctions.

For a start, the SAS is not part of the Infantry or indeed of any other branch of the Army, and it has its own Directorate. Individual members, both troopers and officers, cannot be named or identified publicly, which to the general public would seem to bestow a 'cloak and dagger' image, but such a policy is essential in view of the SAS's operational and peacetime roles. The number of soldiers within the SAS is never disclosed, nor is their participation in any particular campaign, although their involvement in Northern Ireland was announced as the result of a political decision. Another 'distinction' is that the SAS uniform or badge is seldom seen worn in public, for very often SAS members assume the uniforms or badges of other regiments, especially during counter-insurgency operations.

From all the above, it will be seen that the SAS is very much an undercover unit with an operational role in peace and war that will seldom gain much public recognition. To many the very nature, or indeed the existence of the SAS, may seem to be at variance with the generally established form of

Corps Badges. 1 *The Royal Pioneer Corps.* **2** *The Royal Army Education Corps.* **3** *The Royal Army Medical Corps.* **4** *The Royal Army Dental Corps.* **5** *Queen Alexandra's Royal Army Nursing Corps.* **6** *The Royal Army Veterinary Corps.* **7** *The Army Physical Training Corps.* **8** *The Corps of Royal Military Police.* **9** *The Military Provost Staff Corps.* **10** *The Ulster Defence Regiment.* **11** *The Royal Army Chaplains' Department.* **12** *The Gibraltar Regiment.* **13** *The Royal Army Pay Corps.* **14** *The Women's Royal Army Corps.* **15** *The Royal Military Academy Sandhurst.* **16** *The Royal Military School of Music.*

modern society, but such are the enemies who are set against the way we live that it is inevitable that corresponding measures have to be taken. The SAS has assumed some of those measures and its operational role has evolved from them—those who decry the activities and existence of the SAS would do well to remember why it is necessary.

The Small Arms School Corps

The Small Arms School Corps is a relatively small but important adjunct to the School of Infantry, based at Warminster. Stated briefly, its role is to maintain a high level of small arms skill and impart the same skills to the Army as a whole and the Infantry in particular. The SASC tends to regard itself as rather an Infantry elite, which indeed it is, for its role has an impact out of all proportion to numbers.

The SASC makes up the staff of the Small Arms Wing of the School of Infantry. This is divided between Warminster, which primarily caters for the man-carried weapons, and the Support Weapons Wing situated at nearby Netheravon. At both establishments, and the various depots and training establishments where SASC instructors spread their message, the SASC is concerned with the expertise necessary to use and maintain Infantry weapons in the field, and apart from the mere mechanics concerned, the corps has established an enviable reputation for marksmanship, a cachet borne out by the high number of Bisley prizes won by the SASC and the degree of expertise gained by the snipers trained by the corps. Perhaps one of the most important present-day influences of the SASC can be seen in the firepower philosophy of the Army. Prompted in no small way by the tactical situations prevalent in Northern Ireland, the accent on marksmanship imparted by the SASC has meant that the modern Army is now almost alone in devoting so much effort and training to the skill. Many other armies have now adopted the 'area fire' method of spraying areas with barrages of automatic fire to saturate any possible target. While this may be argued as effective, it is very wasteful in ammunition and manpower, and these are two assets the British Army does not possess. Consequently the British soldier is trained to make every shot tell, to conserve ammunition and to maintain a high degree of fire discipline.

Apart from maintaining a pool of highly skilled weapons technicians, the SASC also has a trials and development function based at Warminster. It is thus involved with the current trials being carried out with the 5.56 mm Individual and Light Support

SASC marksman using the 7.62 mm L42A1 sniper's rifle.

Weapons and also with the introduction of Milan into service.

The Royal Corps of Signals & Gurkha Signals

The role of the Royal Corps of Signals within the modern Army is much the same as it has been ever since the corps was first formed in 1920. Its role is to provide and maintain rapid, accurate and reliable communication systems for the Army, both when it is at peace or when it is engaged in a war. While the role may not have changed, the importance of effective communications certainly has, for a modern army cannot fight, move, feed, be maintained or be supplied without vast networks of inter-connecting communications of every conceivable kind. It might even be stated that modern warfare as it is now envisaged quite simply cannot take place outside the umbrella of costly and sophisticated command communication networks. With this in mind it can be seen that the task of the Royal Signals is thus essential to the smooth-running fighting effectiveness of the Army in times of war, and in peacetime it is no less essential for the day-to-day running and routine.

The importance of signals to the Army can be seen in that at any time 8.8 per cent of the soldier establishment is made up of Royal Signals personnel. Among officers the percentage is around seven per cent. As with all the other regiments and corps of the Army, all members of the Royal Signals are fully trained soldiers capable of carrying out all the many duties of fighting troops. What separates them from the rest of the Army is the involved and intensive technical training that enables them to use some of the most modern and effective communications equipment in operational use anywhere in the world. The varied and complicated signals equipment issued to the Army is equal or superior to any comparable equivalent anywhere, and the Royal Corps of Signals is more than equal to its task and provides a service to the Army that is capable of meeting any challenge. From telephones to communication satellites, the corps has a role and a task, and wherever the Army is stationed, there you will find the Royal Signals.

Signals in BAOR

Within 1 (Br) Corps there are the three armoured divisions, each of which has a signals regiment at headquarters level—indeed the signals regiment also supplies the main establishment of the armoured divisional headquarters, which gives an indication of the importance of the Signals role to the modern Army. Each signals regiment has an establishment of 700-800 men, divided among eight signal squadrons. In the armoured division, apart from the headquarters role, the Royal Signals provide and maintain telecommunications down to task force level, not forgetting the vital links to rear. Below the task force level each individual unit is responsible for its own particular communications equipment but the Royal Signals also provide partial repair facilities for front-line sets by supplying repair units at battalion and other levels—these repair units are concerned only with front line repairs.

Above the divisional level is 1 (Br) Corps Headquarters which has two Corps Signals Regiments, one concerned with forward communications (ie, towards the front line) and the other to the rear. Both these regiments at present use the Bruin command communication system but by the time these words are read this may well have been supplanted by Ptarmigan, the first phase of which was due to be initiated during 1979-80 at a cost of £130 million. Both Bruin and Ptarmigan provide modern and advanced command networks, but Bruin has several disadvantages that the Army will remove by the delayed introduction of Ptarmigan, not the least of which is that Ptarmigan will extend to the rear as far as the Channel Coast, an asset not shared by the present Bruin system. It is planned that Ptarmigan will effectively replace the Bruin set-up by 1983, but this should not detract from the fact that Bruin is a system well in advance of any other similar system at present in operational service anywhere in the world. It provides rapid and versatile telecom-

munication switching facilities for command networks with far greater facility than anything comparable, but it is made up mainly from commercially available components and units and thus lacks the complete battle-readiness that the Ptarmigan system will provide with its more advanced solid-state technology.

Ptarmigan will provide communications down to divisional and even task force level from where the Clansman (and perhaps Larkspur, if any sets are still in service) combat networks take over. The Clansman system is very much a 'user arm' facility, and the user arms themselves organise how the Clansman networks should be set up and operated, but the Royal Signals are always on hand to advise and make basic running repairs.

Also in the Corps/armoured division network will be the Wavell automatic data processing system which is expected to be in full use by the mid-1980s. In time this will be joined by BATES, but both will depend on the Ptarmigan network.

One innovation, first introduced in 1979, was the establishment of a new Royal Signals responsibility in the shape of an electronic warfare formation at 1 (Br) Corps level. This unit is the 14th EW Regiment which has the active roles of locating and disrupting enemy communications, combined with the passive role of intercepting and listening to enemy signal traffic. At the time of writing the full equipment for this unit had yet to be decided.

While Ptarmigan can be extended to the Channel Coast, it is intended as a command network only. For the bulk of the day-to-day and routine signal traffic the Army relies on STARRNET, a microwave signal link that connects all the main garrisons and headquarters within the BAOR area. This is yet another Royal Signals responsibility for 4 Signal Group both controls and commands STARRNET from the joint headquarters at Rheindahlen.

A more peaceable role for the Royal Signals, under their Communications Project Agency (or CPA—they were also involved in STARRNET), is the provision of television for the British Forces and their families in Germany. This important link with the United Kingdom and 'home' is still being developed and expanded, with the home link at Wembley and the main control link in Germany at Rheindahlen.

Apart from the services provided to BAOR, the Royal Signals also have responsibilities for other arms of the Forces and NATO allies. The Royal Signals provide ground communications for the Royal Air Force squadrons using the Harrier GR Mark 3 in support of ground forces. Other Royal Signals units provide links with NATO armies on either side of 1 (Br) Corps operational area within NORAG. There is a Royal Signals component at SHAPE, and also at AFCENT.

Like so much else in BAOR, the present Royal Signals establishment is likely to alter to meet changing operational requirements. New equipment and methods are always being introduced and once the full Ptarmigan/Clansman networks have been established along with their attendant services and user systems, the Royal Signals will be in control of the finest combat signals network the world has yet seen, notwithstanding the fact that their present systems have no parallel.

Signals in the United Kingdom

Whereas the main function of the Royal Signals in BAOR is a straightforward one of being prepared for a possible conflict, the function of the Corps in the United Kingdom is rather more complex. The Royal Signals not only retain their normal duties of providing communications for the Army (and partially for the other Armed Services and NATO), but also provide a back-up force for BAOR and at the same time have to stand ready for possible use anywhere in the world.

The general shape of the Royal Signals organisation within the United Kingdom can be generally seen in the organisational chart overleaf. Very roughly there are four signal brigades dealing with 18-plus signal regiments and two independent signal squadrons (No 240 based at York and No 241 based at Edinburgh). Of the four signal brigades, No 1 has a very active role in that it not only provides the 'go-anywhere' component in 30 Signal Regiment, based at Blandford, but it also provides the headquarters and signal squadrons for each of the three infantry brigades based in the United Kingdom, and also provide a signal squadron for the AMF(L) force—this is 249 Signal Squadron based at Old Sarum.

The other three signal brigades, Nos 2, 11 and 12, have a total of 14 Signals Regiments, ten of which are Regular and four Territorial, but a fair proportion of some regiments is made up from civilian personnel. Some of these regiments are intended for use in Europe in an emergency while others will support 5 Infantry Brigade or home-based garrisons. To this end, United Kingdom-based signal units generally use a mixture of Clansman and Larkspur equipments but instead of the combat networks set up in Germany, local commanders will use a signal system known as MOULD. MOULD is a VHF command net system which is roughly equivalent to the existing police radio relay networks and is operated by a system of remote repeater stations

that are almost entirely automatic to the extent that they switch in alternative components in the event of equipment failure. The remote nature of the system can be seen in the fact that only about 12 men are needed to service the whole of the national MOULD network. MOULD operates within each Military District, but is a command network for use in times of emergency—the more usual day-to-day communications are carried either by normal Post Office land-lines or BOXER micro-wave links.

The United Kingdom signals organisation is also responsible for the many and varied tasks that are given to the Army whenever diplomatic or emergency conditions necessitate sending formations on overseas missions. As mentioned above, No 1 Signal Brigade becomes involved on these occasions and as it is often moved to some rather remote locations, the use of space satellites for signal relay comes into play. The Royal Signals is equipped for this role with four rather elderly TSC-502 ground-based signal stations which can be carried by Land Rovers. The satellite used when possible is Skynet 1 which is fixed in orbit over the Indian Ocean (a relic of the days when larger British forces were stationed in the Middle and Far East), but other satellites can be used. These far-flung stations are used to provide rear links back to the United Kingdom only.

Signals in Northern Ireland

The peculiar nature of the presence of the Army in Northern Ireland has led to some rather unique signals situations in that province. The organisation there consists mainly of four independent signal squadrons. The overall command is exercised by a Lieutenant-Colonel who commands one of the squadrons as well.

As the Army is working directly with the civilian police force the choice of suitable communications equipment has been met by purchases of commercial models such as the Pye Westminster and Stornophone CQP 863. Some of these have fared less well than their military counterparts might have done but the conditions in some areas of Ulster would render communications difficult under any circumstances. One relative innovation that has been highly developed in Northern Ireland is the use of colour television as a command and surveillance aid. In the command role, unit commanders regularly attend closed-circuit operational or information briefings, and Heli-telly is in regular use.

The four Signals units permanently in Ulster are 223 Signal Squadron (Northern Ireland), 3rd Infantry Brigade HQ and Signal Squadron, 8th Infantry Brigade HQ and Signal Squadron and 39th Infantry

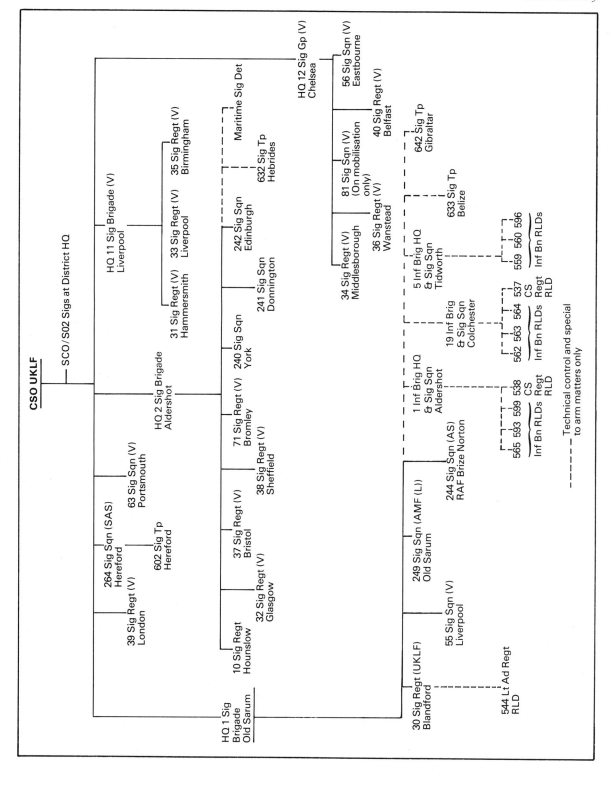

Brigade HQ and Signal Squadron. Together they provide a radio relay system, and ULSTERNET which covers the whole of the Six Counties.

Signals training

The 'home' of the Royal Corps of Signals is now Blandford in Dorset, despite the fact that many serving officers and signallers were initially trained to regard Catterick in Yorkshire as their base. The Royal Signals Headquarters Mess moved from Catterick to Blandford in 1967 and it is there that the School of Signals is situated today. The school provides both officers' and NCOs' training courses in all aspects of military signalling and the associated technologies involved, but it has other roles. These include the development of new signal equipment, the running of the various trials involved in such a task, and even at times the very manufacture and testing of the 'one-off' or specialised pieces of equipment.

Catterick still remains the main training base for the Royal Signals as it is the home of the Training Group Royal Signals. This group has three main elements. The first is 11 Signal Regiment, based at Catterick itself. This regiment is entrusted with basic recruit training and also concerns itself with the Junior Signallers Wing at Ouston, near Newcastle. The largest of all the Royal Signals regiments is 8 Signal Regiment, also at Catterick, which usually has around 1,000 men under trade training at any one time. The third of the training group elements is the Army Apprentice College at Harrogate, which is now concerned only with the training of junior technicians for the Royal Signals. All three of these elements are commanded by the Training Group Headquarters.

Mention must also be made of the Signal Training Centre in Scarborough which acts as a training centre and base for Royal Signals TA units. Some regular refresher training also takes place at Scarborough.

Signallers have a choice of five different types of trade grouping within the Royal Signals (not including bandsmen). These are electronics, telegraphy, combat, administrative and supervisory. (Electronic warfare [EW] specialists are mainly contained in the telegraphy group.)

It would not be possible to mention the Royal Corps of Signals without making some mention of its display team, the White Helmets. This motor cycle display team is now world-famous, and anyone who has witnessed its high-speed routines can be excused from forgetting that the motor cycle is now no longer used operationally by the Royal Signals, which puts the White Helmets into the same bracket as the King's Troop, RHA.

NATO communications

One of the most important requirements of NATO is secure and reliable communications between the member nations, both on a military and a political level. Ever since the Washington Treaty was signed a great deal of time and effort has been expended on the subject of inter-NATO telecommunications and the work continues even now. From the outset the British Army, and in particular the Royal Corps of Signals, has been involved in all the several systems that have been set up, and it will also be involved in the many future developments.

The basis of most inter-NATO communications was, and still is to a great extent, the existing telephone networks set up by the various Post Office agencies of the member nations. Calls to and from the military are often carried on public lines or on lines rented from the agencies for exclusive military use. While this has the advantage of using an existing system, it can be expensive and security is an ever-present problem. As a result, a decision was taken during the late 1950s to set up an exclusive NATO communications network that was partially completed in the early 1960s and known as 'Ace High'. The 'Ace High' network uses the tropospheric-scatter system, is primarily concerned with the NATO early-warning system and is almost completely used as a command level network. 'Ace High' covers the NATO area from Norway to Turkey, and provides high capacity microwave links for voice and telegraph circuits. The equipment used varies from country to country and is usually readily available material.

By the late 1960s 'Ace High' was given the backing of another high-level system known as the NATO-Wide Communications System (NICS), mainly reserved for top-level exchanges of political and intelligence information. At this stage the decision was taken to extend the reliability and eventual survival of NATO communications by the use of space satellite links. This became reality in March 1970 when the first of two satellites was launched and later the same year SATCOM came into service. SATCOM is the acronym for NATO Satellite Communications, and nearly every NATO member nation has a ground relay station. The system is at present being extended to provide a battlefield tactical network.

Another current programme is to provide a more modern, all-automatic, NICS with fully automatic message switching and dial telephone facilities along the lines of the various STD systems used by many European telecommunication agencies. The new NICS will not replace 'Ace High' or any of the earlier networks but will use their existing facilities in a more modern integrated form.

The British Army is deeply involved in all the various NATO networks and is partially responsible for the links within the United Kingdom. All three British armed services use the BOXER microwave link system mentioned earlier. Originally known as MUKRCS, BOXER provides links between all the major garrisons of the United Kingdom and their various command centres. It has been designed to involve as little manpower as possible and interconnects not only with the various NATO networks (of which it is the United Kingdom carrier) but also with STARRNET.

Ptarmigan

Modern armies depend to a far greater extent on their communications than they have ever done before in the history of warfare. Today, mobile forces can only move, fight and even exist within the framework of commands, information and all the mundane day-to-day routine provided by the links of their communication systems. Thus, in the modern British Army the provision of reliable and secure communications is as important as the provision of modern weapons. By the time these words are published the Army will be using some of the most advanced communication equipment in service anywhere in the world in the shape of Ptarmigan.

Ptarmigan provides the main information links which route all the Army's routine and tactical information from corps HQ down to the front line units. It is a mobile, automatically switched and secure area communication system designed to provide a very high measure of reliability and traffic capacity. It is also compatible with existing NATO systems.

Like so many programmes of a similar nature, Ptarmigan development has a fairly long history. The British Army was for years after the war searching for the answer to the secure area communications problem to replace the rather cumbersome systems built up during the war years and retained only because there were no funds to replace them. One of these early development projects was 'Project Hobart' which had to be abandoned due to the high costs that would ultimately have been involved. Then came 'Project Mallard', an international project involving the United Kingdom, Australia, Canada and the USA. The project began in 1967 but ended in 1969 when the US withdrew as the result of a political decision. But Project Mallard had shown the needs and the basic outlines of what any new system would require. Already the basic outlines were approaching the hardware stage as the 1 (Br) Corps in Germany began to be issued with the interim Bruin communication system, in the

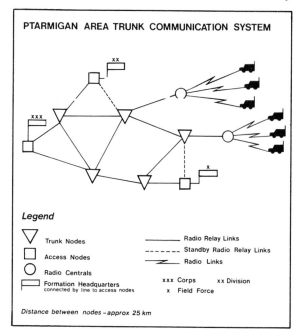

PTARMIGAN AREA TRUNK COMMUNICATION SYSTEM

Legend

▽ Trunk Nodes
☐ Access Nodes
◯ Radio Centrals
⊏ Formation Headquarters
   connected by line to access nodes

——————— Radio Relay Links
- - - - - - - Standby Radio Relay Links
⚡ Radio Links

xxx Corps   xx Division
      x Field Force

Distance between nodes – approx 25 km

hopes that Project Mallard would eventually replace it. With the demise of Project Mallard, Bruin was improved somewhat and its expected service life was extended.

Bruin is still a unique communication system in that it employs a secure system of links using a digital-based switching system. Despite its advanced nature and widespread use it does have several disadvantages which the Army wishes to have eliminated. One of these is that it has a distinct limitation on the amount of traffic it can handle, and there are restrictions on its operational flexibility. On the technical side, much of the equipment used was obtained from existing commercial sources and consequently some items lack the capabilities required. For example, most of the switching is carried out by electro-magnetic gear with all their attendant maintenance and reliability problems. Another difficulty is that, although messages are transmitted in pulsed (digital) form, they have to be converted to and from conventional electrical waveforms (analogue) before transmission and after reception—this adds to the reliability and maintenance workload.

Despite its present problems, Bruin provides 1 (Br) Corps with the outlines and experience of the next generation of communication systems. The British Army decided to adopt their new system, soon known as Ptarmigan, in 1973, and at the time of writing development is almost complete with a date into service stated to be in the early 1980s.

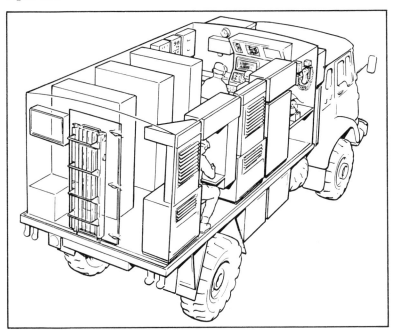

Far left *Basic layout of a Ptarmigan system* (MoD). **Left** *A Ptarmigan installation on a 4-tonne truck* (Plessey). **Right** *Triffid equipment installed here in a building* (Marconi).

From the outset, experience gained with Project Mallard was used but even so, a large number of agencies were involved. The British communications industry was deeply involved from the start and Plessey were appointed prime contractor in 1973. The Ministry of Defence, the Royal Signals and Radar Establishment (RSRE) and the Army School of Signals were also involved in the resultant series of studies and trials. Production of the actual hardware began during 1979 with a large number of firms involved, still under the overall direction of Plessey.

Ptarmigan uses thoroughly up-to-date technology to the extent that it is digital throughout. This means that switching and all the various message routing can be carried out swiftly and reliably using well-proven solid-state techniques. Very basically the Ptarmigan system is not unlike a modern telephone subscriber system in that each 'customer' unit has its own unique 'identify' number. If any unit wishes to contact any other unit the identify number is transmitted over a radio frequency. The code is picked up at one of what may be several switching stations, or nodes, in the area and directed along a selected radio path to its destination. All the switching involved is done automatically and electronically. There are three different types of switching node, each with its own particular task, but they all have basically the same function. For in-

stance, the Headquarters/Access nodes are an integral part of all divisional and other formation headquarters and can receive and transmit information not only to units under their control but also to other units in the general corps area.

One great advantage which the Ptarmigan system shares with Bruin is that it can deal not only with conventional voice traffic but also with the traffic associated with data links such as Wavell, teleprinter traffic, facsimile transmission and even pulsed video signals. The basic heart of the system lies in the switching nodes themselves which are usually contained in mobile container bodies carried by 4-tonne trucks. In a normal corps area there are about 20 of these nodes which intercommunicate with each other by UHF radio links involving a Ptarmigan sub-system which rejoices in the code name of Triffid. (This sub-system is provided by Marconi Communications Limited and the Triffid designation has been given purely to identify the components involved from the rest of the Ptarmigan system.) The various nodes are constantly in touch with at least three (and usually more) other nodes to provide a constant and flexible routing network for traffic. If any one node goes out of action, either for repair, maintenance, enemy inflicted damage or the need to move to a new location, traffic is automatically switched to its destination along other links. The link with the front-line battlefield radio nets is via Radio Central switching stations which can thus link the front-line units direct into the complete network. No matter in which form a message enters the system, it is converted into a standard pulsed (digital) form which it retains until it is decoded by the receiver station.

For extra information, each of the switching nodes can be up to about 25 kilometres apart, although this can vary according to local conditions. Each radio link can have either 16 or 32 channels, two of which are permanently occupied for technical purposes leaving the rest for the actual communication network. Using a digital system, each message can be transmitted at a very rapid rate (a normal signal can be transmitted in a time scale measured in milliseconds). Apart from the usual message transmissions the whole network can be used for broadcast messages and, at the other end of the scale, secure and 'hot line' channels can be provided. Full cryptographical coverage of all messages is provided. As mentioned elsewhere, Ptarmigan is used for BATES and Wavell, but it also has many technical facilities which it is not possible to describe in a general work of this nature.

With the introduction of Ptarmigan into service 'in the early 1980s' the British Army will have a communication system that will be in advance of many other comparable systems available elsewhere. Doubtless, in time its traffic capacity and mobility will be increased even further to meet ever-changing needs but for the foreseeable future Ptarmigan will be capable of almost any communication demands made upon it.

Clansman

Clansman is the cover designation given to a range of battlefield telecommunications equipments which together provide an integrated and compatible system for use by front-line formations and their vehicles. The Clansman designation covers seven different types of set—originally there were five but two have optional 'add-on' units and a further two have been added to the range. However, the Clansman compatability extends not only to the sets but to the wiring harnesses involved, their aerials, and also to the test and repair equipment involved. In addition, the British communications industry manufactures many other equipments built to the same exacting standards as Clansman which are compatible with the Service equipments.

When Clansman was first introduced, the British Army had more than 20 different types of radio equipment in service and general use. The bulk of these belonged to the Larkspur range, many of which are still in use, both in the front lines and elsewhere. The Larkspur range is a legacy of the days when the Army had a full global role, but once that had gone, many of the Larkspur sets were no longer really suitable for the European theatre (mainly for various technical reasons). Also the number of types of set was too many for logistic comfort. The decision was thus taken to introduce an entire new family of equipments embodying as many proven technical innovations as possible. The new Clansman sets were thus to be smaller, lighter and more reliable than Larkspur. After the usual issue of specifications, production of Clansman began during 1976 so that by the end of 1978 some front-line units had been issued and trained with the new sets. But by late 1981 Larkspur had still not been entirely replaced and even after it has passed from front-line use it will no doubt continue to be used by the TA and other formations.

Apart from their overall reliability, Clansman equipments are built to very tight and rugged specifications. Almost every set uses voice as a general medium but most can be converted for morse, facsimile transmission and data transmission, and all are compatible with Bruin and Ptarmigan. By the use of various 'add-on' units nearly every set can have its frequency range or combat range extended, and adaptors have been

The interior of a Royal Signals FV432 (MoD).

produced to enable hand sets to be able to feed direct into the Wavell system, or into other NATO networks. Most sets also have such refinements as microphone amplifiers for 'whisper' voice inputs, and every set has automatic aerial tuning when frequencies are changed. Vehicle sets can also have cryptographic devices attached.

Considering the number of different types of component involved in the Clansman system, it is not surprising to learn that nearly every manufacturer involved in the British telecommunications industry has become enmeshed in Clansman production. For overall production of the manpack sets, Racal have been involved, but Plessey are responsible for one set. Marconi and MEL produce the vehicle range, but many other companies produce such items as test equipment, aerial tuners, wire harness switch boxes and all the many other similar essential items.

This book is not the place for a complete run-down of all the technical detail of the Clansman range, but the following table provides a general appreciation of the salient points. The outlines are only basic and do not provide for the fact that many of the sets can be altered and improved by the use of 'add-on' units. At the time of writing many Clansman improvement packages are in the pipeline or under trial, so the list may be yet extended.

Clansman equipment	Frequency (MHz)	RF power	Range (approx) (Km)	Weight (Kg)
Manpacks				
UK/PRC-344	225-399.95	2.5W	10	7.6
UK/PRC-349	37-46.975	0.5W	2	1.5
UK/PRC-350	36-56.975	2W	5	3.6
UK/PRC-351	30-75.975	4W	8	6.3
UK/PRC-352	30-75.975	20W	16	9.1
UK/PRC-320	2-30	30W	50	10.8
Vehicle equipments				
UK/VRC-353	30-75.975	0.1-50W	30	22
UK/VRC-321	1.5-30	40W	60	23
UK/VRC-322	1.5-30	300W	80	52

Wavell

Wavell is a mobile, computer-based information system designed for service within 1 (Br) Corps, and using modern automated data processing equipment (ADP) converted to serve the needs of the modern Army. The need for some form of ADP system has long been painfully evident to higher command echelons, for the scale and demands of mobile warfare have grown to the stage where the passing and sifting of routine combat information and intelligence can submerge the command function. The introduction of Wavell is intended to place this flow of information under the control of an ADP system so that the command levels can deal with the command process alone, and the everyday routine of the task is reduced to a minimum.

Wavell has been under development by Plessey ever since the first ADP design contracts were issued during 1976. The introduction of Wavell into service has not proved easy as for some time after 1976 the system parameters were so undefined that it proved almost impossible to move into the hardware stage. But by the end of 1979 the first phase of its introduction had been completed. This involved HQ 1 (Br) Corps and only one division (2nd Armoured Division), while the actual hardware was confined to nine processing centres. The cost was some £6 million, but the results have been so encouraging that the second phase has now been given the go-ahead at a further cost of £31 million. The final number of centres will be 33 and they should be in service by the early 1980s.

The overall system can be roughly outlined as follows. At Corps HQ there will be a main Wavell terminal consisting of a central computer data bank using both floppy disc and bubble data storage. Included will be a paper ('hard') print-out for any required data, and a visual display unit (VDU) along with racked ADP modules, communications equipment and switching gear. All this is contained in a special air-conditioned container body carried on a 4-tonne truck. The central system is switched into either the Bruin trunk system or eventually Ptarmigan—Bruin has two channels reserved for Wavell use only, and Ptarmigan will also devote two channels to the system. Divisional HQs will also have a Wavell terminal which will be the same as that used at Corps HQ, but in most circumstances there will be an alternative installation in another location, also switched into the Wavell network. Below divisional level there will be at least two further Wavell installations in FV432s, but these will be employed at task force level and will have only input and output terminals. During the Phase One

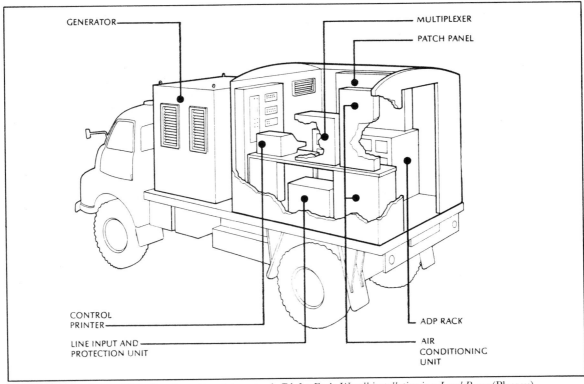

GENERATOR

MULTIPLEXER

PATCH PANEL

CONTROL
PRINTER

LINE INPUT AND
PROTECTION UNIT

ADP RACK

AIR
CONDITIONING
UNIT

Above *The future layout of Wavell equipment in a 4-tonne truck.* **Right** *Early Wavell installation in a Land Rover* (Plessey).

trials a number of hard-topped Land Rovers were used both as switching vehicles and as forward terminals.

The whole purpose of Wavell, for all its seeming complexity, is to act as a data switching system from corps HQ down to the task forces and back again. Data inserted into the system at task force level can be examined and acted upon at corps and divisional level, and as command HQs move from location to location, Wavell is carried with them ready to be switched into the network for almost immediate use. The information can be read out on a VDU or it can be printed out on to a 'hard' paper copy. Each formation can build up its own particular data bank, but this can be switched into any other formation's data bank, or the central HQ bank, at any time.

The introduction of ADP into the Army command structure has not been without its difficulties and prior to the first phase of introduction there were several problems that had to be ironed out. One was the possible amalgamation of Wavell and BATES, but for several reasons this was not proceeded with, although there will have to be interface communications between the two systems. There will also have to be interface with other NATO command systems such as the West German

HEROS and the US Army TOS (Tactical Operations System).

The Phase One Wavell system was mostly adapted from commercial equipment and was based on the PDP 11/35 central processor. This uses a tape and disc memory, but the Phase Two installations will be based on a military computer, the GEC 4080M. The Phase One VDUs were commercial Cossor DID400 units adapted to military needs but with Phase Two they will be replaced by more compact units.

There are doubtless many more problems left to be solved before Wavell is in full-scale service but the Phase One installations proved to be so successful that they are to be retained until the Phase Two equipments are ready. With the old 2nd Armoured Division the use of Wavell was extended to include Artillery, Engineer and logistic functions and doubtless other uses for the system will be found. But already some questions are being asked. It is noticeable that the downward chain of information and input ends at the task force level while it is foreseen that battle groups may well be useful input and output customers. Another age-old problem is that when the data is finally put into use at any level it still has

During 1976 Marconi Space and Defence Systems exhibited their range of cryptographical coding and decoding equipment known as the 'CRYP' series (even to exhibit such a range gives an idea of the professed unbreakability of the codes employed). The CRYP series uses an offshoot of modern solid-state logic circuit techniques by imposing another sequence of pulses over the original message. All communication equipments now in service employ a digital (pulsed) transmission system so if the message is combined with a pre-selected pulse sequence the result is unintelligible to anyone intercepting the resultant transmission. With the CRYP series the choice of random imposed pulse sequences is almost infinite (Marconi have offered each potential customer 10,000 billion possible codes which will be unique to him). The selected code setting can be entered on to the CRYP equipment but the device will not start to work until a secrecy cover is closed. The long and complex code sequence then commences and continues until the device is either switched off or a new code is selected. Any messages fed into the device are combined with the sequence at any point, so that no end or commencement signal is transmitted to aid decoding by an interceptor. Only pre-set equipments on the receiving end can decode the actual message but in the event of an equipment being captured or 'read' the sequences can be altered at pre-determined (and often random) intervals.

There are several forms of CRYP equipments, each designed to deal with one particular form of signal traffic, as follows: CRYPDIX—net radio (eg, Clansman); CRYPDEX—data transmission (eg, Wavell); CRYPMUX—trunk communications (eg, Ptarmigan, Bruin); CRYPFAX—facsimile transmission; CRYPTWIX—teleprinter; CRYPCOMM—radio telephone; and CRYPFONE—general telephone use.

to be converted into visual form on the familiar perspex-faced map by hand. Input into Wavell will remain via a VDU keyboard for some appreciable while, but future developments may include the direct keying into the system via miniature keyboards plugged into radio equipments in the front line.

When Wavell is in full service it will conserve valuable manpower and time that is at present employed in sending, switching and receiving routine data and reports. Wavell will also act as a data sorting and storage bank that can be consulted at will, providing the information that commanders need, when they need it, and in a manner that all levels can assimilate and understand. The importance of Wavell to the Army of the future can be seen in the fact that the 1980 Defence White Paper estimates that it will cost £55 million to implement.

Communication cryptography

Not surprisingly, not a great deal has been revealed regarding the secretive subject of cryptography in the modern Army, but some information has been released on the equipments used in conjunction with Clansman, and to a lesser extent with such systems as Bruin and Ptarmigan.

STARRNET

Keeping troops in Germany is not a cheap exercise and the Army is at all times watching out for methods and means of keeping down the overheads inherent in carrying out its European role. Wherever possible, any means of reducing costs is examined and many savings have been made in the day-to-day running of the Army in Germany, even if the initial capital costs may at first sight seem rather daunting. Typical of the cost-cutting exercises carried out in the past has been the reduction of the everyday telephone communication expenses that are inevitable if links between garrisons in Germany and the United Kingdom are to be maintained and the numerous message-

Off to the next job—a REME FV434.

passing admin tasks are to be continued. After 1945 and up to 1964 the vast bulk of the Army's day to day telephone costs had to be paid to the Deutches Bundespost, and the outlay was at times heavy. To make some savings the Army decided to set up its own secure microwave telecommunication links between the various garrisons. The result is known as STARRNET.

STARRNET is the acronym for Static Radio Relay Network, which works on the line-of-sight microwave principle. There are 300 channels available for telephone, telegraph and data transmission circuits, and it is possible to link STARRNET with both the United Kingdom and the Berlin Garrison, not by line of sight transmission but by tropospheric scatter—this consists of 'bouncing' a microwave beam off one of the various layers in the troposphere. The system was commissioned in 1964 and ever since then it has paid for itself over and over again—it had virtually saved its initial costs within four years. The system is run by the Technical Control Centre at JHQ Rheindahlen. In operation it has proved to be so reliable that the Rheindahlen centre is the only one that is permanently manned. Each station has a 'hot standby' facility in that if one main set should produce a fault it automatically switches to a standby set.

The Rheindahlen station is controlled by 4 Signal Brigade which is thus responsible for the overall command of STARRNET within Germany. The United Kingdom link is at Dover. At the time of writing STARRNET is still being modified to extend its coverage and capabilities.

The Royal Electrical and Mechanical Engineers

The Royal Electrical and Mechanical Engineers, or the REME to give its more usual name, is a branch of the Army with a well-defined role—it is to keep the Army's wide range of equipment fit and ready for operational use. By the Army's standards the REME is still a relatively young formation since it was only raised in 1942, but ever since then it has established itself as probably the Army's most technical and versatile grouping of specialists. The REME provides the tradesmen for all branches of the Army, and where you find the British soldier, the REME tradesman is not very far away.

If it were possible to reduce the tasks of the REME from their wide-ranging complexities to a basic statement, it would be apposite to state that the REME is the Army's repair branch, but needless to say it is much more than that. It does have a repair task but it has many others as well, not the least of which is that of equipment recovery for re-use. Throughout this book it will become obvious that modern warfare is a frighteningly expensive business and any recovery or economics produced by the turnround or repair of damaged or worn items is an essential part of the Army's battle readiness. At the 'teeth' end, the battlefield recovery of damaged or broken-down tanks or other vehicle casualties could be essential, while further to the rear the repair of weapons and other equipment enables logistic and manpower loads to be diverted to supply other needs. In the front line and in the rear areas, the REME has an essential role to play in keeping the Army ready for battle, and in both sectors it is organised accordingly.

The importance of the REME to the modern Army can be seen in the way that the REME is incorporated into every strata of the Army's organisation. Two examples of this will suffice to illustrate the point. At the United Kingdom-based Infantry battalion level are 12 or 13 REME tradesmen who are tasked with keeping the equipment and weapons of that battalion ready for use. In Germany, each armoured division has its own Armoured Workshop of 15 officers and about 328 tradesmen (plus some non-REME personnel) geared to supply the requirements of the whole division. In between these two extremes there are many other levels of organisation and manning, but throughout all REME establishments the underlying theme is one of organisation and equipment designed to suit the particular needs of the types of unit they serve.

The composition of each of these particular types of REME establishment can be seen in the tables that accompany these words. From these it will be seen that most BAOR formations have field workshops—the Infantry and Cavalry units have light aid detachments, or LADs. The role of the LAD is to accompany its particular units into battle and provide running repairs and recovery as and when they are needed. These repairs are very much

Types of REME organisation within BAOR

The vehicles mentioned include only 'A' and specialised vehicles.

1) Armoured Regiment (Type A) LAD. Manpower: 2 officers + 90 soldiers. Vehicles: 5 FV434s, 4 FV432s, 4 FV4204 Chieftain ARVs and 1 Recovery Vehicle Heavy. Outline: regimental HQ and HQ squadron with 1 FV434 and 1 Recovery Vehicle Heavy; four sections each with 1 FV434, 1 FV432 and 1 FV4204 Chieftain ARV.

2) Infantry Mechanised Battalion LAD. Manpower: 1 officer + 69 soldiers. Vehicles: 5 FV434s, 5 FV432s and 1 Recovery Vehicle Medium. Outline: LAD HQ and battalion HQ fitter section with 1 Recovery Vehicle Medium; HQ company fitter section with 1 FV434 and 1 FV432; four mechanised fitter sections each with 1 FV434 and 1 FV432.

3) Armoured Division Engineer Regiment Workshop. Manpower: 2 officers + 76 soldiers. Vehicles: 3 FV106 Samsons, 2 FV434s, 4 FV432s and 1 Recovery Vehicle Heavy. Outline: HQ and maintenance section with 1 Recovery Vehicle Heavy; field support squadron section with 3 FV434s and 1 FV432; three field squadron sections each with 1 FV106 Samson and 1 FV432.

4) Armoured Reconnaissance Regiment (Type A) LAD. Manpower: 1 officer + 55 soldiers. Vehicles: 1 Ferret, 2 FV103 Spartans, 4 FV106 Samsons and 1 Recovery Vehicle Medium. Outline: LAD HQ and HQ squadron fitter section with 1 Ferret, 1 FV106 Samson and 1 Recovery Vehicle Medium; close support recce squadron fitter section with 1 FV106 Samson; two recce squadron fitter sections each with 1 FV103 Spartan and 1 FV106 Samson.

5) Anti-tank Battery LAD. Manpower: 21 soldiers. Vehicles: 1 FV106 Samson.

6) Armoured Division Transport Regiment Workshop. Manpower: 1 officer + 52 soldiers. Vehicles: 2 Recovery Vehicles Heavy. Outline: workshop HQ and main repair section with 2 Recovery Vehicles Heavy; two squadron sections each with 16 soldiers.

7) Field Regiment (Abbot/M110A1) Workshop. Manpower: 2 officers + 79 soldiers. Vehicles: 3 FV434s, 4 FV432s, 1 M578 ARV and 1 Recovery Vehicle Heavy. Outline: workshop HQ and HQ battery section with 1 Recovery Vehicle Heavy; three FV433 Abbot battery sections each with 1 FV434 and 1 FV432; one M110A1 battery section with 1 FV432 and 1 M578 ARV.

8) Field Regiment (Abbot/Blowpipe) Workshop. Manpower: 1 officer + 80 soldiers. Vehicles: 3 FV434s, 3 FV432s, 1 FV106 Samson, 1 Recovery Vehicle Heavy, 1 TC Shop FACE and 1 TC Shop Cymbeline. Outline: HQ and HQ battery section with 1 Recovery Vehicle Heavy; three FV433 Abbot battery sections each with 1 FV434 and 1 FV432; one mortar location troop section with 1 TC Shop FACE and 1 TC Shop Cymbeline; one air defence battery section with 1 FV106 Samson.

9) Armoured Workshop. Manpower: 15 officers + 328 soldiers (plus RAOC stores platoon). Vehicles: 12 FV434s, 7 FV4204 Chieftain ARVs, 7 Recovery Vehicles Medium, 5 Recovery Vehicles Heavy, 2 automobile repair shops, 3 TC electrical workshops GP, 6 TC electrical workshops screened, 2 TC injection repair shops and 2 TC instrument repair shops. Outline: each armoured workshop organisation is decided by each CO armoured workshop. Operationally, each armoured workshop will be divided into two FRGs and two MRGs.

10) Other units in BAOR. Each Armoured Division HQ has a REME establishment of 5 officers and 54 soldiers carried on HQ vehicles. Each Armoured Division Ordnance Company has a detachment of 4 REME tradesmen.

first line—any major tasks are carried out by the rear echelons. The field workshops supplying the needs of the support arms are usually situated further to the rear of the main battle lines and do not need this forward element, although they often have one. All the BAOR-based REME formations are equipped with tracked vehicles, where possible. United Kingdom-based formations use wheeled vehicles, with only a relatively few tracked types. Like the BAOR REME units, each particular unit has its REME component tailored to suit its individual requirement.

To return to the BAOR organisation, each armoured division has its own armoured workshop which is a REME-manned unit (plus some personnel from other arms) and which is completely mobile. Each individual armoured workshop has its own individual internal arrangements to suit the particular tasks and scope of its operations but in battle it is usually split into four sections. Two of these sections are the forward repair groups, the FRGs, and the other two are the main repair groups, or MRGs. The FRGs operate within a task force area (the LADS will be in the battle group areas), and they operate as far forward behind the battle lines as possible. Their task is to carry out the repair and recovery tasks the LADs cannot handle. These will include such major operations as engine pack changes and weapon replacements. The MRGs are usually further to the rear and carry out those jobs that involve specialised repair or test equipment and bench work. To illustrate the differences between the types of armoured workshop unit, the FRG will change an engine pack but the MRG will replace a component of that engine pack.

As well as their battle roles, the armoured workshops also have peacetime functions. In addition to the day-to-day repair and maintenance functions, the workshops look after garrison vehicles and equipment and operate limited production and re-furbishing tasks. In peacetime, civilians are used to augment manpower levels.

Above divisional level come the Corps echelons which consist of a Mobile Corps Workshop, a Special Electronic Workshop (also mobile), and Aircraft Workshops, which are not fully mobile but are at least portable.

Backing up the corps REME units are two large Base Workshops. These are run by REME personnel but are almost entirely manned by civilians. The biggest unit is 23 Base Workshop which deals with AFV major repairs and overhauls. It is much the larger of the two as 37 (Rhine) Workshop deals with instruments, electronic equipment and all the many other specialised forms of Army equipment. Further support is given to BAOR by the four Central

Workshops based in the United Kingdom. These are run along factory lines with planned workloads, schedules and all the many other disciplines normally associated with commercial concerns. They are almost entirely civilian-manned but are run by the REME. The largest of them is 38 Central Workshop which, like its BAOR equivalent (23 Base Workshop), deals with AFVs. It is established at Chilwell. In contrast the smallest establishment is 33 Central Workshop at Newark which deals with telecommunications. The other base workshops are 35 at Old Dalby which handles electrical and electronic equipment, and 34 at Bovington, dealing with gun systems, small arms and other weapon equipment. In addition to their routine work, the Base and Central Workshops are capable of producing various types of specialised equipment and major semi-production tasks such as the retrofitting of extra armour and accessories to the vehicles used in Northern Ireland. Other production examples are machine-gun mountings and specialised internal security equipment.

Overseas there are REME workshops in Hong Kong, Cyprus and at Suffield in Canada. Northern Ireland has its own REME establishment, and there are similar bases in Gibraltar and Belize. As mentioned above, wherever the Army goes, the REME goes with it.

The home of the REME is at Arborfield, the location of the REME Officers' School and the Army Apprentice College. It is also the home of the School of Electronic Engineering while the School of Electrical and Mechanical Engineering is at Borden.

Offering as it does such a wide range of trades and skills, recruiting is seldom a problem for the REME and the annual intake of around 1,200 entrants is often over-subscribed. Once taken into the REME the recruit is offered an enormous range of possible trades, all of which can lead to the highly skilled level of artificer or specialised technician. There are many different types of trade, including such really unique skill forms as bandsman, shipwright and metalsmith, but they fall into six main groupings. These are electronic, aircraft, vehicle, weapons, driving and administrative. In each group there may be several sub-divisions. For example, in the vehicle group there are fitters and mechanics ('A' and 'B') and various types of electrician, while in the aircraft group there are aircraft technicians and avionics technicians.

With the advent of more and more complex electronic and optical equipment, the importance of the REME within the Army is bound to increase, and with this has come a novel and significant role. All new military equipment is now scrutinised by

Left *A combination of the No. 16 and the No. 43 Modular Distribution Systems. This is a field materials handling system designed to lift and handle containers (No. 16) and even vehicles (No. 43)* (MoD). **Right** *REME fitters at work on a Stalwart. The fitters are all wearing the full NBC Mark 3 suits and respirators* (MoD).

REME personnel at almost every stage of its design and development, not only with a view to ensuring that it lives up to its performance specifications, but also to ensure that it has as much built-in reliability as possible and that it can be repaired and maintained with the minimum of cost, time and specialised back-up. The REME is not the only arm of the service involved in this detailed assessment, but it is one of the more important. The new role is carried out as part of one of the four maintenance advisory groups, or MAGs, and the REME personnel are usually officers with specialised knowledge of their particular field. The Vehicle MAG is based at Chobham, the Aircraft MAG at Middle Wallop and the Weapons MAG at Woolwich. The fourth MAG is concerned with telecommunications and radar and is based at Malvern.

The Royal Corps of Transport & The Gurkha Transport Regiment

The Royal Corps of Transport (RCT) Year Book for 1977 opens with these words: 'The chief responsibility of the Royal Corps of Transport is to organise and operate the means of transport which support the British Army in war and peace. In ad-

dition, the corps executes the movement of men and material worldwide, operates ports and performs certain functions in connection with air movement and air logistic support.'

It would be difficult to find a more succinct statement of the role of the RCT, but to assess that role is a complex task. To simply state that the RCT deals with transport hardly deals fairly with all its varied operations, for the corps transports the Army not only on land (by road and rail), but also helps to move it by air and even carries some of the Army's loads by sea.

The Depot for the RCT is at Buller Baracks, Aldershot, but the Corps is based wherever the Army goes. It is to Buller Barracks that the new recruit is sent for his basic Army training and while there he is also given his Army driver training course. More advanced driving instruction is given at Leconfield in Humberside, and from there the qualified drivers go to their respective units for further instruction and duties.

Drivers can be assigned to a number of specialist units but the basic RCT formation is the Transport Squadron which forms part of an RCT Transport Regiment. Each squadron is made up of two or three troops with about 20 trucks apiece, and each troop is usually equipped with only one type of truck, either 4- or 10-tonne. Each 1 (Br) Corps armoured division has its own transport regiment. These transport units are the main carrying components of nearly all the Army's long- and short-haul operations, ferrying stores, fuel, ammunition, food and all the other items needed to keep the Army functioning.

Apart from the transport squadrons, the RCT also mans the Ambulance Squadrons and drives the ambulances for the RAMC, both tracked and wheeled versions. There are also Car Squadrons which operate staff cars at all levels from Land Rovers to six-seater saloons. At the top end of the scale are the Tank Transporter Squadrons which have the most highly qualified and experienced of all RCT drivers, namely the driver specialists. Perhaps the most prestigious unit in the RCT is 20 Squadron, which operates the six vehicles used to carry the Queen's Baggage Train.

There are several other driving skill trades open to soldiers in the RCT. The top driver is the Master Driver, a highly competent and experienced Warrant Officer who has the task of advising all other branches of the Army with reference to driving skills. Another specialist is the Driver Radio Operator who has a variety of communication roles.

The Army has its own railway specialists who operate the Army's own diesel railway based on Detmold. The function of this is not only to carry stores, but also to act as the training location for the Army's railway staff who can become qualified as shunters, guards, signalmen, yardmasters and controllers. All of these personnel would take over some civilian railways in an emergency. The unit that operates the Detmold complex is 79 Railway Squadron, which is backed up by 275 Railway Squadron (V), a part-time unit largely drawn from British Rail staff.

Perhaps the greatest surprise to many scholars of the Army comes when they learn that the Army has its own maritime detachment, with its own military port at Marchwood, on Southampton Water. Marchwood Military Port is operated by 17 Maritime and Port Regiment RCT (which also maintains troops in Cyprus and Hong Kong), but the majority of the maritime trade training is carried out at nearby Gosport (apart from the trade of Port Controller). These maritime trades include seaman, marine engineer, navigator and navigator ocean watchkeeper. All these naval-sounding trades are carried out by soldiers, and the RCT also has its own divers for various duties.

The shipping of the RCT is largely operated by 20 Maritime Regiment RCT. Pride of the Army's fleet are two Landing Craft Logistics (LCL) named HMAV *Ardennes* and *Arakan*. Both are used on the Marchwood to Antwerp run to supply BAOR, but they are also used to carry supplies to Northern Ireland and the various Army outposts and ranges in the Hebrides and other Scottish islands. A variety of smaller craft is operated by the RCT, some in association with the Royal Navy. The great bulk of the Army's wartime supplies would be carried on the Landing Ship Logistics (LSL) fleet of about 12 vessels operated by the Royal Fleet Auxiliary.

Supplies dropped by aircraft of the Royal Air Force to Army units in the field are the responsibility of another RCT unit, namely 47 Air Despatch Squadron. This squadron packs Army supplies, loads them into the aircraft and is also responsible for dropping them from the aircraft in flight. The RCT members of the unit are known as Air Despatchers, and the squadron is mainly based at RAF Lyneham in Wiltshire, but they travel with the aircraft (now nearly all C-130 Hercules) wherever they are needed as part of the aircraft's crew. The squadron also carries out some air despatch tasks for the Royal Navy and the Royal Marines, and deals with RAF Wessex, Chinook and Puma helicopters.

The moving of any number of soldiers and their families involves the RCT in yet another of its functions, this time movement control. The RCT has a specialised and far-flung formation known as 29 Movement Control which has a large and varied number of movement control detachments operating everywhere the Army is likely to travel to and from. These detachments carry out the essential tasks of administering and supervising all aspects of the Army on the move and they operate at ports, railway stations, airports and road locations.

An important part of the RCT's functions are centred on the AMF(L) Squadron, RCT, which is the central part of the AMF(L)'s Logistic Support Battalion. This squadron is a versatile and adaptable one for not only does it deal with wheeled transport but it also handles the support and despatching of the various types of helicopter likely to be used by the AMF(L) nations.

The Intelligence Corps

The Intelligence Corps, or 'I' Corps as it is often referred to, is one of the Army's newer formations, having been formed as recently as 1940 in the aftermath of the Battle of France. The precise duties of the 'I' Corps are not easy to put into a few words, but it is a body with a myriad of functions and tasks which fall into two main categories: security and combat intelligence.

There is often a considerable overlap between these. For instance, a security operative in Germany may have to be fully conversant in a language other than the usual English and German while at the same time having a considerable insight into the working methods and procedures of his possible opposite number on the enemy side. Combat intelligence operatives also have to have a good grasp of basic and battlefield security methods, with all that that entails. From this simple pair of examples it will readily be realised that the work of the 'I' Corps can be very varied and often extremely involved.

Soldiers joining the 'I' Corps are trained in both branches of their particular skill after going through the same basic training that all new Army recruits have to experience. Specialisation commences after the basic intelligence courses have been completed but there are several possible paths open to anyone joining the corps. The task of the security operatives is fairly straightforward in intention, as it is to deny access to any of the Army's premises, equipment, documents and personnel by a potential enemy. The task involves many specialised skills from knowledge of a language through to photography, co-operation with civilian police and other organisations, a good grounding in locks, and many other similar areas of knowledge.

Combat intelligence covers another wide area. Put once again into a very basic form, it is to supply to a commander all the whats, whys, wheres and whens of an enemy's intentions. This once again involves many skills from the rapid identification of items of enemy equipment through to the interpretation of aerial photographs. Language knowledge is an obvious asset in this field as the interception and analysis of enemy signal traffic is often involved.

In both branches of 'I' Corps skills, co-operation and liaison are necessary with virtually all the other arms of the Services, and at all levels. Members of the 'I' Corps, at both commissioned and NCO level (soldiers joining the 'I' Corps usually assume junior NCO rank soon after their basic training) have to be able to express themselves in clear and organised terms, both verbally and in writing, and have to be able to pass their information to all levels of command. This latter requirement alone is what often limits the entry level into the corps, but at both commissioned and NCO level what is required is a well-organised and systematic mind with the ability to absorb information, the ability to adapt to new situations and the ability to learn. Life in the 'I' Corps is seldom dull, for when not on fully active duty the job's basic knowledge is always being updated and improved. Language tuition is seemingly always under way with courses being run at the Army School of Languages, situated at Beaconsfield. The corps depot is at Ashford in Kent, and it is there that the intelligence skills are given. Considering the requirements of the 'I' Corps it should come as no surprise to learn that the chances of gaining a commission from the ranks are thought to be higher than in any other branch of the Army. Many serving members transfer from other branches of the Army and once in, very few seem to transfer out.

The Royal Army Ordnance Corps

The usual image that comes to mind when the Royal Army Ordnance Corps is mentioned is that of a storeman working away amid piles of racking and odd-shaped cardboard boxes. The RAOC does indeed have such a stores function but it has many other roles as well. Basically the RAOC provides a fast and efficient supply service for the Army, but in these days of mobile warfare with all its attendant complexities, supply is no longer just a matter of stores. It is a complex and highly technical affair and thus the RAOC is one of the most technically diverse and specialised of all the support functions of the Army.

The RAOC has many bases but one of the main centres is at Deepcut where there is a sizeable training establishment at which recruits are given basic training in the 15 nominal trades open to RAOC recruits. These range from that of storeman to such specialities as ammunition technician or

A Coles Crane on a AEC 10-tonne chassis, typical of the handling devices used at the many depots and stores run by the RAOC.

photographer. Once past this training the RAOC technician or officer can find himself posted throughout the Army for the RAOC is a widespread and highly-involved corps.

Every fighting formation has an RAOC component somewhere in its organisation ready to supply whatever the soldier in the field needs. The armoured divisions in 1 (Br) Corps each have an ordnance company under the control of their division HQ. The role of the ordnance company is direct supply support of the troops in the field so each of these companies is mobile. The strength is about 100 men and the company carries around 10,000 different items with it on its own transport, ready for direct issue to the combat arms. They in their turn are backed up by combat supply battalions which contain nearly all the various tradesmen maintained by the RAOC. These two RAOC combat formations supply just about everything the troops need, from food to fuel and from transport vehicles to ammunition.

Further back are many more RAOC units that range from store and vehicle depots to bakeries and salvage platoons. Their role is to supply the needs of the forward RAOC units and they in turn are supplied by the large static depots with their huge parks of vehicles and warehouses full of spares, uniforms, ammunition and all the many other items the modern Army needs to function.

To service this massive organisation the RAOC has a pool of skilled tradesmen, many of whom are retrained for their roles within the RAOC itself, ie,

they have to serve within the RAOC for a period before they receive their retraining. This can be seen in the stores function itself for there RAOC personnel (assisted by some WRACs) have to master all the technicalities of stock control using ADP and computers, handling techniques, accounting and many other such skills. RAOC stores have to handle well over 500,000 separate items. These all have to be kept in serviceable condition, have to be readily available and have to be taken to where they are needed with the minimum of delay. This is particularly true where vehicles are concerned so the RAOC has its own vehicle specialists who are trained to maintain and drive all the many vehicles the Army has on its inventory—ranging from Chieftain tanks to Engineer equipment.

One of the most important functions is that of fuel supply. Fuel is perhaps the most important single item needed to keep present-day forces in the field and a correspondingly large proportion of RAOC effort is devoted to keeping the Army supplied with the vital POLs (Petrol, Oil and Lubricants). Today, the accent regarding fuel supplies is on bulk transport methods in which the jerricans of the 1939-45 war are replaced by bulk storage and supply using modern technology. BAOR is a case in point. The normal routine peace-time fuel supplies for BAOR are met by the huge petro-chemical complex situated around Hamburg and other such commercial concerns, but such plants cannot supply all the specialised needs of the Army. Some of them still have to come from the United Kingdom and a fair proportion pass along the NATO Central European Pipeline System (CEPS) which covers four nations and is run by a joint NATO staff based at Versailles (this is the Central European Operating Agency, or CEOA). Most of the fuel destined for BAOR travels from Antwerp or Rotterdam but some also comes from Marseilles and other ports. At each of these ports is a pumping station which transfers the fuels from their bulk transit carriers, which could be either fuel tankers or, in forward areas, dracones, which are huge rubber containers towed behind tugs. There are no restrictions between the different types of fuel that flow down the pipes. Petrol can be followed by kerosene along the same pipeline as the buried pipes would be too expensive to duplicate. When two differing fuels have to follow each other along the pipeline they are separated by huge steel spheres known as 'pigs'. On each side of the 'pig' there is a section which consists of a mixture of both fuels and the system is so arranged that these mixed sections are 'cut out' at the receiving station and passed into prepared slop tanks. At the receiving station the fuel is then passed into tanks ready to be further transferred into bulk carriers or more dracones which may be either simply laid on the ground surface or buried beneath ground. From there the fuels go to the units. The CEPS is a complex affair with 105 pumping stations and 53 storage depots. If one pipeline is put out of action, the fuel can be switched to another line, and in some areas of potential damage risk the pipelines are duplicated.

The RAOC is mainly responsible for the British Army side of the fuel operation although there is considerable RE and RCT involvement as well. To give an idea of the many types of POL the RAOC has to handle and supply there is a list of the main British POLs at the end of this section. Not all of these are handled in bulk. Some of the really specialist items are issued only in small containers or tubes, while others are issued in amounts that vary from a few litres up to thousands of litres—it all adds to the complexity of the RAOC supply function.

Stores sections are a vital part of many of the Army's support functions, and the RAOC provides a service to many other corps. There is an RAOC supply section at each REME workshop at all levels and there are similar supply sections serving with the Royal Artillery, the Royal Engineers and the AAC, as well as several other arms. The RAOC has a supply function for the Royal Navy and the RAF as well.

After fuel, perhaps the next most important supply item for the Army is ammunition. The RAOC not only stores and supplies ammunition but is also responsible for its maintenance and repair. This responsibility ranges from guided missiles to 7.62 mm ammunition and it is carried out not only in base depots but in field locations. An off-shoot of the ammunition technician branch is Explosive Ordnance Disposal, more popularly known as bomb disposal. The RAOC is the corps responsible for the safe disposal of the types of explosive device used by terrorist or criminal organisations, but they are also used to dispose of unwanted or time-expended explosives. The RAOC EOD role in Northern Ireland is now well known. The EOD role is shared with the Royal Engineers but the Engineers deal mainly with bombs and other devices dropped from aircraft and the like—the RAOC deal with the rest.

The RAOC trains and provides the Army's photographers and deals with the bulk of the Army's printing requirements. The RAOC also supplies clerks, but here there are two categories. The RAOC technical clerks are used only within the RAOC, mainly as inventory specialists. The other category is the staff clerk, a rather more attractive employment for they are employed as clerks at British Embassies all over the world. They are also used at NATO Headquarters and other similar locations.

Food is another prime RAOC function and the corps trains and mans the staff used in field bakeries and butcheries. These units are usually mobile and are backed up by RAOC cold stores at base depots.

There are many other RAOC functions as corps personnel are trained as crane operators, laundry operators, textile refitters and military programmers. RAOC officers are educated in a variety of management skills and are often on hand at all levels of Army command to advise on supply matters.

The RAOC is a diverse operation. In terms of the amount of capital the RAOC 'manages' and controls it must rank among the largest of all British business concerns, and its manpower and resources are among the most cost-effective in the nation.

RAOC-supplied POLs

Listed below are the different types of POL supplied by or through the RAOC. The designations given are British ones but where an asterisk (*) is used, the substance has an equivalent common to all NATO forces.

Fuels: AVGAS 100LL*, AVCAT*, AVCAT/FS11*, AVTAG/FS11*, AVTUR/FS11*, CIVGAS*, COMBATGAS*; Regular 47/0 DIESO*, General Purpose UK DIESO, General Purpose UK(MT) DIESO, DIESO F-76*, 3/50 FFO, 36/50 FFO, 125/50 FFO, 370/50 FFO, KERO/A, KERO/B*.

Oils: OC-65, OC-160*, OC-600, OEP-38*, OEP-70*, OEP-71*, OEP-215, OEP-220*, OEP-740, OM-1*, OM-11*, OM-13*, OM-15*, OM-16*, OM-17, OM-18*, OM-21, OM-33*, OM-58, OM-70*, OM-71*, OM-100*, OM-160, OM-750*, OM-1300*; OMD-30*, OMD-40*, OMD-45, OMD-60*, OMD-75*, OMD-113*, OMD-160*, OMD-250*, OMD-330*, OMD-370*; OX-7, OX-8*, OX-10, OX-14*, OX-18*, OX-26*, OX-38*, OX-165, OX-300, OX-320*.

Greases: XG-220, XG-235*, XG-250*, XG-264*, XG-271*, XG-276*, XG-279*, XG-284*, XG-285*, XG-293*, XG-300*, XG-315*.

Specials: ZX-1*, ZX-2, ZX-6*, ZX-8*, ZX-13*, ZX-16, ZX-20*, ZX-30, ZX-33, ZX-34*, ZX-38*; PX-3*, PX-4, PX-6, PX-7*, PX-10, PX-11*, PX-15, PX-19, PX-24*, PX-25, PX-26*, PX-28, PX-29, PX-30, PX-31; AL-11*, AL-14*, AL-34, AL-36, AL-38, AL-39, AL-40.

The Army Catering Corps

While the Royal Navy have their 'Fly Navy' recruiting slogan, the Army have their own counter —'Eat Army'. To clarify what I mean, the Army is fed by the Army Catering Corps, or ACC, an establishment which has still to overcome the image inherited from its often untrained predecessors, for it was only established in 1941 and by the time it had become fully operational and working properly the Citizens' Armies of 1939-1945 had already formed their uncomplimentary opinions. Since 1945, however, the standards of Army catering have improved out of all recognition, and the modern soldier is well fed and usually has a wide choice of types of meal on most occasions.

The Depot and Training Centre of the ACC is at Aldershot where a large and modern training establishment has been set up to teach cooking and catering at all levels of expertise. The new recruit to the ACC undergoes the usual basic soldiering skills course and then is taken through an elementary Army catering course. This provides for all the essentials of modern catering from basic cooking techniques up to menu planning, food budgeting and food preparation and care. The course lasts 21 weeks during which the trainees often leave the kitchen behind to carry out practical cooking in the field under full operational conditions, which includes camouflage and self-defence of the area.

From the Training Centre the ACC cook is posted to a unit. This could be almost anywhere in the Army, ranging from a large garrison to an operational unit in Germany. On the large bases the ACC establishments are run along civilian lines with specialisation being very much the rule, but the new cook is usually given as much experience as possible. On a large base the ACC also has to provide for special diets for sports or medical purposes, while the ACC cooks on large RAMC establishments often have to work very closely with RAMC personnel to provide special medical foods and diets.

The ACC cook with a field unit frequently has to provide a wide range of meals at what can be very short notice. When in the field or on exercise, the units themselves often provide their own catering facilities, based on the various forms of 'Compo' ration pack. These mostly utilise tinned foods which require a minimum of preparation other than heating and opening, and are issued on the basis of one pack being adequate for so many men for so many days—the types of pack vary. They provide an adequate diet, and even include such luxuries as sweets and chocolate (not forgetting such essentials as tin openers and toilet paper!) but they are meant to be supplemented by fresh vegetables and fruit when available, and after even a few days on compo rations the diet tends to become rather dull. This is where the ACC becomes such a morale booster for, using the same basic compo rations, a trained cook can provide really good and adequate meals from his knowledge and the extras he carries. The ACC in the field uses 4-tonne trucks which carry tools, supplies and cooking ranges fitted to a special trailer towed by the truck. Water boilers are carried for the essential tea, and for utensil cleaning purposes. The trucks also carry tents and some tables and other basics. With such equipment the ACC can serve simple hot meals which can transform units from tired men into refreshed soldiers. The number of cooks assigned to a unit varies from place to place and according to the type of unit itself—for instance a BAOR armoured regiment has an ACC complement of 16 men.

Troops in garrisons and permanent bases are often fed to the point of distraction and to the extent that the 'Fit to Fight' campaign has to be really put into active use. A visitor to some garrison messes will be greeted by a lunch menu with a long list of hot courses, salads and the almost inevitable curry. Other meals are just as varied.

Away from the day-to-day catering, the ACC has the opportunity to further its more delicate skills in such fields as pastrywork, the preparation of seafood and meat and all the other more advanced cooking skills. To assist in these areas the ACC Centre has prepared all manner of food routines and menus to suit almost any occasion—even the cooks in the field are issued with detailed menus and cooking guides. As the ACC cook proceeds through his Army career he can try for any number of civilian catering qualifications which will stand him in good stead in civilian life, and many famous civilian chefs were taught their trade in the ACC.

Many WRAC members are also taught alongside ACC personnel, and carry out the same duties as the men apart from the fact that they are not usually assigned to field duties.

The Royal Pioneer Corps

If there is one word that sums up the role of the Royal Pioneer Corps today, it is versatility. The modern RPC is a very far cry from the days when its personnel were the Army's labourers. Today their presence is an essential one for the Army, but there is no single role. The RPC assists in moving stores, loading and unloading the thousand-and-one items the Army needs to move and function, and also provides dog handlers. But first and foremost the Pioneers are fighting soldiers and the task they carry out in Northern Ireland is one in line with that of the rest of the Army.

The main depot and training centre of the RPC is at Northampton, where recruits go to be trained as Infantrymen. Thereafter they are trained in what is their central role, namely that of materials and stores handling. To this end they have to master all the many forms of handling equipment the Army employs, from Eager Beavers to dock cranes. This role is carried out not only in stores and base depots but also in the field in direct support of forward units. At any one time at least 40 per cent of the RPC strength is serving with other arms of the Army such as the RE and the RAOC. With the RCT the Pioneers not only assist with the loading and unloading of the vehicles but also act as drivers and even help in the running of the RCT railways.

The RPC is also involved in man management. The bases in Germany employ a great deal of local labour for the hundreds of tasks needed to keep the garrisons and bases functioning. A large proportion of this local labour is recruited, administered and supervised by RPC officers and soldiers.

Selected RPC soldiers are trained to be dog handlers for various tasks. Most RPC handlers are used in security roles at ammunition and other sensitive stores depots, being trained for their role by the RAVC.

To top its versatility, the RPC is also used in an Infantry role on occasions and has frequently been used in this way in Northern Ireland. When the first RPC units were stationed there, either on roulement or as part of the Ulster garrison, they had to draw on their flexibility yet again for they often had to build their own billets and guard posts while at the same time carrying out their various security duties.

Despite all its many modern tasks, on occasion the RPC has to revert to its original pick and shovel role. This usually occurs when the corps is in support of the RE road and bridging units when permanent structures have to be built—but Pioneers are also involved in the combat roles of the RE as well.

Whenever the Army has some unusual task that cannot be met by any particular corps or regiment, the RPC usually finds itself given the job. Such rapid and varied roles call for a large measure of adaptability and problem approaches which are met by giving all members of the RPC a sound grounding in all manner of military skills ranging from driving to stores management and layout. Senior NCOs and officers are given considerable training in management skills and problem solving. To add to its all-round capabilities the RPC often works with the Royal Navy and the Royal Air Force.

The Royal Army Education Corps

The Royal Army Education Corps consists of the Army's schoolteachers, and is also one of the Army's few all-officer corps. All RAEC officers are fully qualified in one sphere or another and it is their task to provide a comprehensive educational service to the Army, and to the Army's families.

The RAEC is stationed wherever the Army goes. Most RAEC officers are based at the Army's many training centres and particularly at such locations as Junior Leaders establishments where basic schooling is still an essential part of the training. But such training is also needed at the many technical schools where basic education is as important as the technical information given. The RAEC is also present at almost every major military establishment to carry out all manner of teaching from basic three-Rs up to advanced studies for promotion examinations and civilian qualifications.

The RAEC also provides some specialist courses for the Army which can range from the various 'war studies' to language courses. International affairs and instructional techniques are also among the many Army-orientated courses run by the RAEC. Overseas, the corps also provides basic education for Army families and in this its personnel are often assisted by WRAC officers seconded to the RAEC.

The Royal Army Medical Services

The Royal Army Medical Services are formed from three different corps, as follows: The Royal Army Medical Corps (RAMC), The Royal Army Dental Corps (RADC) and Queen Alexandra's Royal Army Nursing Corps (QARANC). Of these, the largest is the RAMC which has its main depot and training centre at Keogh Barracks at Ash Vale near Aldershot. Within the RAMC the differentiation between a war- and a peace-time footing is most marked, for in peace corps personnel are mainly based at the various Army hospitals but in war a large proportion of them will leave their bases to man forward field hospitals and other field force units. In both capacities the RAMC provides a complete medical service to the Army and the civilians attached to it as well. The duties of the RAMC include not only medical care, although that is one of their prime functions, but also general hygiene, the control of insects and other such pests, and the general supervision of food and water supplies. All RAMC doctors have commissions and are usually trained doctors or well through their medical

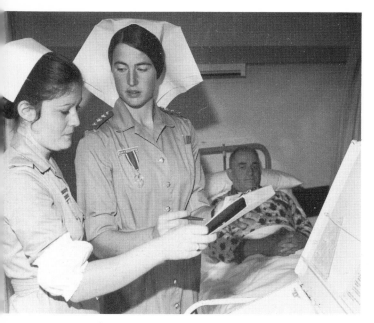 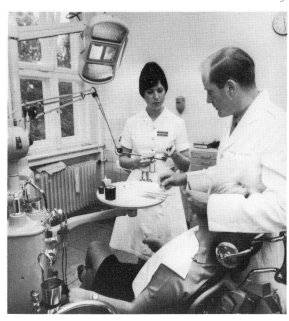

Left *QARANC staff on duty at the Duchess of Kent's Military Hospital at Catterick* (UKLF PR). **Right** *RADC staff in action at the British Military Hospital, Rinteln* (MoD).

courses when they apply to join, but there are also non-medical commissions in the RAMC such as technical, administrative and quartermaster officers in addition to nursing officers. Non-commissioned RAMC soldiers can be either laboratory technicians, physiotherapists, radiographers, dispensers, operating theatre technicians, student nurses, clerks, environmental health assistants, medical assistants, storemen or pupil nurses. All these have their civilian equivalents.

Although the main body of the RAMC is based at the various hospitals, even in times of peace each battalion or regiment has its RAMC personnel for everyday routine medical duties. Each combat unit also has its own RAMC personnel and for example, each armoured regiment has one RAMC officer. But the main body of the RAMC remains in the base hospitals which are situated as follows: In the United Kingdom—Royal Victoria Hospital, Netley; Cambridge Military Hospital, Aldershot; The Duchess of Kent's Military Hospital, Catterick; Colchester Military Hospital; Military Wing, Musgrave Park Hospital, Belfast; Louise Margaret Maternity Hospital, Aldershot; and the Queen Elizabeth Military Hospital, Woolwich. In addition to these the RAMC has staffs in several civilian teaching and casualty hospitals—of the latter, perhaps the best-known being the Royal Victoria Hospital, Belfast. In Germany there are British military hospitals at Munster, Rinteln, Hannover, Iserlohn

and Berlin, while further afield there are hospitals at Dhekelia, in Cyprus, at Hong Kong, and perhaps the most distant, the British Military Hospital at the Ghurkha base at Dharan in Nepal.

All these military hospitals are run very much on civilian lines and may have some civilians on their staffs. Their facilities and equipment rival any civilian hospital and their responsibilities to the large Army civilian population can be seen in the provision of the maternity hospital at Aldershot.

In times of conflict, however, the RAMC assumes its war footing with the provision of forward field hospitals. These may have either tented or more substantial accommodation and are situated just behind the main battle zone. Forward of them, the unit RAMC personnel are responsible for the physical well-being of their unit. A regiment or battalion usually has one doctor and a small number of medical assistants, usually at HQ company or squadron level where they are based around an ambulance FV432 or FV104 Samaritan— wheeled units have the FV18067 ambulance. In 1 (Br) Corps each division has the support of a field ambulance unit which can provide extra vehicles to carry casualties to the rear, and for really large scale casevac, trucks can be used—these are manned by regimental personnel. Helicopters also have their role in casualty evacuation from forward areas and all AAC helicopters can be fitted out for the ambulance role—the Scout, for instance, can be fit-

Left *The RAMC in action in Northern Ireland* (MoD). **Right** *The training of the explosive-sniffing dogs used in Northern Ireland and elsewhere is carried out by the RAVC* (MoD).

ted with external stretcher panniers. Whatever their mode of conveyance, casualties are taken to the field casualty stations or field hospitals where their wounds can be treated with all the medical care and attention that would normally be given at a base hospital.

The RADC is the dental equivalent of the RAMC and has its main depot and training centre at Aldershot with more facilities at nearby Blackdown. Like the RAMC, RADC personnel are stationed wherever there are British soldiers and the standards they work to are as high, if not higher, than those available to the average civilian. Normally, RADC officers and soldiers are stationed mainly in the base hospitals but there are some field units which take their skills directly to the soldier who is unable to reach the RADC base facilities.

The RAMC provides some male nursing staff but the main nursing unit for the Army is the QARANC which numbers about 1,500 personnel, of whom about 500 are officers. The women of the QARANC can be either State Registered Nurses or State Enrolled Nurses, or they can join the QARANC and obtain their qualifications in the service. Their main training centre and depot is at Aldershot but much of the training is carried out in the main base hospitals and at the RAMC centre at Keogh Barracks. Some members of the QARANC also serve as dental technicians, clerks and hygienists with the RADC.

There are several TA medical units, the largest of which is 208 (Merseyside) General Hospital RAMC(V), and all three branches of the Royal Army Medical Services are represented in this unit.

The Royal Army Veterinary Corps

In a world where armies travel on tracks or wheels propelled by the internal combustion engine, it comes as rather a surprise to learn that the British Army still keeps a considerable number of animals for all manner of purposes. The Army's long association with the horse has still not come to an end, and horses are still 'kept on the books' with duties ranging from the ceremonial to the recreational. The horses are joined by dogs that are used in a number of military roles, but the poor old mule is no longer a British Army animal—the last of them went some years ago. To add to the list, many regiments still possess mascots ranging from ponies to goats, and most garrisons have cats in one form or another. In fact the Army still has so many animals that it needs a corps to look after them— this is the Royal Army Veterinary Corps, or RAVC.

The Directorate of the RAVC is at Droitwich, but the main RAVC training centre is at Melton Mowbray. There are other RAVC centres at Aldershot and in some of the German garrisons, such as Sennelager. RAVC officers are all fully qualified veterinarians but the non-commissioned ranks of the corps contain farriers and other such qualified specialists. The Army's horses are all looked after by RAVC specialists, although the various units themselves care for their own animals on a day-to-day basis. But the RAVC does provide horse clinics and hospitals, and its vets run highly organised diagnostic laboratories. The main centres of 'horse activity' in the Army are at Knightsbridge Barracks in London (for the Household Cavalry), St Johns Wood (for the King's Troop, RHA), and Aldershot (where there are several horse establishments including the RMP Mounted Troop).

Today, the Army horse is now outnumbered by the Army dog which is used in a number of roles. Dogs are used by the RMP in a police dog role, by the RPC in a general security role, and by various units where they are used as 'war dogs' in a tracking role. There are even dogs used to 'sniff out' explosives. All these animals are trained, along with their handlers, by the RAVC at Melton Mowbray. The police dogs are employed much as their 'civilian' counterparts, and can be used to discover drugs and explosives. The security dogs are trained to be used mainly in a guard role, although they too are often called upon to carry out other duties. Usually the police and security dogs are Alsatians but the dogs used to discover explosives, as they have been for some years in Northern Ireland, are often Labradors. Labradors are frequently preferred for this dangerous role in Ulster as their normally gentle disposition makes them much more amenable to the variations in general routine and transport methods. Early experience with Alsatians in the sniffing role soon showed that they did not take kindly to the interiors of helicopters which circumstances frequently dictate as their mode of transport, while Labradors took such noisy things in their tolerant stride. The explosive-sniffer dogs and their handlers (who are volunteers from all branches of the Army) undergo a basic three-month course before they can be assigned to their area, and even there training continues. In Ulster the dogs have proved to be very successful in finding explosives, and as their training teaches them to indicate anything unusual, they have often been instrumental in arms and ammunition finds. There have been casualties among the Ulster dogs, although not many, but a dog's service life is relatively short and the Army generally needs a turnover of about 350 a year to keep up the numbers. To obtain this operational number the Army has to find some 700 or so dogs as the course failure rate is about 50 per cent.

Tracker dogs are also used for search purposes, but as their name implies they are mainly used to track suspects or escaped prisoners. Any item left at the scene of a terrorist crime will often provide a useful scent and many arrests have been the result of tracker dog activity. Both Alsatians and Labradors are employed in this role. Although tracker dogs have been mainly used in Ulster, they are also trained for use in Germany for a variety of roles, often connected with discovering infiltrators and behind-the-lines agents.

The RAVC staff are frequently assisted by members of the WRAC assigned to them in a number of capacities ranging from laboratory technicians to kennelmaids.

The Army Physical Training Corps

The popular image of the APTC is one of early morning physical jerks on a freezing cold parade ground or in a draughty gymnasium, and to be strictly accurate there still is some small measure of truth in this image. However, these days the role of the APTC is the little-mentioned but important one of keeping the Army fit. Only over the last few years has it become painfully obvious that modern warfare will be even more exacting an experience for the soldier in the field than any previous conflict. Any future war will involve troops having to remain at their combat posts for days at a stretch and rest or sleep will be almost impossible. Physical fitness and stamina therefore become just as essential to the soldier as his weapons and equipment, and this is where the APTC takes on its important role.

Over the last few years the physical fitness of the Army has been improved beyond all recognition by the imposition of a new physical training routine far removed from the PT exercises of old. Today the soldier has to reach a fixed standard of fitness which is shown by his ability to cover a fixed distance in a prescribed time. At one time it was 1½ miles in 11 minutes, with a further 1½ miles within a further period. If any soldier could not achieve this, he was immediately placed on a course of dietary and physical exercise until he could. The programme was launched as the 'Fight the Flab' campaign and was so successful that it even had its effects on civilian life. The programme still continues and as a result the British Army is one of the fittest in Europe, a status rather improved by the extra toning-up programmes entered into before 'Operation Banner' tours in Northern Ireland. The body responsible for the overseeing and implementation of the fitness campaign is the APTC.

Based at Aldershot, the APTC is one corps that rarely recruits direct from 'civvie street' as most of the NCOs in the corps are recruited from within the Army itself, and even then not until at least one year has been served by any prospective member. After the usual specialist training courses at Aldershot the APTC NCOs are drafted throughout the Army, usually at the rate of one NCO to every battalion or regiment, although in some formations there may be more. Once with their unit they are responsible for its fitness and carry out physical training programmes, run combat obstacle courses, organise route marches and provide any specialist training that might be needed for unit sports teams. Needless to say they are also actively involved in all the many and varied Army sports activities which range from cricket to skiing. The Army's involvement in sport of all kinds is usually carried out under individual unit auspices, but the APTC is involved when the sport expertise reaches a higher level such as national and Olympic levels. The APTC is a corps that rarely hits the headlines but it is one that is essential to the combat efficiency of the modern Army.

Corps of Royal Military Police & Military Provost Staff Corps

The men of the Royal Military Police are among the most widely known of all the soldiers of the Army for their very appearance marks them as being soldiers of note. Their red caps have given them their nickname, and their duties have often bought them into direct contact with many members of the general public, sometimes in odd circumstances. Within the Army, though, they have a definite function which is simply to serve and assist the rest of the Army to carry out its duties. The old days of the Redcaps seeking out off-duty soldiers in order to give them a dressing down and subsequent punishments have long since departed. The modern military policeman is a very different character, in himself a model soldier and an example to all.

In practical terms this means that the Royal Military Police have two roles. In time of peace the MP carries out all the normal everyday policing of the Army. As with his civilian counterpart, this includes everything from traffic control to all the normal powers of arrest. In time of war the MP's main role is traffic control, mainly getting the right traffic to the right places at the right time.

The men of the Royal Military Police are formed into two main branches. The largest is the General

Cancam motor cycles used by the Royal Military Police.

Police Duties Branch, or GPD. All members of the RMP pass through this branch after their initial training which is given at the RMP training centre at Chichester. In the GPD branch all the basic policing skills are taught with the addition of such military extras as the use of the 9 mm pistol and the sub-machine-gun. Training is given in first aid, photography, military law, traffic control, driving (both vehicles and motor cycles) and signals. Once trained the soldiers of the GPD branch are then assigned to the Provost companies.

The basis of all Provost companies is the platoon, but the Provost platoon bears no resemblance to any other Army platoon. Each Provost platoon is commanded by a Staff Sergeant. Together with a driver and a cook, he forms a small platoon 'headquarters' overseeing two sections with a Sergeant and four Corporals in each. The number of platoons to a Provost company varies widely, but within BAOR most companies have five platoons. The platoons within 1 (Br) Corps all come under the control of HQ 1 (Br) Corps, but are assigned specific roles. Each of the divisions has its own Provost company. Each of these Provost companies is fully mobile and uses Land Rovers and Cancam motor cycles. Also under the control of HQ 1 (Br) Corps are a further two Provost companies for control of the corps rear area, each with five platoons, and there are a further two three-platoon Provost companies to control the large rear combat zone—in an emergency these latter two companies would be augmented to six platoons by the arrival of men from TA Provost companies.

In time of war, these Provost companies would be kept very busy controlling traffic, routing and maintaining route signs, redirecting and re-routing stragglers and lost units, apprehending PoWs and maintaining the general security of unit headquarters. The RMP are constantly kept in training for this role but they also have an important peace-time role which keeps them very busy. The Army in Germany maintains large garrison and base areas and the GPD branch of the RMP has the unenviable task of policing these against all the normal day-to-day occurrences that are likely to arise. Thus the RMPs are kept constantly busy with patrols, traffic control, road safety, the checking of premises and the general overseeing of the conduct of both the soldiery and the civilian elements who live and work in the British areas. To carry out these many duties there are only the wartime establishments available, so they are kept very busy. Also in Germany there is 247 Provost Company as part of the Berlin Brigade, with seven platoons. A further platoon forms the Autobahn Control Detachment based at Helmstedt.

In the United Kingdom there are seven Provost companies. Normally they are stationed wherever there are sizeable concentrations of troops in such locations as Aldershot, Catterick, Edinburgh, Donnington, Bulford, Colchester and the London District. In an emergency four of these companies would travel to West Germany, and one of them, 158 Provost Company at Bulford, forms a nucleus for the British MP contingent assigned to the ACE Mobile Force (Land). Two companies (probably attenuated to provide manpower for elsewhere) would be assigned to 5 Infantry Brigade. The London District Provost Company would stay where it was. All the home-based and BAOR units would be augmented in an emergency by members of the Royal Military Police Volunteers from the eight Territorial Army MP units.

Northern Ireland is at present absorbing a considerable amount of RMP effort for it now is the working area for the 1st Regiment RMP. Apart from a small regimental HQ and an administrative element, this regiment has five Provost companies including 181 Provost Company WRAC. These companies are assigned to each of the three brigades in Northern Ireland where they are employed and stationed according to the local situation.

Provost companies are also stationed in Cyprus, Hong Kong and Belize, while at BATUS in Canada a single RMP NCO keeps local order. There is also a six-man RMP unit in Gibraltar.

All the above units are part of the GPD branch. The other RMP branch is the Special Investigation Branch, or SIB, which is charged with the prevention of crime within the Army and the subsequent apprehension of offenders. It is the military equivalent of the civilian CID and operates along much the same lines. All members of the SIB are carefully selected from within the GPD branch and have to complete a six-month probationary period with the SIB before they are even trained. Basic training for the SIB is carried out within the RMP but further training is often carried out at civil police establishments.

There is one further RMP establishment to mention, the Mounted Troop based at Aldershot. Competition to join the Mounted Troop is very keen as it has only 20 horses, and a potential recruit has to have at least two years' service before he can even apply to join. Once in the troop any RMP member will find himself kept busy. The horses are used mainly for the patrolling of the ranges and open areas around Aldershot, but they also have ceremonial and display duties.

As is normal with civilian police forces, the RMP do not have a detention role. If a soldier commits a crime that merits imprisonment he is sent to a civilian prison, but if a soldier's conduct warrants a period of detention he is sent to the Army's only remaining detention centre at Colchester. There the offender will be placed under the control of the Military Provost Staff Corps, the military equivalent of the civil Prison Service. Once inside the Colchester establishment the MPSC has the task of turning a bad soldier into a good one. The regime is onerous but not over-rigorous. If any indication of the conduct of the modern Army was needed it is the fact that there is now only one Army detention centre—not so many years ago there were many, many more, and all of them were kept busy. It is a measure of the standard of education and general behaviour of the modern soldier that the number of centres remains at but one.

But to return to the RMP: any recruit for the ranks of the corps must meet certain physical standards. He must be at least 1.7 metres tall (5 feet 7 inches) and fulfil weight, fitness and eyesight standards. He must also have a clean record. Once trained, the Military Policeman is segregated from the rest of the Army and messes separately. He has his own particular uniform distinctions of the red-topped service cap or the red beret. On duty he wears a red armband and a whistle and chain. At all times he has to maintain an example to all, and his conduct, bearing and appearance must be beyond reproach.

Ambush drills are essential for the UDR. Here one is being carried out in Cumberland on a typical UDR training course (MoD).

In the words of the Provost Marshal, the officer responsible for both the RMP and the MPSC, (incidentally the title of Provost Marshal is one of the oldest military titles still in use as it dates back to the time of William the Conqueror, and maybe before then), 'The Royal Military Police provide only two per cent of the Army, but they like to think they give ten per cent in value.'

The Ulster Defence Regiment

The Ulster Defence Regiment has to be dealt with separately from other branches of the British Army for several reasons. One reason is that it is the largest single regiment in the Army, being around 8,000 strong. It is the only regiment that recruits women as well as men (at the time of writing there are over 700 women serving with the Ulster Defence Regiment—or UDR). It is also the youngest of all the Army's formations, being formed as recently as April 1 1970. A further distinction is that it is the Army's only 'part-time' regiment, as its roles and duties are quite distinct from that of the Territorial Army. If any further distinctions were needed, the UDR is the only regiment of the Army that is continually in the front line, for it was formed to combat the form of political terrorism that is prevalent in the troubled province of Northern Ireland.

The UDR was formed to partially replace the Reserve elements of the Royal Ulster Constabulary that were disbanded for political reasons in 1970. The UDR's duties are straightforward enough, for it exists to provide assistance and aid to the Royal Ulster Constabulary in its task of safeguarding lives

and property against the extremists who have found Ulster such a fruitful ground for their destructive activities. Apart from a relatively small cadre of full-time officers and NCOs, all the members of the UDR are part-time soldiers. When they are off-duty they resume their normal places in society and carry on their everyday civilian tasks. For them there is no chance of relaxing in well-guarded barracks. They have to carry on their normal lives as part of the local community, with all the risks which that involves. Consequently the UDR is constantly in the front line. On uniformed duty its men are always possible targets for terrorist action. Off-duty they have, in the past, been singled out for all manner of terrorist activity which has ranged from intimidation and local unpleasantness to the extremes of the bullet and the gun—in this latter respect each edition of the *UDR Journal* has, in the past, contained a sizeable obituary section. But the spirit of the UDR is amazingly high and recruiting is never a problem. If there is one continuing area of concern with the membership of the UDR it is that the sectarian nature of the Northern Irish community is reflected in its membership—only about three per cent of UDR members are Roman Catholics despite the fact that UDR membership is open to all sections of the population. Originally the proportion of Catholics in the UDR was higher but social and terrorist intimidation by the PIRA and its sympathisers has led to the creation of the present social imbalance, and indeed, the continuing membership of the serving Catholics must be a point worthy of special mention.

In its fight against terrorism, the UDR has several routine tasks. The patrolling of built-up and rural areas is perhaps the most obvious activity but there are others. UDR units also set up and operate the road blocks that are such a feature of anti-terrorist measures, but perhaps the most important contribution to the Army's activities comes from the

UDR members themselves. They are all very much a part of the local community, they know intimately the area they are patrolling and serving in, and they usually know the members of the population as well. Consequently they are well able to sense the times when something suspicious or out of the ordinary has occurred, or when someone or something unfamiliar is in the area. Such local knowledge is invaluable in anti-terrorist operations and the UDR uses this valuable attribute to the full in arms searches and the supply of tactical intelligence.

Despite its part-time nature, the UDR has proved time and again that it is a very professional and effective force. It often serves alongside Regular army units and Regular units frequently come under the command of UDR officers when on duty. This efficiency is the result of the years on duty since 1970 when some of the early efforts of the UDR were open to criticism, mainly as a result of equipment and training deficiencies. Those early days are now well past and any new recruit to the regiment is soon made very aware of the dedication which the UDR applies to its often thankless tasks. New recruits are always put through a screening process to prevent some of the more undesirable elements of Northern Irish society from gaining admission to the ranks, not only from a security point of view (to prevent the infiltration of UDR activities by terrorist sympathisers) but also to prevent UDR weapons and training from being misused. Unfortunately, this screening has not always been effective enough, as the political enemies have often been quick to point out, but by and large the members of the UDR have proved themselves to be more than worthy of the philosophy of their regiment, which is to be non-sectarian, impartial, courteous and fair. In the troubled nature of the Northern Irish situation, such a philosophy would try the patience of angels but the UDR manages somehow. Under such circumstances it is no wonder that the UDR sometimes attracts criticism, usually from the very people who are disposed towards the forces the regiment was formed to combat. To counter this the UDR has also attracted the praise and thanks of many more by far.

Once accepted by the UDR, the recruit is given a one-week basic training course before company duties are assumed. Further training takes place within the company, both locally and sometimes in the United Kingdom. For the part-timer there are 15 full days of training every year, but the amount of time spent on active duties varies from area to area and is dependent on a number of circumstances. If the occasion demands, the UDR can be called out for full-time duty, but normally the only full-time UDR members are the CONRATES who carry out the administrative and training functions for the regiment as well as the security and guard duties for UDR bases. Most part-timers devote at least one evening a week to UDR duties, and most weekends as well. Patrolling is the usual form of active duty (apart from the guarding of essential services and locations) and the patrols can be by foot, vehicle or helicopter. Some battalions have boat sections (using Dell Quay light launches on the numerous loughs and waterways), and nearly all companies have dog sections used for guard and explosive search purposes.

The women members of the regiment deserve their own special mention for they serve alongside the men as full UDR members. Known throughout Ulster (and elsewhere) as 'Greenfinches', they carry out numerous duties. They are trained to administer first aid, act as mobile communications operators or telephonists, assist at check points or road blocks for search purposes, and also act as clerks, storewomen and cooks.

The equipment used by the UDR is similar to that used by other Infantry regiments. The basic weapon is the L1A1 rifle, along with the L2A3 submachine-gun and the L4A4 (Bren) machine-gun. UDR members whose normal civilian duties present them as potential terrorist targets are sometimes issued with personal XL47E1 Walther pistols. On patrol the UDR uses the ubiquitous Land Rover fitted with armour and other fittings to suit the anti-terrorist role, and the regiment is the main user of the FV18061 Shorland armoured car. Some battalions have been issued with the SB.301 armoured personnel carrier.

The UDR is at present organised into 11 battalions. Each has the usual headquarters unit which administers the companies under its command—there are usually at least three companies in each battalion. The main UDR headquarters is at Lisburn with the various battalion headquarters situated as follows: 1st (County Antrim) Battalion UDR—Ballymena, Co Antrim; 2nd (County Armagh) Battalion UDR—Armagh, Co Armagh; 3rd (County Down) Battalion UDR—Ballykinler, Co Down; 4th (County Fermanagh) Battalion UDR—Enniskillen, Co Fermanagh; 5th (County Londonderry) Battalion UDR—Limavady, Co Londonderry; 6th (County Tyrone) Battalion UDR—Omagh, Co Tyrone; 7th (City of Belfast) Battalion UDR—Holywood, Co Down; 8th (County Tyrone) Battalion UDR—Dungannon, Co Tyrone; 9th (County Antrim) Battalion UDR—Antrim, Co Antrim; 10th (City of Belfast) Battalion UDR—Belfast; and 11th (Craigavon) Battalion UDR—Portadown.

There is no doubt that the UDR is a unique formation but in its relatively short life it has proved to be as willing, efficient and operationally effective as any Regular unit based in Northern Ireland. A small measure of this effectiveness can be seen in the attention it has drawn from the security forces of many nations who have expressed keen interest in the organisation and methods of the UDR, often with a view to instituting similar formations in their own potential troubled areas. But without a doubt, the UDR would not have proved to be the successful counter-terrorist regiment it has become without the dedication, hard work and application of the ordinary men and women of Ulster who have joined its ranks. Their decision to counter and fight the political terrorist is the vital factor that motivates the UDR, and it is they who put meaning into the regimental byword—'Peace through Strength'.

The Royal Army Chaplains' Department

In the same way that any society depends not only on material things but on some other spiritual or moral guidance or order, the Army has its own department for its continuing Christian ministrations. In an age when it would seem that the soldier has become a mere cog in a huge fighting machine, it is still apparent that the Christian faith has a place in British life, including the Army. Within this structure the Royal Army Chaplains' Department carries out the spiritual guidance of the Army and its associated communities. It has five Churches represented within its numbers, those of England and of Scotland together with the Methodist, Roman Catholic and United Board (Baptist and Congregationalist) Churches. There is also a Senior Jewish Chaplain to the Forces, but he is a member of the Territorial Army.

Chaplains who administer any of these religions and who wish to minister to the Army have to undergo their normal religious instruction at civilian establishments. All Army chaplains undergo, after joining, a further training period at the training centre at Bagshot Heath. From there they join a regiment or the equivalent and, as their career in the Army progresses, they may be assigned to a garrison or a Junior Leaders' regiment. Wherever they go they will minister not only to soldiers but to their families and all the other personnel attached to the establishment.

The Army chaplain is given a commissioned rank but his role is to guide all ranks. While doing this he shares the hardships, upheavals and discomforts of the men and women under his guidance, and is expected to take part in all their activities. But the RAChD is the only section of the Army where the personnel do not undergo weapon training or carry weapons. This does not mean they do not assimilate military skills, for the chaplain has to be able to conduct himself sensibly on a battlefield to preserve life and limb, and he must be able to appreciate the tasks of the units he is assigned to. Perhaps the most extreme example of this can be seen with the chaplains assigned to the Parachute Regiment, who have to go through the full parachute course and 'jump' with their units into whatever situations the regiment may find itself.

The General Service Corps

The General Service Corps is a rather odd formation with no real existence at the present time other than as a tiny cadre for possible administrative purposes. It remains in existence purely for convenience as it provides a ready holding unit to enable the Army to place specially recruited or short-service civilian specialists within its 'ranks' for a short period. It also provides a 'home' for any specialists who are assigned to the Army to carry out any function that does not enable them to be readily assigned to any other regiment or corps. But for most of the time, the General Service Corps is a 'paper' formation.

The Gibraltar Regiment

At one time, wherever the Army became established it raised formations of local inhabitants as adjuncts to the local garrisons. In time many of these levies grew into magnificent armies, of which the largest and finest was perhaps the old Indian Army. More modest establishments flourished elsewhere, many of them romantic like the various Arab State units, the others who provided sound functional formations such as the Royal Malta Regiment, the Cyprus Regiment, the King's African Rifles, and many, many more. With the withdrawal from Empire, most of these have been incorporated into their national forces and today, only one remains under British guidance (apart from the Gurkhas, who are really in a different category) and that is the Gibraltar Regiment.

Formed in 1939 as the Gibraltar Defence Force and renamed in 1958, the Gibraltar Regiment has as its primary task the defence of Gibraltar. For this it is divided into three main units. There is a Headquarters unit that administers and controls the two main units, an infantry company and an artillery battery. The Regiment is 256 strong of whom 45 are regular soldiers, and the Regiment takes its duties very seriously. Their training sessions are always fully attended, there is a thriving social side, and the Regiment even has its own 19-strong Corps of

Drums (all volunteers). Apart from its purely defensive role the Regiment has several other tasks to perform, among these being the maintenance of some of the relics of the past that still exist on the Rock.

Pride of place must go to the splendid 9.2-in coastal defence guns of O'Hara's and Lord Airey's batteries. These magnificent guns are situated on some of the highest points of the Rock and command views that have to be seen to be believed. As the guns are now the property of the people of Gibraltar, the Gibraltar Regiment is charged with their upkeep and presentation, and present them they do. The guns are kept in fully working order and from time to time they are shown off complete with all the correct gun drill of their period, which lasted until the 1960s. Other artillery relics kept in shape by the Regiment include the massive 17.72-in calibre 100-ton rifled muzzle-loading gun at Rosia Bay, and the sealed-off 5.25-in anti-aircraft guns of the 1950s Princess Anne's battery. One unique duty carried out by a full-time Sergeant and Private of the Regiment is the care and general welfare of the Rock's apes. The Regiment also participates in many of the ceremonials carried out in Gibraltar, including the Ceremony of the Keys, a movable feast that takes place three to four times a year.

The Infantry Company has three platoons and a Company HQ. They are equipped with the normal infantry weapons but the heaviest they use is the GPMG. Every year they travel to the United Kingdom to undergo training that cannot be carried out locally due to the rather obvious space restriction. Both sections provide their own independent signals.

The Artillery Battery has two sections, a Field Troop and an Air Defence Troop. The Field Troop has two 105 mm Pack Howitzers, the last operational examples of this weapon, and the Air Defence Troop has four 40 mm L/70 Bofors guns, the very last of their kind still in Army use. As with the infantry, every year both Troops travel to the United Kingdom for range training, the Field Troop to Larkhill and the Air Defence Troop to Manorbier. On the Rock, both troops fire the salutes from the four 25 prs at Devil's Gap. Both troops and the infantry platoons carry out the same training requirements as any UK-based Territorial Army unit, apart from the fact that the local enthusiasm is almost overwhelming. From time to time range firing is carried out at sea targets but space precludes many training activities that would otherwise be necessary. Both sections hope to obtain new weapons eventually. The Field Troop hope, one day, to be given 105 mm Light Guns, and the Air Defence Troop hopes for Blowpipe, or even Rapier.

The Royal Army Pay Corps

The men of the Royal Army Pay Corps are the Army's accountants, looking after all the many aspects of finances and associated tasks. Every unit in the Army has a member of the RAPC attached to administer its monetary affairs, either in the shape of RAPC unit paymasters or RAPC clerks.

The basic matter of pay for the Army is no longer carried out by the time-honoured and time-wasting procedure of pay parades (except where local conditions make them necessary) but via a computer-based system located at the RAPC's home at Worthy Down. The computer there is the central segment of the Army's pay and salary system and funds are assigned from it into individual bank accounts. The computer also deals to a large degree with the many and various allowances, allotments to families, and even with pensions. Worthy Down is also the home of the RAPC Training Centre.

Although every Army unit has its own RAPC personnel, the 'teeth' units of the corps are the field cash offices assigned to the four divisions of BAOR. The field cash offices are kept in being and train constantly but are normally only put into the field in an emergency or on exercises. The sums of money handled by these offices can be quite considerable, but the role of the RAPC extends down to such transactions as hire purchase advice for individual soldiers and the running of tote offices for regimental point-to-point meetings. All ranks of the RAPC are, however, still fighting soldiers and they are all trained in essential combat skills.

The field cash offices are usually formed of an RAPC officer, two or three senior RAPC NCOs and a number of Corporals employed in a clerical capacity. Other RAPC personnel act as drivers and general administration staff. The office is fully mobile, usually using Land Rovers carrying accommodation, safes and the inevitable desks and furniture. The offices go wherever they are needed and administer not only pay and allowances to troops in the field but also unit funds for such purposes as local purchases, currency exchange and general finances.

The Women's Royal Army Corps

The WRAC was established as a Regular corps in 1949 from the old Auxiliary Territorial Service which was the formation that really established the role of women as a practical and functional part of the Army structure. Today, the WRAC consists of

Junior Leaders from the WRAC display the five different types of uniform worn by the Corps (MoD).

approximately 5,000 women who serve in just about every branch of the Army other than the front-line combat units (and even there the WRAC can sometimes be found). WRACs are very much full-time members of the Army. They go wherever the Army goes, they carry out the same support and administrative functions as their male counterparts, and they share also in the upheavals and uncertainty of Service life in general.

The depot for the WRAC is at Guildford in Surrey, and it is there that recruits carry out their basic Army training. Trade training is carried out at the normal schools, eg, Signals operatives are trained at Catterick, stores personnel at Deepcut, and so on. Once trained, the WRAC personnel are then assigned to Army camps and depots where they have their own accommodation, but apart from that one rather obvious necessity, the WRAC takes its place in normal Army activities with few other concessions. The WRAC does have its own officer corps (about 700 strong in 1979) who combine the roles of administering and controlling their WRAC rank and file, along with carrying out the everyday officer tasks in all branches of the Army. In this latter respect, some WRAC officers have reached positions of considerable responsibility, albeit usually in an administrative role—some WRAC officers have become adjutants in field batteries and other units.

WRAC personnel can select their trade from the following: analyst, clerk/shorthand writer, communication centre operator, cook, driver, experimental assistant gunnery, hairdresser, intelligence and security operator, kennelmaid/ groom, medical orderly, Military Policewoman, musician, physical training instructor, postal and courier operative, radar operator, regimental store-woman, stewardess, switchboard operator, technical clerk or technical storewoman.

As will be seen from the above, the WRAC is integrated in nearly all branches of the Army, but it has now become even more involved with the introduction of small-arms training to some trades open to the WRAC. Ever since women joined the Army's ranks it has been a basic rule that female fingers were not to pull triggers, even though they were often in a position to issue orders to open fire. That policy was changed during 1979, partly as a realisation of the trends of modern sociological changes, and partly from the practical viewpoint that WRAC MPs have been on active security duties for some years in Northern Ireland and elsewhere.

The Royal Military Academy Sandhurst

The purpose of the Royal Military Academy Sandhurst is well set out in its Charter which states the following aims: To give the officer cadet a broad view of his profession as a whole and his responsibilities as a servant of the Crown; to develop the essential characteristics of leadership and man management, sense of discipline and sense of duty; and to develop his physical fitness.

All officers who are given the Queen's Commission have to pass through the RMAS at some stage or other of their military careers, usually at the beginning, and many return there either for further training or to become part of the instructional staff. Thus the RMAS is as important a part of the modern Army as it has been since the twin academies of Woolwich and Sandhurst were established during the 18th century. Now only the RMAS remains.

There are several different types of commission but all involve a period of training spent at the RMAS. For the direct entrant there is the Standard Military Course lasting about six months. Both short-term and career cadets take this course together, but the long-term cadets then go on to take a further six-month curriculum known as the Regular Career Course. In addition to these two basic courses there are more specialised ones run for entrants who will be going on to university, and for TA officer cadets.

Since the Standard Military Course is the one that most officers encounter it will be dealt with in some detail. It is an involved and exacting course involving all aspects of the future officer's work. As with other basic forms of military training the initial emphasis is on drill (in all its forms), weapon training and essential tactical skills. Where the RMAS differs from the rest of the Army is in the degree of expertise the officer cadet is expected to achieve—he must excel. Further basic military skills are imparted, not only in the Infantry role but in all the other arms of the Army as well. This intensive education is interspersed with lectures and practical training on the administration and organisation of the Army, leadership, military history, physical training, adventure training and sport. Sport plays an important part in the Sandhurst timetable and the facilities available range from the usual athletic pursuits to the almost inevitable horsemanship, and even flying.

Apart from the sporting aspects, the facilities at Sandhurst are first class in every respect while the instructional staff are drawn from well-qualified civilians and the military alike. The RMAS is set in several hundred acres of pleasant country near Camberley in Surrey and contained in its grounds are ranges, tactical training areas and all the accommodation needed for the cadets. The RMAS itself is divided into three colleges, 'Mons' (the Mons Officer Cadet School was joined on to the RMAS in 1972), 'Old' and 'Victory'.

The largest of these is Mons as this college is the one that caters for the Standard Military Course. It has two Wings, each divided into three companies as follows: Wing 1—Alamein, Burma and Normandy Companies; Wing 2—Arnhem, Rhine and Salerno Companies.

The officer cadets who will be going on to the Regular Career Course pass on to the Old College where they will be assigned to one of four companies, namely Blenheim, Dettingen, Waterloo or Inkerman. The third college is Victory, which caters for the university graduates and the like. It has three companies, Salamanca, Amiens and Gaza.

The RMAS also has five departments— Mathematics, Science, Political and Social Studies, War Studies and Languages. Each department is involved in all stages and forms of officer cadet training, but they are especially involved in the Regular Career Course where they combine to provide an extensive and comprehensive military education that will form the basis of the officer cadets' eventual career outlooks. The course lasts 21 weeks and covers such items as contemporary affairs, military technology in all its many aspects from basics to computers, ADP and electronics, further war studies and the essential techniques of in-

struction. The training is first-class and, although involved, is backed up by modern facilities and extensive libraries.

The RMAS education can also lead to further education at university level, either at the civilian universities or the Royal Military College of Science at Shrivenham. Further education comes from the officer cadets themselves, who now come from all walks of life, rather than the rather narrow band of the more privileged classes as of yore, and also from overseas. The overseas cadets usually come from the old colonies and British-influenced states, and on their return many have, in the past, gained high positions in their own armed forces or governments. This social aspect of the RMAS is one that is discreetly encouraged for the formation of character and leadership is just as important to the graduate officer as the technicalities of his calling.

The RMAS has over the years provided its own particular traditions, some of which have been passed down from previous academies such as that as Woolwich. Perhaps the most widely known oddity that the RMAS brings to mind is that of the Adjutant riding his horse through the Grand Entrance at the end of the Sovereign's Parade, but there are others. The RMAS is the last home of traditional body armour in the British Army for the cadets still retain the gorgette as part of their parade dress. Numerous trophies are competed for every year—the best known being the Sword of Honour.

The Royal Military School of Music

The Royal Military School of Music is based at Kneller Hall, near Twickenham, and is the home of British military music. Nearly every regiment and corps of the Army has its own band while some have more than one—for example, the Royal Artillery has three: the Royal Artillery (Woolwich) Band, the Royal Artillery (Mounted) Band and the Royal Artillery (Alanbrooke) Band. One of these will soon be disbanded.

Most military musicians join a band of their own choosing but usually spend one year at Kneller Hall learning all aspects of their trade. After service with their own corps or regiment band they may return to Kneller Hall for the Student Bandmaster's Course which lasts some six months. If they pass all the necessary stringent criteria they can eventually become bandmasters with Warrant Officer rank. In time they may become eligible for commissions as Directors of Music.

Military musicians do not normally have to carry out military duties and in most cases do not receive the standard military training. But they have to comport themselves in a military manner and their dress and bearing on parade is of a high order. They have to turn their hands to music of every description from ceremonial parade marches, through classical music to dance music for informal occasions. Most musicians are taught to play more than one instrument, eg, a brass instrumentalist may well double as a string musician for mess occasions, and all are taught the theory behind the music they read and play. Kneller Hall provides the background training for all this and much more.

The Territorial Army

The modern Territorial Army has a long history stretching back over several centuries to the era when every able-bodied man had to practice weekly with his longbow, but as the years went by its many forms gradually emerged as local militia units raised to be called upon in times of national emergency. Where the present-day Territorial Army (the TA) differs from its forebears is that it is no longer an armed force separate from the rest of the Army. Today the TA is an integral part of the Army's structure and its manpower and units form a large part of the Army's fighting strength.

The main strength of the modern TA lies within its 38 Infantry battalions. In addition to this total there are another 17 fighting units ranging from Gunner and Engineer formations to the two Yeomanry armoured reconnaissance regiments. But this is not all the TA can provide for, in addition to the major units, there are another 250 or so minor ones that vary from map-making squadrons to specialised Signal units. There are even two TA SAS units and three battalions of TA Parachute Regiment troops (described elsewhere).

The TA is made up mainly of part-time soldiers drawn from all walks of civilian life. Reservists and ex-Army soldiers who wish to retain some measure of the social and regimental spirit that the Regular Army provides add a valuable contribution to the technical skills needed by the modern TA, but the main training and administrative cadres are formed by Regular soldiers and officers. All arms of the modern Army are represented in the TA. Every unit is in some manner affiliated to a Regular formation and wears that regiment's badge. Their 'parent' formation usually provides some training facilities and other support and in time of emergency would become fully responsible for its mobilisation and deployment. However, many TA units have already been assigned their wartime roles. About 50 per cent of all TA units are intended for use in West Germany in an emergency. Some of these will be necessary to make 1 (Br) Corps up to its full numerical complement, but the majority of them will be combined with Regular units to form part of 1 and 19 Infantry Brigades. Those TA units remaining in the UK, apart from a few specialist formations, will form part of 5 Infantry Brigade for home defence. In this role they will be assigned to the various Military Districts and will be commanded by the local District Commanders. Regular units, along with troops raised from the various base and training establishments in the United Kingdom, will also be assigned to 5 Infantry Brigade.

As the modern TA is such an integral part of the Modern Army, its equipment is in most cases exactly the same as that of the front line units. However, especially with units intended for 5 Infantry Brigade, the accent is on wheeled rather than tracked vehicles. This has the combined attraction of lower costs coupled with less demanding maintenancing and training requirements. Thus an Infantry support weapons company would carry its Wombats and 81 mm mortars in Land Rovers rather than FV432s. Apart from this stricture the weapons involved are the same. Recently, some TA units have been issued with new equipment in advance of Regular units, but here and there some of the recently replaced front-line equipment takes on a new lease of life with the TA. An example of this can be seen in the adoption of Larkspur signal equipment by some home-based TA Signal units after they have been replaced by their Clansman counterparts. But generally speaking the TA units train with the same weapons and equipment as the Regular Army. Of course, there are some exceptions to this.

The present strength of the TA is around 55,000 men. To this may be added nearly 4,000 women who belong to WRAC TA units. As mentioned above, members of the TA come from all walks of life and by joining they take on various training and attendance committments. Each member of the TA has to attend at least 44 training days a year, of which 15 are spent full-time at a training camp or establishment. Many TA members exceed this total by a considerable margin. In return they are paid by a system of Regular pay scale rates and bounties. The minimum period of engagement is three years.

Despite the fact that some TA units are not up to full strength, the general standard of training is very high for the simple reason that members are all volunteers and do not join unless they wish to. The training is often hard, for some weekend training sessions take place in the field under all manner of conditions. TA soldiers often have to leave work on a Friday evening, travel straight to their training areas and commence their training exercises immediately. To make maximum use of the limited time available the exercises often carry on throughout the weekend without a break so that the soldier returns to work on the Monday morning after only a limited amount of rest. But they still turn out for the next weekend.

The annual training camp is a full-time affair and in many cases takes place in other locations than the United Kingdom. Units assigned to the 6th and 7th Field Forces often travel to West Germany, and small numbers of TA personnel have even made the long journey to Suffield in Canada. During the annual camp period, the TA units are treated exactly the same as their Regular counterparts but usually, such is their spirit and morale, they often try to outdo their colleagues in efficiency and expertise. To this extent there is a considerable degree of inter-unit competition between the TA units and other formations with trophies being awarded for specific tasks and competitions. Added to this is the considerable kudos that a TA soldier can obtain from being associated with such elite formations as the Parachute Regiment, while some TA units also have considerable social sway. Typical of the latter category is the Honorable Artillery Company based in London. As well as providing an Artillery regiment for ceremonial and field duties, the HAC also has a position of some social prominence in London life. It also provides another of the Army's structural anomalies. By tradition it is an Artillery unit but it is not part of the Royal Regiment of Artillery—in practice it is associated with the Gunners but it's constitution makes it a separate body.

Finally, mention must be made of the two basic types of TA unit—these are the Independent and the Sponsored unit. The Independent unit is what it says it is—it is one which can be formed with its own resources alone, and has its own centre. By contrast the Sponsored unit does not have its own centre and is dependent on a Central Volunteer Establishment of their own corps or regiment. The bulk of TA units (82 per cent) are Independent. Nearly all the Sponsored units are highly specialised and as a result have different training commitments.

Listing of the major TA units

The following list is provisional as TA units have been known to be rather prone to short-notice and short-term amalgamations or title changes. The list contains only those units of regimental size or status—there are many more units of smaller size. The units are not presented in order of precedence.
The Royal Yeomanry
The Queen's Own Yeomanry
The Wessex Yeomanry (now Infantry)

The Mercian Yeomanry (now Infantry)
The Duke of Lancaster's Own Yeomanry (now Infantry)
The Honorable Artillery Company
1st Battalion, 52nd Lowland Volunteers
2nd Battalion, 52nd Lowland Volunteers
1st Battalion, 51st Highland Volunteers
2nd Battalion, 51st Highland Volunteers
3rd Battalion, 51st Highland Volunteers
5th (Volunteer) Battalion, The Queen's Regiment
6th/7th (Volunteer) Battalion, The Queen's Regiment
5th (Volunteer) Battalion, The Royal Regiment of Fusiliers
6th (Volunteer) Battalion, The Royal Regiment of Fusiliers
5th (Volunteer) Battalion, The Royal Anglian Regiment
6th (Volunteer) Battalion, The Royal Anglian Regiment
7th (Volunteer) Battalion, The Royal Anglian Regiment
4th (Volunteer) Battalion, The King's Own Royal Border Regiment
5th/8th (Volunteer) Battalion, The Queen's Lancashire Regiment
1st Battalion, The Yorkshire Volunteers
2nd Battalion, The Yorkshire Volunteers
3rd Battalion, The Yorkshire Volunteers
4th (Volunteer) Battalion, The Royal Irish Rangers
5th (Volunteer) Battalion, The Royal Irish Rangers
1st Battalion, The Wessex Regiment (Rifle Volunteers)
2nd Battalion, The Wessex Regiment
1st Battalion, The Mercian Volunteers
2nd Battalion, The Mercian Volunteers
3rd (Volunteer) Battalion, The Royal Welch Fusiliers
3rd (Volunteer) Battalion, The Royal Regiment of Wales (24th/41st Foot)
4th (Volunteer) Battalion, The Royal Regiment of Wales (24th/41st Foot)
3rd (Volunteer) Battalion, The Worcestershire and Sherwood Foresters Regiment (29th/45th Foot)
5th (Volunteer) Battalion, The Light Infantry
6th (Volunteer) Battalion, The Light Infantry
7th (Volunteer) Battalion, The Light Infantry
4th (Volunteer) Battalion, The Royal Green Jackets
4th (Volunteer) Battalion, The Parachute Regiment
10th (Volunteer) Battalion, The Parachute Regiment—London
15th (Scottish Volunteer) Battalion, The Parachute Regiment
21 Special Air Service Regiment (Artists) (Volunteers)

23 Special Air Service Regiment (Volunteers)

31 (Greater London) Signal Regiment (Volunteers)—Hammersmith

32 (Scottish) Signal Regiment (Volunteers)—Glasgow

33 (Lancashire and Cheshire) Signal Regiment (Volunteers)—Liverpool

34 (Northern) Signal Regiment (Volunteers)—Middlesborough

35 (South Midland) Signal Regiment (Volunteers)—Birmingham

36 (Eastern) Signal Regiment (Volunteers)—Wanstead

37 (Wessex and Welsh) Signal Regiment (Volunteers)—Bristol

38 Signal Regiment (Volunteers)—Sheffield

39 (City of London) Signal Regiment (Volunteers)—London

40 (Ulster) Signal Regiment (Volunteers)—Belfast

71 Signal Regiment (Volunteers)—Bromley

Royal Monmouthshire Royal Engineers (Militia)

71 (Scottish) Engineer Regiment (Volunteers)

72 Engineer Regiment (Tyne Electrical Engineers) (Volunteers)

73 Engineer Regiment (Volunteers)

74 (Antrim Artillery) Engineer Regiment (Volunteers)

75 Engineer Regiment (Volunteers)

111 Engineer Regiment (Volunteers)

100th (Yeomanry) Field Regiment Royal Artillery (Volunteers)

101st (Northumbrian) Field Regiment Royal Artillery (Volunteers)

102nd (Ulster and Scottish) Air Defence Regiment Royal Artillery (Volunteers)

103rd Lancashire Artillery (Volunteers) Air Defence Regiment Royal Artillery (Volunteers)

104th Air Defence Regiment Royal Artillery (Volunteers)

The Army in Northern Ireland

As these words are written, the present troubles in Northern Ireland have been extended over a period of more than ten years. That period has seen the Army always in the thick of whatever unpleasantries the inhabitants of Ulster have chosen to inflict upon one another, and they have always borne the brunt of the open aggression so freely doled out by all the many sides in the multi-faceted social and political circumstances that continue to bedevil the Six Counties. During the past decade, the Army has come in for more than its share of 'blame' for events in Northern Ireland, but it has been called upon to carry out a thankless task that any other Army would have turned into something approaching a bloodbath, and it has to be stated as a fact that if the Army was not present in Ulster as it now is, ie, in strength and well-trained, life in Ulster would be a good deal worse than it is already.

The Army is no stranger to Northern Ireland. For many hundreds of years the Army has been a well-established part of the social and political landscape. Ever since William of Orange took over the sovereignty of the Province, and long before that, the people of Ulster have had soldiers of the Crown in their midst. The soldiers manned the garrison towns in the Province and raised many famous regiments that served the Crown well in numerous conflicts, and some of these regiments survive to this day. After 1922 the Province continued to supply men for the Services, and it should be remembered that between 1939 and 1945, Northern Ireland was excluded from the various Conscription Acts for the reason that so many Irishmen were crossing the Border to sign on for the British forces that conscription was never necessary.

When the present troubles 'began' in 1969 the Army was already present as part of the normal peace-time garrison. Within a very short time the prevalent social and political unrest erupted into open insurrection and rioting to the extent that the local civil and police authorities were completely unable to contain the violence and uproar that broke out in nearly all the major urban centres of Ulster. The Army was called in by the local government authorities to assist the Royal Ulster Constabulary to maintain order, but the strength of the local Army units was insufficient to take on such a task. Troops were brought into the Province from the United Kingdom to swell the available numbers and they have never been able to return.

The Army in Northern Ireland is engaged in that most unloved form of military duty, 'action in support of a civil power'. This point has to be stressed for it is not widely understood that the Army by itself does not possess autonomous powers of action. In Northern Ireland the Army comes firmly under the control of the local civic authorities and their various offices. In Ulster that means the Army comes under the direction of the Royal Ulster Constabulary which in its turn takes its references from the United Kingdom Home Office, via an appointed Crown Minister. Acting under such a control the Army often finds itself in some very tricky legal circumstances. The Army does not have an automatic right to search or arrest. If soldiers are attacked or fired on, their powers to retaliate are carefully and rigidly proscribed. Such restrictions of the Army's activities are very necessary if our

A patrol of the Royal Fusiliers about to set off on a patrol. There are several items of note in this photograph, apart from the PR-minded sniffer dog. The soldier in the left foreground has a 30-round magazine on his L1A1, and all the patrol have SUIT sights fitted. Note the extra Macralon armour panels fitted to the Land Rover, and note also that some patrol members still wear the distinctive and colourful Fusilier hackle in their berets, despite their obvious attraction to a sniper (Army PR HQ NI).

carefully preserved liberties are to be retained, but the restrictions often hamper the Army in their task of apprehending suspects and generally keeping the peace. All too often the Army has had to place itself and its members in positions of extreme risk with all too often no chance to effect redress or carry out any counter-activity.

The last ten years *have* produced their results. These words are being written in the aftermath of the Mountbatten and Warrenpoint murders when it would seem that all the efforts of the last decade or more have been for nought, but the Army and the RUC have been able to effect some degree of success in their fight against the modern political terrorist. Starting from a rather shaky beginning, the Army has had to re-learn and retrain for the counter-insurgency role to the extent that it is now the finest and best-equipped such force in the world. Despite all the killings, bombings and attacks, the last ten years have seen a gradual shift of terrorist activities from the main urban centres to the more open country of the Border between the province and the Irish Republic. Murders, bombings and at-

tacks still occur in Belfast, Londonderry and the other large towns but they are on nothing like the scale that was the virtual norm in the years just after 1969 and 1970. Despite the recurring incidents in the towns and cities, life there can now be said to be virtually normal and fairly safe. In rural areas it can still come as a pleasant surprise to find large tracts of country untouched in any way by the present troubles. Only the long and open borderland remains 'bandit country' where the terrorists still find it fairly easy to carry out their nefarious tasks.

The cost of the long campaign against the terrorist in Northern Ireland has been very high. At the time of writing well over 300 soldiers have lost their lives, many more have been maimed and injured, and thousands of soldiers will carry mental scars to their grave. In monetary costs, the keeping of the peace has caused a constant drain on the Exchequer running to millions of pounds, but the main problem for the Army is that the Northern Ireland commitment has been a very difficult one to meet at a time when manpower and equipment has been at a constant premium.

There is still a permanent Northern Irish garrison with a basis of five Infantry battalions together with the normal supporting arms, some of which have been augmented to support the extra manpower involved in the 'roulement' process. All the Six Counties contribute to the Territorial Army, and the locals also have the option of joining the Ulster Defence Regiment. Even so, the permanent manpower in the Province cannot supply all the needs of the authorities, so the 'roulement' system has been evolved.

To overcome the general shortage of manpower and still maintain the extensive NATO commitments in Europe, the Army has had to resort to a constant rotation, or 'roulement', of units from the United Kingdom and BAOR. All the arms of the service provide units for this duty, be they Infantry, Gunners, Drivers, Pioneers, Signallers, or whatever. The 'roulement' units normally operate a 4½-month tour in the Province, but in practice their involvement extends over a much longer period. The programme is generally known as 'Operation Banner'.

Well before a Northern Ireland tour commences, a unit detailed for the task has to virtually leave its normal operational task and retrain for the counter-insurgency role. Experience gained early on in the Northern Irish troubles showed that it was no use just diverting an operational unit to Northern Ireland and expecting it to take up its complex duties without preparation. The counter-insurgency role demands careful training, careful briefing and the need to master all the varied items of equipment involved in the new task. Normally, operational units receive very little counter-insurgency training so this usually means the time-consuming process of starting from scratch. An entirely new 'set of rules' has to be absorbed, the new equipment has to be mastered, and new drills have to be rehearsed. All this is frequently to the detriment of the normal operational duties and skills, but considerable attention is also paid to honing up some of the more basic skills such as musketry, and a physical fitness course is also carried out to counter some of the more obvious depredations of the ACC and the local brewers. The training itself is intensive and thorough. Riot drills and tactics are taught in simulated mob conditions. The desperate and intensive skills of street fighting are imparted in special training areas, both in the United Kingdom and Germany, that have been constructed to closely resemble Northern Irish towns. In these areas the buildings are constructed to simulate the Ulster urban scene, down to Northern Irish street signs and pub exteriors—even the style and variety of the many graphic forms of Irish graffiti are reproduced on the walls. While this training is still in progress, officers and NCOs from the unit visit their future 'patch' in Northern Ireland to learn the local conditions and the prevailing activities to ensure that the handover from one unit to the other is as smooth as can be made possible.

After the training is complete, the unit travels to Northern Ireland—by air from Germany, and usually boat and train from the United Kingdom. Once the tour is completed, each unit usually gets a block leave of ten days or so, and then has to return to the job of re-learning and practising its normal role, a job that usually takes many more months. In this way, the effect of a Northern Ireland tour can spread over the best part of a year. The present pool of manpower within the Army is not unlimited so some units have had to return for roulement tours time and time again. Some units have been on Ulster tours seven times or more. By contrast, the permanent garrison units normally serve for a period of 18 months, but some specialists such as EOD personnel are posted there for a minimum of two years. The time interval between 'Operation Banner' tours is now around 2½ years for any individual unit.

The basic equipment used in the Northern Ireland campaign is much the same as that used by the ordinary foot soldier. The standard L1A1 rifle (usually fitted with a SUIT sight, although some soldiers have purchased their own Singlepoint sights in the past) is the normal weapon carried, while specialist soldiers carry the L9A1 pistol. The L2A3 sub-machine-gun has few applications in urban conditions, and the L4A4 (Bren) machine-gun is often preferred to the L7A2 GPMG for foot patrols. In riot situations the L1A1 'riot gun' is carried along with the special IS combat helmet and riot shields. Flak jackets are virtually *de rigueur* on all occasions. Mobile patrols use a variety of vehicles ranging from the ubiquitous Land Rovers (fitted with extra Macralon armour and toughened windscreens) to the handy 'Pigs' and FV603 Saracens. Ferrets are also used for rural patrols and convoy escorts. All these vehicles are fitted with extra armour and such accessories as wire mesh windscreen covers, anti-grenade mesh shields, barricade-clearing rams and leg shields to protect soldiers using the vehicle for cover. Many of these 'extras' have been designed and produced by the Army themselves in REME workshops. In this bracket come barricade-clearing grapnels, 'scissor-type' folding road blocks, and the steel stanchions fitted to nearly all vehicles in Northern Ireland to cut through wires strung across urban streets at head height. More extensive tasks, such as the 'Operation Bracelet' up-armouring of the 'Pig' carriers, have been undertaken in conjunction with the Royal Ordnance Factories.

Specialist equipment abounds, from the various types of CS grenade to the many forms of night surveillance devices and movement-spotting radar. Operational practice with such devices as the L1E1 'Twiggy' image intensifier will doubtless prove invaluable on the conventional battlefield, but the same cannot be said to apply to such highly-specialised EOD devices as Wheelbarrow and Marauder, nor to the water cannon held in readiness in some urban centres.

The tactics used by the Army in their counter-insurgency and peace-keeping campaign are many and are constantly being varied. At all times the constant threats of the sniper or the mine/bomb ambush are present, and the Army has to function inside a situation of impending danger. The bulk of the Army's work consists of constant patrolling, by foot and by vehicle. In some of the more isolated country regions, helicopters are also used. The constant patrolling has several functions. One is simply to deny an area to the terrorist—with the Army and the RUC constantly in the vicinity, it will be difficult for the terrorist to move about and carry on his underhand activities. Another patrol task is general surveillance and intelligence gathering. The patrols also have the added advantage of reminding the ordinary law-abiding citizens that they are being safeguarded and that the forces of law and order are still functioning—in a counter-insurgency campaign this alone can prove vital. Apart from the patrols, the Army also becomes involved in the constant round of road-blocks, checkpoints, and the ever-present job of guarding the important public utilities such as electricity stations, telephone exchanges and water supplies, to say nothing of the constant guards on the security premises themselves. The Army is also involved in the searches of areas and premises for weapons, explosives and wanted persons. They also have to clear areas around suspect or known terrorist explosive devices, and to add to their general burden, they often have to be held in reserve for public disturbances or riot duties.

Of late, the RUC has gradually resumed its proper role in such street disturbances, but at certain times the Army has to be held in reserve. Typical of these occasions are the July Ulster marches which have a tendency to break out into violence on such a scale that the RUC cannot cope alone. When the Army does become involved in riot duties, and of late such occasions have been fewer and further between and on a smaller scale than in the past, the role of the Army is always to try and persuade the gathering to disperse peacefully. Unfortunately, Ulster riots have a tendency to follow a sequence of stone or brick-throwing along with the erection of barricades. The barricades often take the form of the burning of stolen public vehicles such as buses or lorries, but fortunately such barricades are more emotive than practical and can be moved or demolished by Army vehicles fitted with rams or grapnels. Engineer construction plant has often been employed for this task.

The stone-throwing is countered by the use of riot shields, either carried by the individual soldiers or erected on the vehicles present. If the necessity arises, the use of baton rounds to keep the stone-throwers at a harmless distance can be brought into play, while CS canisters can be fired or thrown to break up the crowds. These tactics can be varied by the use of lightly equipped 'snatch squads' to apprehend and detain ringleaders or particularly active offenders. In most riot situations still and video cameras are now commonly employed to keep a record of events, and at all times one officer or NCO is in use as a 'secretary' to keep a full log of all orders and events. Helicopters are another relative innovation in riot suppression—both Skyshout and Heli-Telly have obvious applications.

Underlying all the Army's present operations in Northern Ireland is the use of intelligence. The aim of intelligence-gathering is to undermine the operational network of the terrorist and his (or her) guerrilla tactics, and the operational base from which they work. This involves the penetration of the cell network that the PIRA and the other terrorist factions employ, and also the penetration of

their supply system. With a long border as wide open as that between Ulster and the rest of the Irish Republic this is a seemingly impossible task, but it is one that the Army just has to tackle. The intelligence-gathering is both overt and covert. The constant patrolling is an obvious source of overt information, but the covert gathering is much more difficult. In the past the Army has gone to the extent of setting up bogus business concerns to penetrate areas of the Province hostile to the security forces, but some of these early efforts resulted in violent terminations. At all times, certain Border crossing points and suspected premises are kept under surveillance from carefully concealed hides. Further information is often handed in by the law-abiding public, often at great risk.

The net result of all this constant inflow of information is carefully checked and handled by the use of automatic data processing and the storage of information in computers that can supply their data to all parts of the Province. The results are often startling, but their full import is usually lost on the lay public. In many areas the local activists are known to the security forces and patrols often take photographs on patrol with them of wanted persons. Indications can often be sensed of forthcoming terrorist operations and several times in the past security forces have mounted some spectacular ambushes. But the terrorists, operating as they can without warning, scruple or seeming reason, will always retain the vital initiative, and can strike as and when the occasion pleases them. In these circumstances the need for good intelligence is vital, and it is one area where the Army is always active. Their past success rate against the terrorist in the urban areas, due in no small part to effective intelligence, can be seen in the switch of the bulk of terrorist activities to the Border areas, and the constant use by the terrorist of murder and violence against suspected 'informers'.

Life for the ordinary soldier in Northern Ireland is far from comfortable, and at times it is fraught with danger. The constant patrolling often takes many long hours in all weathers, and in some urban areas even the very atmosphere is unpleasant and unfriendly. Off-duty hours have to be spent in cramped billets or barracks although there are compensations in the shape of an extra food allowance and the odd spot of home leave during a tour. But Ulster is not all gloom for the Army. The soldiers on duty know they are carrying out an essential task, and they have the added knowledge that with the general shift of terrorist activity from the towns to the country, they are gradually taking the initiative and overcoming the threat of insurgency. Ulster is a soldier's job, and as the modern Army is an all-volunteer force, the soldiers know what is expected of them and act accordingly.

Apart from the beneficial effects of the Ulster campaign on morale and junior leadership, another positive advantage for the Army is that its basic military skills such as field work and the standard of marksmanship is unexcelled by any other army anywhere. The insistence of the Army on the use of accurate firepower means that the general level of musketry is way above that of the other NATO forces. Overall, the very existence of an ongoing 'combat' situation in the Province has given the Army that fine edge that only comes with action, and while the end result would have been far less costly in lives, money and facilities, the general training level of the Army would have been nowhere near so high had the campaign not taken place.

Perhaps the most lasting impression that comes from the Ulster experiences has been the overall morale improvement. Peace-time exercises can produce a lethargy that is almost impossible to disperse, but when real action is an ever-present possibility, the general level of trust and team-work within units takes on a marked improvement. The end result of this trust and general acceptance of an unloved task is almost always shown in the everyday level of personal conduct of the ordinary soldier. The general moaning is ever-present but the gripes usually take on a less important aspect and the job in hand is tackled in a manner that would be impossible to a less well-motivated individual. Perhaps out of all the misery and sheer unpleasantness that the last decade in Northern Ireland has produced, has come a most unexpected product. As an outcome of all the involvement the Army has had to endure, the end result is a positive one. The Army is now the finest counter-insurgency force extant. Morale is high and the general level of military skills is the envy of many other military forces. The hapless soldier on yet another foot patrol in Belfast would no doubt disagree with this proposition and so, no doubt, would many bereaved families, but out of all the misery, something worth while has emerged.

To round off this section and give an idea of the scale of involvement the Army has in Northern Ireland, listed below are the units based there during 1981.

Headquarters Northern Ireland; three brigade headquarters; one armoured reconnaissance regiment; three Engineer squadrons; five Infantry battalions—resident; seven units acting in an Infantry role—on 'roulement' (Operation Banner); one SAS squadron; two AAC squadrons plus one further flight; and 11 UDR battalions. These units are organised into three brigades, 3, 8 and 39 Brigades.

The Falklands

It is still too early to provide a full summary of the Army's contribution to the Falklands Islands campaign other than to mention that it performed magnificently. All the units involved, and especially the 2nd Battalion The Parachute Regiment, have added to their laurels but the supporting arms should not be forgotten. As this is written all three regular battalions of 5 Brigade are forming a garrison, along with a Gurkha battalion. They are supported by a 105 mm Light Gun regiment and numerous Engineer and other support troops. Long-term arrangements have yet to be announced but the Army will be involved in the Falklands garrison for some time to come.

The land campaign on the Falklands was an arduous slog enlivened by the Battle of Goose Green where the Paras performed a remarkable feat of arms against a well established force twice its size. The final taking of Port Stanley was just as hard but throughout the campaign full marks must go to the unsung support echelons who kept the troops in the field supplied. Casualties were surprisingly light, despite the carnage at Bluff Cove where the Welsh Guards lost many men and much of their fighting equipment.

The Falklands campaign was a soldier's battle. There was little scope for advanced or heavy equipment and the soldier had to carry his supplies on his back over some rough country. He had to live out in the open in dreadful weather, and at the end of it all, he had to storm the enemy in time-honoured style. The campaign will go down in history as a classic of its type, a type that the Army has fought so well in the past and is still able to carry out now. It will not be easily forgotten.

NBC

The abbreviation NBC stands for Nuclear, Biological and Chemical warfare which combine to form one of the most unpleasant and horrific facets of modern warfare. All three aspects of this nasty form of conflict produce their own particular hazards and combat risks but their effects can all be minimised by much the same form of defence, namely protection, and NBC defence is one area where the British Army is well provided for, to the envy of many Western armed forces.

Nuclear warfare is now seen as an almost unavoidable feature of any future conflict so protection against it has to be provided for by any armed force. For the soldier in the field Nuclear warfare means the battlefield use of tactical nuclear weapons

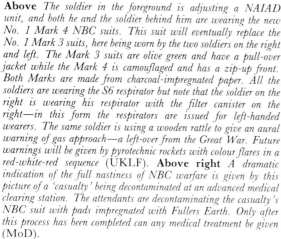

Above *The soldier in the foreground is adjusting a NAIAD unit, and both he and the soldier behind him are wearing the new No. 1 Mark 4 NBC suits. This suit will eventually replace the No. 1 Mark 3 suits, here being worn by the two soldiers on the right and left. The Mark 3 suits are olive green and have a pull-over jacket while the Mark 4 is camouflaged and has a zip-up front. Both Marks are made from charcoal-impregnated paper. All the soldiers are wearing the S6 respirator but note that the soldier on the right is wearing his respirator with the filter canister on the right—in this form the respirators are issued for left-handed wearers. The same soldier is using a wooden rattle to give an aural warning of gas approach—a left-over from the Great War. Future warnings will be given by pyrotechnic rockets with colour flares in a red-white-red sequence (UKLF).* **Above right** *A dramatic indication of the full nastiness of NBC warfare is given by this picture of a 'casualty' being decontaminated at an advanced medical clearing station. The attendants are decontaminating the casualty's NBC suit with pads impregnated with Fullers Earth. Only after this process has been completed can any medical treatment be given (MoD).*

delivered by a number of means. These are weapons that are relatively small in the nuclear sense and will thus be of the power of around 10-20 kilotons of TNT. Such weapons produce three main hazards—heat, blast and radiation, with the latter being both immediate and residual ('Fall-out'). While defence against nuclear devices is a complex and involved study, the main protection can be simply stated as the provision of adequate shelter. The immediate effects of a nuclear explosion can be considerably reduced by the use of even quite simple shelter but the long-term effects of nuclear radiation involve forms of filtering radioactive particles from the atmosphere. Thus simple digging can provide rudimentary defences for soldiers in the open but in the long term some forms of filtering and other measures must be taken.

Armoured vehicles can provide a great deal of their own protection and all British armoured and other vehicles have integral air-cleaning systems as part of their normal equipment. In a radioactive environment foot soldiers can still gain a measure of protection by the use of specialised clothing but generally speaking they cannot function or survive long so they have to go underground. The Army has a considerable number of mobile shelters known as the Field Shelter Mark 2, or Mexeshelter, which can be fairly rapidly constructed by digging trenches, erecting the shelter frame and its flexible walls and roofing, and filling in the sides and top with earth. This shelter, with its built-in air-filtering system, can also be used as a defence against chemical and biological attack.

Chemical warfare involves the use of various war gases which can range from the well-tried blister and choking gases through to the modern 'nerve' gases and other horrors which are as yet unrevealed. They are usually dispensed in cloud or aerosol forms by a number of methods which can range from ground-mounted cylinders to airborne dispensers. Of these thoroughly unpleasant forms of attack, the modern nerve gases are among the most lethal. There are several different forms, eg, Tabun, the V-agents, GB, etc, but they all interfere with some aspect or another of the human body's basic functions and even small amounts can produce an unpleasant death. The only protection against such agents is to completely cover the body with a layer of impervious material, and the use of respirators to filter the air the soldiers breathe. The same measures can be taken against biologial warfare, which can be loosely regarded as an adjunct to chemical warfare except that the agents involved are intended to inflict a range of lethal or incapacitating diseases ranging from anthrax to 'artificial' diseases produced in laboratories.

In the British Army, the protection measures against chemical and biological warfare consists of the Mark 3 NBC Suit and the S6 respirator (see the uniform section for further details and illustrations). Wearing the Mark 3, or 'Noddy' Suit, is not a pleasant experience and a soldier's fighting capabilities can be somewhat reduced by even a relatively short period encased in its total envelopment. The British suit does, however, at least provide some measures that enable some air circulation around the body, a feature not shared by many similar suits in service elsewhere. Wounded soldiers can be protected by being enclosed inside an all-enveloping Casualty Bag, and walking wounded can be covered by a bag which extends over the head (a vision panel is provided) and is secured at the waist. There are various decontamination measures available from simple water sprays to remove agents from vehicles and weapons through to special cleansing kits for personal decontamination.

But all the protective measure can be to no avail if there is insufficient warning or time to take them. Here the British Army is well in advance of many others with the provision of various forms of detection equipment. These can vary from simple treated papers up to one of the most advanced chemical detectors in service anywhere. Although it is still undergoing the final stages of development, the new detector, known as NAIAD, will become one of the most important defences against Chemical Warfare for it is a 'Black Box' that can synthesise the natural chemistry of the human body and thereby detect any agent that might prove harmful. NAIAD has two units. One is the detector and the other a remote alarm unit that can be placed up to 500 metres away from the detector. Thus a unit in the field can be given some measure of warning of the approach of harmful agents. The complete NAIAD system weighs 14 kg.

One other protection against the nerve gases is the use of small automatic hypodermic injectors which can inject the chemical atropine through the soldier's clothing into the body. Atropine has the property of reducing or minimising the effects of some nerve gases on the human body but it must be used quickly, hence the designation of Autoject No 2 Mark 1. Each soldier in the field is issued with at least one of these along with his other NBC first aid and decontamination kit. Other protective measures

are still the subject of considerable research and development at a number of establishments. One of the most widely known is the civilian establishment at Porton, but the Army has its own Defence NBC Centre at Winterbourne Gunner. A great deal of the development work involving protective clothing is carried out by the Stores and Clothing Research and Development Establishment (SCRDE) at Colchester.

The Army and the Royal Air Force

The modern Army and the Royal Air Force are more interdependent than they have ever been. The Army relies on the RAF for much of its long-range and close-support weapons delivery, to say nothing of the tactical reconnaissance it provides, and the RAF relies on the Army for the overall defence of its bases and also for a fair portion of its logistic support and supply. Thus a full account of the modern Army cannot be given without some mention of the role the RAF carries out in Germany, where the bulk of the Army will have to fight.

The RAF has three main roles that it carries out for the Army. They are close air support, interdiction and tactical reconnaissance.

The first mentioned, close air support, is the direct involvement of the RAF in the Army's land battle. In effect, it replaces the role played in the past by the heavy artillery, but today's modern air support is much more flexible. For the Army the main weapon involved is the remarkable Harrier, the vertical or short take-off and landing ground support aircraft. They are well supported by tactical strike Jaguars.

Interdiction is the penetration of the enemy's rear areas to attack, disrupt and generally harass the sup-

C-130 Hercules unloading an FV101 Scorpion. The Hercules is the main transport aircraft used in moving the Army.

ply columns, supply depots and communications. At present this role is carried out by the ex-naval attack bomber, the Buccaneer, but it will eventually be taken over by the Tornado.

The term tactical reconnaissance is self-explanatory and is essential to the Army commanders. It involves the photography of ground areas and other sensor equipment may also become involved. Both Jaguars and (to a lesser extent) Phantoms are involved.

All these roles are carried out for the Army by RAF Germany which provides squadrons for the NATO 2nd Allied Tactical Air Force, or 2nd ATAF. The RAF Germany squadrons are only part of the general NATO air support effort but in effect the British Army will be mainly supported by RAF units.

RAF Germany has a basic cadre of 13 squadrons with four Rapier airfield defence squadrons, a single Bloodhound air defence missile squadron and one RAF Regiment field squadron for airfield defence.

The squadrons based in Germany can be quickly reinforced by further squadrons from the United Kingdom, mainly from No 1 Group Strike Command, with the transport element being supplied by the transport aircraft of No 38 Group. The United Kingdom will also provide aircraft for the United Kingdom Mobile Force (Air), or UKMF (Air), which will have one Jaguar squadron and a Puma helicopter squadron. The air component of the AMF provided from the United Kingdom will comprise of a Harrier squadron, a flight of Puma helicopters and an RAF Regiment field squadron.

The RAF Germany aircraft squadrons are as follows:

Unit	Aircraft type	Role	Base
2 Sqdn	Jaguar GR1/T2	Tactical recce	RAF Laarbruch
14 Sqdn	Jaguar GR1/T2	Tactical strike	RAF Bruggen
17 Sqdn	Jaguar GR1/T2	Tactical strike	RAF Bruggen
20 Sqdn	Jaguar GR1/T2	Tactical strike	RAF Bruggen
31 Sqdn	Jaguar GR1/T2	Tactical strike	RAF Bruggen
3 Sqdn	Harrier GR3/T4	Close air support	RAF Gutersloh
4 Sqdn	Harrier GR3/T4	Close air support	RAF Gutersloh
15 Sqdn	Buccaneer S2B	Strike	RAF Laarbruch
16 Sqdn	Buccaneer S2B	Strike	RAF Laarbruch
19 Sqdn	Phantom FGR2	Air defence	RAF Wildenrath
92 Sqdn	Phantom FGR2	Air defence	RAF Wildenrath
18 Sqdn	Chinook HC1	Harrier support	RAF Gutersloh
60 Sqdn	Pembroke C1	Communications	RAF Wildenrath

The tactical strike Jaguars can fire rockets or drop bombs and in the latter role they are directed by forward air controllers (FACs) who travel with Army formations and operate close to the front line. Individual targets can be marked by laser target designators operated by these FACs or by Artillery FOOs.

The Harriers operate very close to the front lines and are supplied by the Army. The Royal Engineers build the aircraft 'hides', the RCT delivers the ammunition and some of the fuel and the Engineers are also responsible for the bulk fuel installations. Infantry often guard the operation perimeters.

The Phantoms are used to defend the RAF bases but are also used on occasion for tactical reconnaissance. In an emergency they would be among the first RAF units to be supplemented from the United Kingdom. Further airfield defence is provided by the RAF Regiment field squadrons with their Blowpipe missiles and their specialised air defence squadrons with a mixture of Rapiers and Bofors L/70 guns. Airfield ground defence is augmented by the use of RAF Regiment FV103 Spartans and FV107 Scorpions. The Bloodhound air defence squadron is for general high-altitude defence and has only a very limited low-level capability.

Up and away after unloading a section of troops, a Puma shows its paces at a public display.

Weapons and equipment

The section devoted to the modern Army's weapons and equipment has been compiled from as many sources as has been found possible while at the same time having regard to security restrictions. I have attempted to make this section as comprehensive and up-to-date as possible but inevitably the scale of the modern Army's equipment is so vast that not every item can be included. Some of these items are still 'under wraps', while others are in use in such small numbers that they can be omitted, despite their relative importance to the units that use them. In this latter category come some rather odd and long-in-the-tooth items such as the FV13203 Commer Q4 trucks still used by some REME units based in Germany. Other elderly trucks still survive in some TA units and their omission has had to be decided upon for the simple reason that to include them all would make this book so large it would be unmanageable. However, in some cases the older equipments do rate a mention, if only to give a general idea of the gradual development of the modern Army's weapons and equipment.

Equipment designation system

The British Services have adopted a system for identifying and labelling all the equipment used by them that enables each item to be clearly differentiated from all the other items in use. At first sight, the system appears complex and not very clear but it is actually straightforward once the following guidelines have been understood.

Each item of equipment has a designation in a set sequence. The first part of the sequence describes exactly what the item of equipment is, eg, Gun, Howitzer, Rifle, Carriage, etc.

This is followed, where applicable, by the essential characteristics of the particular item. For instance, the term Rifle is followed by its calibre of 7.62 mm in the form Rifle, 7.62 mm. A howitzer is described as Howitzer, 8 inch.

Then comes the model number, which in the Army is usually prefixed by the letter 'L'. In this

context the L stands for 'Land Service'. If an item starts with a prefix L it is usually an approved and in-service item. If it is itself prefixed by an 'X', it denotes it is still in the development or experimental stage, and in some cases the same letter is used to indicate a limited procurement item. Returning to the rifle example we thus have Rifle, 7.62 mm, L1A1.

To explain the further import of the 1A1 after the L in the last example, the 1 refers to the model number, ie, Rifle, calibre 7.62 mm, Land Service Model 1. The A1 part of the quoted example refers to the modification state of the model, ie, it is still unchanged from its state when it was introduced into service. In the unlikely event of the standard rifle being extensively modified for some reason it would become the L1A2. X prefixes use E numbers in this context, eg, Pistol, Automatic Walther Type PP XL47E1. Note that this example amplified its essential characteristic identification by the addition of a commercial name.

At this point it must be mentioned that a designation is not necessarily peculiar to one particular item. To quote an extreme example it is possible to have a Pistol L1A1 and a Gun Carriage L1A1—the L1A1 must be prefixed by the basic name of the item concerned.

Needless to say there are some variations to this system, usually when American designations are carried into British use. The American system is similar to the British one in many ways but each item model number is prefixed by the letter 'M'. In many cases the American designation is used in place of the British one, eg, Anti-personnel Mine M18A1.

Another anomaly arises with the use of the old designation system in use until just after the end of the Second World War. This involved the use of numbers of each item of equipment and Mark numbers. In many cases to avoid the duplication of a great deal of paperwork on items that were expected to go out of service in time anyway, the old system was retained. But in some cases the old items are still in use and some anomalies remain with them. An example is the Trailer, Tank Transporter, No 1 Mark 3. (Asterisks (*) were added to Mark numbers to denote substantial alterations to the state of the Mark that did not warrant a new Mark number.) The old system was dropped mainly because, although it seems fairly straightforward, in practice it became very complex and cumbersome. The present L system is more versatile, shorter in use, and more in line with similar systems used by other Allied nations.

FV designations will be found wherever they can be accurately attributed throughout this book. It is applied to all wheeled or tracked vehicles, whether powered or not. The letters FV refer to 'Field Vehicle'.

Infantry weapons

9 mm Pistol Automatic L9A1

Calibre 9 mm; **Length** 0.196 m; **Length of barrel** 0.112 m; **Weight empty** 0.88 kg; **Weight loaded** 1.01 kg; **Muzzle velocity** 354 m/s; **Magazine capacity** 13 rounds; **Rate of fire** Single-shot; **Maximum effective range** 40-50 m.

The design of the Browning pistol was finalised in 1925 but it was not until 1935 that production commenced at Herstal in Belgium. During World War 2 production continued in Belgium for the German forces but drawings shipped to Canada

enabled the firm of John Inglis, situated in Toronto, to manufacture slightly modified pistols for issue to the Allied armies. In February 1943 drawings were finalised for a version known originally as the Pistol, Browning, F.N. 9 mm H.P., No. 2 Mark 1*, and soon afterwards this version was issued to various special-purpose formations such as Commandos and airborne forces. Thereafter the use of the 9 mm automatic gradually spread throughout the forces, at first supplementing and finally replacing the existing .38 revolvers in service. The pistol finally gained the seal of approval by being termed as available for issue in February 1961 by which time there were few .38 revolvers left. Now designated the L9A1, the pistol is the general service issue pistol for all branches of the Service.

The L9A1 is an unusual pistol in that its magazine holds 13 rounds. Not only can this be a valuable asset in combat but the oversize grip provides a good hold for above-average shooting, even by relatively untrained personnel. Normally the L9A1 is carried in a webbing belt holster, but it has on occasion been issued with a shoulder holster for plain-clothes undercover missions.

7.65 mm Pistol Automatic Walther Type PP XL47E1

Calibre 7.65 mm; **Length** 0.173 m; **Length of barrel** 0.099 m; **Weight empty** 0.68 kg; **Weight loaded** 1.00 kg; **Muzzle velocity** 290 m/s; **Magazine capacity** 8 rounds; **Rate of fire** Single-shot; **Maximum effective range** 40 m.

Left *A Military Policeman on the range with a 9 mm L9A1 pistol* (MoD). **Right** *The PP XL47E1 Pistol.*

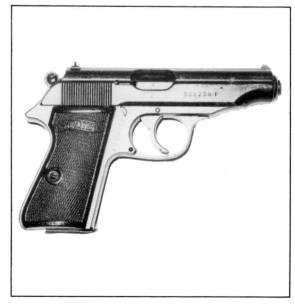

Relatively few of these pistols are in use as they are normally issued only to those who carry out what are categorised as 'special duties'. This usually entails undercover and plain-clothes tasks. The pistol is a German commerical model designed for easy concealment, has been widely used by many police forces ever since it was first introduced in 1929 and is still in production. Designed and made mainly by the German Walther concern, its commercial designation is Model PP (PP—Police Pistol). Recently this design has rather fallen from favour with many civilian police forces as it was the model involved in the now-infamous attempted kidnapping of Princess Anne in The Mall in 1974, when a police example failed to fire. However, it must be stated that when correctly maintained the PP is an excellent pistol for its role.

Sub-Machine Gun 9 mm L2A3

Calibre 9 mm; **Length (butt folded)** 0.482 m; **Length (butt extended)** 0.69 m; **Length of barrel** 0.198 m; **Weight empty** 2.7 kg; **Weight loaded** 3.5 kg; **Muzzle velocity** 390 m/s; **Magazine capacity** 34 rounds; **Rate of fire (cyclic)** 550 rpm; **Rate of fire (practical)** 102 rpm; **Rate of fire (single-shot)** 40 rpm; **Maximum effective range** 200 m.

Known unofficially as the 'Sterling', the L2A3 had a rather protracted development timespan as the original version, then known as the Patchett, was used for troop trials in action in 1945. It was not until 1951 that the first service model (the L2A1) was produced, followed in 1953 by the L2A2. In 1954 the type was adopted as the standard British sub-machine-gun as the L2A3, after which it gradually replaced the well-tried Sten. Since 1954 the L2A3 has undergone some slight changes but it is still in production at the Sterling Armament Company Limited at Dagenham, and is in use by well over 80 police and military formations.

Construction of the L2A3 is extremely robust and its blow-back mechanism has proved to be reliable under a wide range of conditions. The side-mounted magazine is designed to hold 34 rounds but in practical service two or three rounds less than this number are loaded. The breech block has inclined splines which effectively clear any debris which enters the receiver and reduces the likelihood of jamming. A small bayonet can be fitted to the muzzle. The main users of the L2A3 in the British Army are tank crewmen, the Artillery and second-line support services.

Sub-Machine-Gun 9 mm L34A1

Calibre 9 mm; **Length (butt folded)** 0.654 m; **Length (butt extended)** 0.857 m; **Length of barrel**

A Sergeant from the 6/7th Queen's (V) on the Ash ranges with an L2A3.

0.198 m; **Weight empty** 3.54 kg; **Weight loaded** 4.25 kg; **Muzzle velocity** 308 m/s; **Magazine capacity** 34 rounds; **Rate of fire (cyclic)** 515-565 rpm; **Rate of fire (practical)** 102 rpm; **Rate of fire (single-shot)** 40-45 rpm; **Maximum effective range** 150 m.

The L34A1 is the service version of the Sterling Patchett Mark 5 which was produced in 1964 as the result of a General Staff request for a silent weapon. It was adopted in small numbers and is usually issued to special-duties formations only. The L34A1 is basically the same weapon as the L2A3 but the barrel housing is longer and has a number of holes along its length which vent off the propellant gases, produced after firing, through a wire mesh sleeve into a diffuser tube. These gases are then passed through a spiral diffuser so that by the time they vent around the muzzle they are virtually noiseless. Also, by the time the bullet leaves the muzzle its velocity has become sub-sonic and the overall effect is that the

Above *The L34A1 silenced sub-machine-gun—this particular example is a commercial model with a special plated finish but is exactly the same as the Army version.* Below *A L1A1 fitted with the 30-round magazine from the L4A4 machine-gun.* Above right *An unusual combination of two L1A1 rifles fitted to a buoyancy bag made up from an inflated poncho. The two rifles are ready to fire and the arrangement is one produced by the 2nd Gurkhas in Brunei (MoD).* Below right *A TA para with his L1A1 Rifle—which is fitted with the L1A2 blank-firing attachment over the muzzle.* Below far right *A soldier from the Black Watch on active duty in Northern Ireland with his L1A1. The rifle is fitted with the L1A1 SUIT sight (Army PR HQ NI).*

L34A1 is an effective soundless weapon. Normally the L34A1 would be fired single-shot with the fully automatic feature being used only under special circumstances. Although the firing mehanism is similar to that of the L2A3 a lighter bolt and less powerful return spring are needed. For use at night a Scotos night sight can be fitted.

Rifle 7.62 mm L1A1

Calibre 7.62 mm; **Length overall** 1.143 m; **Length of barrel** 0.5334 m; **Weight empty** 4.337 kg; **Weight loaded (20-round magazine)** 5.074 kg; **Muzzle velocity** 838 m/s; **Magazine capacity** 20 or 30 rounds; **Rate of fire** 40 rpm; **Maximum effective range** 600 m plus.

The LlA1 is the British version of the Belgian FN FAL (Fabrique Nationale—Fusil Automatique Leger) which was selected for service after trials with two versions of the original Belgian model that commenced during 1955. Modifications were made to the basic design, not the least of which was the removal of the fully automatic fire mode of the FAL, and the L1A1 thereafter replaced the Rifle No. 4 Mark 1 as the British Army's standard service rifle. Production was carried out at the Royal Ordnance Factory at Fazackerley, and the Royal Small Arms Factory at Enfield Lock. The early production versions were fitted with wooden furniture but this was later changed to black nylonite.

The L1A1 uses a gas-operated mechanism that is robust and dependable. Field stripping is straightforward and easily carried out. The basic sights consist of the normal 'iron' variety with a sight radius of 553.7 mm, but the SUIT (Sight Unit Infantry

Trilux) L1A1 or L1A2 is now a virtual standard combat fixture adding a further 0.435 kg to the loaded weight. The Infantry Weapon Sight (IWS) L1A2 is another sighting fixture. Other combat accessories include a bayonet (L1A3 or L1A4), and a grenade launcher (L1A2). For training purposes a blank firing attachment can be fitted over the muzzle—this is the L6A1 or L1A2. When indoor or small rifle ranges have to be used the .22-in Conversion Set L12A1 can be employed—this is produced by the West German Heckler and Koch concern.

The rounds fired by the L1A1 are 7.62 mm in calibre and the cartridge cases are 51 mm long—hence 7.62 × 51 mm. There is a wide range of types of ammunition produced in NATO 7.62 mm, not all of which is fired by the L1A1 (for instance, tracer is rarely fired from rifles but is in common use with machine-guns). The more common types in Army use are the Round 7.62 mm Ball L2A2 (standard ball round); the Round 7.62 mm Ball Target L2A2 (selected 'Green Spot' round for target use); the Round 7.62 mm Ball L11A1 (NATO round produced by Raufoss in Norway); Round 7.62 mm Tracer L5A3 (red tip to bullet); the Round 7.62 mm Short Range L14A1 (training round with plastic bullet—little used); the Round

7.62 mm Blank L13A1 (crimped green case nose); the Round 7.62 mm Drill L1A2 (inert round with red grooved case); the Round 7.62 mm Inspection L3A1 (inert round for armourers' use—silver case); and the Cartridge 7.62 mm Rifle Grenade L1A2 (for firing Energa grenade—now little used). With the Ball L2A2 and L11A1 the bullet weighs 9.33 grams and is projected by a charge of 2.85 grams.

Rifle 7.62 mm L39A1

Calibre 7.62 mm; **Length** 1.18 m; **Length of barrel** 0.7 m; **Weight empty** 4.42 kg; **Weight loaded** ? kg; **Muzzle velocity** 841 m/s; **Magazine capacity** 10 rounds; **Rate of fire** Single-shot only; **Maximum effective range** 1,000 m plus.

The Rifle L1A1 is a good combat rifle but does not have the inherent accuracy that is necessary in the exacting sphere of competition rifle shooting. As always the Army is very involved in this field and to keep up its showing at such places as Bisley the Army has to have a viable competitive rifle. NRA rules dictate a non-repeating weapon for all its major contests so the Army decided to convert its old surplus No. 4 Mark 1 and 2 .303-in rifles for competition work. The old Mark 1 rifles proved unsuitable for the role but numerous Mark 1/2 and 2 rifles were selected for conversion which involved replacing the barrel with a new heavier item in 7.62 mm calibre and changing much of the furniture—the basic Lee-Enfield bolt action was retained. The conversions were carried out at the Royal Small Arms Factory at Enfield Lock and the final product is an excellent target rifle which is good enough to be produced commercially as the 'Envoy'. The L39A1 is usually delivered without sights to enable each individual or unit to fit their own choice and the maximum effective range quoted in the table is dependent upon individual skill and choice of ammunition batch. The round most commonly used in competitions is the Round 7.62 mm Ball Target L2A2 ('Green Spot') ammunition produced at the Royal Ordnance Factory, Radway Green.

Rifle 7.62 mm L42A1

Calibre 7.62 mm; **Length** 1.181 m; **Length of barrel** 0.699 m; **Weight empty** 4.43 kg; **Weight loaded** ? kg; **Muzzle velocity** 838 m/s; **Magazine capacity** 10 rounds; **Rate of fire** Single-shot only; **Maximum effective range** 1,000 m plus.

The L42A1 is a sniper's rifle and is a conversion of the .303-in Rifle No. 4 Mark 1(T) to the 7.62 mm NATO calibre. As with the earlier rifle the standard Lee-Enfield bolt action and trigger mechanism have been altered in various ways to ensure better accuracy and the butt has been altered to accommodate a cheek rest. Although normal 'iron' sights are fitted the L42A1 is usually used with the Sighting Telescope L1A1. A special sling with alternative sling swivels on the rifle is another

Below *The L39A1 competition rifle.* **Bottom** *The L42A1 sniper's rifle.* **Above right** *Gurkhas in Hong Kong carrying the M16 rifle* (MoD).

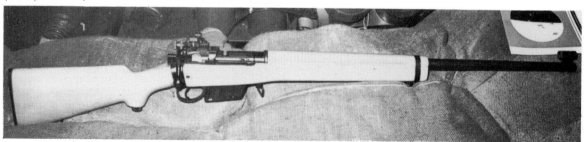

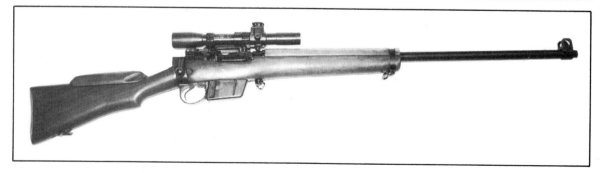

'extra'. The maximum effective range of this weapon depends greatly on conditions and the skill of the individual sniper, and for the sniping role special ammunition batches are selected.

Rifle No. 8 Mark 1

Calibre 5.48 mm/.216 in (.22); **Length** 1.043 m; **Length of barrel** 0.956 m; **Weight empty (approx)** 4.025 kg; **Weight loaded (approx)** 4.025 kg; **Muzzle velocity** 320 m/s; **Magazine capacity** Single-shot only; **Rate of fire** Single-shot only; **Maximum effective range** 50 m.

The Rifle No. 8 Mark 1 was first issued in September 1950 and ever since then its role has been the same, namely that of providing low cost target practice on small or indoor ranges. Over the years it has been issued to virtually every arm of the Service but its use is now largely confined to Army Cadet and Combined Cadet units. Designed and made by the Royal Small Arms Factory at Fazakerley, some were made by BSA at Shirley. The Rifle No. 8 has proved itself to be an excellent training rifle but it has never equalled the standards of accuracy achieved by many commercial target rifles. Numbers are now appearing on the commercial market for disposal to rifle clubs.

Some .22 training is carried out using the semi-automatic Rifle, .22, Sportco, L29A2, which has been purchased from the Australian concern Sporting Arms Limited of New South Wales. This blow-back operated rifle has a ten-round magazine, and weighs 2.61 kg.

Rifle 5.56 mm M16

Calibre 5.56 mm; **Length** 0.99 m; **Length of barrel** 0.508 m; **Weight (gun alone)** 3.1 kg; **Weight loaded (20-round magazine)** 3.68 kg; **Weight loaded (30-round magazine)** 3.82 kg; **Muzzle velocity** 1,000 m/s; **Magazine capacity** 20 or 30 rounds; **Rate of fire (cyclic)** 700-950 rpm; **Rate of fire (practical)** 40-60 rpm; **Maximum effective range** 400 m.

The British Army was one of the very first customers for Eugene Stoner's Armalite AR-15 automatic rifle, and it actually took delivery of its first examples before the US Army, which then went on to become the largest users of this rather controversial weapon. The choice of a miniature rifle calibre has long been a feature of British small-arms development but with the arrival of the 5.56 × 45 mm cartridge it became possible to fully evaluate its worth without the political and economic restrictions imposed by membership of NATO or the threat of imminent large-scale conflict, both of which have intervened to curtail earlier British projects. Apart from this evaluation, the in-

troduction of the M16, or AR-15, was considered as a method of providing light automatic rifles for jungle warfare in the Far East. Since the first purchase in 1961 the M16 has been in action on numerous occasions in that theatre. Although it cannot be confirmed, it would appear that about 10,000 M16s were obtained and most of these are now used by Gurkha regiments based in Brunei and Hong Kong. Units in the United Kingdom use them for training and familiarisation. Most of the AR-15s used by the Army are of the M16 pattern and lack the external bolt plunger fitted to the later M16A1 which is the American Army general issue pattern.

The M16 was manufactured by Colt Firearms at Hartford, Connecticut. It is a gas-operated weapon that uses the rotary locking mechanism that is now almost universally adopted for this kind of firearm, and which has been selected for the new British 4.85 mm Individual Weapon. The construction of the M16 has been carefully designed for ease of mass production, but for all that it is remarkably well-finished and can operate well under a variety of conditions. The 5.56 mm cartridge used by the M16 has for long been the subject of much controversy but its eventual success can be measured by its adoption by many nations and gun designers, and it will doubtless emerge, in a modified form, as the future standard NATO calibre. The 5.56 mm cartridge produces low recoil forces which make the M16 easy to aim and fire and the bullet possesses sufficient striking power to disable an opponent at most combat ranges.

The XL70E3 Individual Weapon.

5.56 mm Individual Weapon XL70E3

Calibre 5.56 mm; **Length overall** 0.77 m; **Weight loaded (20-round magazine)** 4.28 kg; **Weight loaded (30-round magazine)** 4.68 kg; **Muzzle velocity** 900 m/s; **Magazine capacity** 20 or 30 rounds; **Rate of fire (cyclic)** 700-850 rpm; **Combat range** Up to 400 m (unconfirmed).

Ever since before the First World War the British Army has been trying to produce a new small calibre standard rifle for front-line troops but many reasons, ranging from political uncertainties and wrangling to the intervention of large-scale conflicts, have prevented anything in the hardware line ever reaching the troops. A tentative move to a new small round in the early 1950s was quashed by the political imposition of the American .30/7.62 mm round that became the NATO standard, but by the 1970s it was acknowledged that this had been an unwise choice. Even the Americans, who were among the prime protagonists of the 7.62 mm NATO round, had adopted the 5.56 mm round as their standard ammunition during the 1960s, and the British Army, along with most other NATO nations, found themselves saddled with a round that was too powerful and bulky for their current infantry needs.

The British had long anticipated the move to smaller calibres and during the early 1970s began the design and development of their own new small calibre weapons and ammunition. The result then was a new 4.85 mm round and a new weapon to fire it, the Individual Weapon XL65E5. The 4.85 mm round was an excellent performer and was based on the dimensions of the American 5.56 mm cartridge but necked down to the smaller calibre. But the 4.85 mm calibre was definitely non-standard as far as many other NATO nations were concerned, even though some of them were, at the time, attempting to introduce their own national calibres and ammunition types. The result of the varying proposals was a protracted and involved series of international weapon and ammunition trials carried out over a period of years by all the interested nations and manufacturers. The British 4.85 mm round and the Individual Weapon (IW) XL65E5 took part and performed well, but it was competing against a well mooted preference for some form of 5.56 mm round, a choice virtually dictated by the overwhelming availability of manufacturing facilities and weapon types already produced to follow the American 5.56 mm lead.

The 'winner' of the NATO competition was the Belgian 5.56 mm SS109 cartridge with a propellant load slightly more powerful than the American original and firing a bullet with a steel core to increase penetration on impact. There was no overall weapon design 'winner' as it had become obvious almost from the start that each nation would produce its own weapon designs, whatever the competition outcome. The British weapon choice is still the IW but re-calibered to take the new round. As the original 4.85 mm cartridge was based on the 5.56 mm dimensions the actual re-design and re-engineering internally was not too overwhelming a task, but the current model, the 5.56 mm IW XL70E3, appears to be a very different weapon from the 4.85 mm IW XL65E5.

The charges are mainly superficial and aimed primarily towards production expedients rather than any more fundamental reasons. The IW remains a short, handy 'bull-pup' design with the magazine, which can hold either 20 or 30 rounds, behind the trigger mechanism. The length will make the IW easy to stow and carry in the confines of helicopters or APCs where the modern soldier spends so much of his time. The mechanism is gas-operated and uses the rotary bolt-head locking system that is now a virtual standard choice in comparable weapons world-wide. Both single and fully automatic fire can be selected, while the muzzle has provision for a small bayonet and can act as a grenade launcher. Optical sights are fitted as standard, and are known as the SUSAT; they have a x4 magnification. Iron sights for emergency use are mounted on the SUSAT body but the pistol grip contains 'iron' sights for use when required. There is also provision for passive night sighting equipment.

When production finally gets under way, the IW will be produced at the Royal Small Arms Factory at Enfield Lock, Middlesex. Exactly when that will be is uncertain at the time of writing, as development is still continuing. There is even a current of opinion that proposes that production never should begin as it would be cheaper to purchase a foreign design 'off the shelf', but production plans are still under way at Enfield Lock.

Radway Green will produce the 5.56 mm ammunition and types proposed to date include ball, tracer, blank and grenade firing. The weight of a ball round is 12 grams.

5.56 mm Light Support Weapon XL73E2

Calibre 5.56 mm; **Length overall** 0.9 m; **Weight loaded (20-round magazine)** 4.88 kg; **Weight loaded (30-round magazine)** 5.28 kg; **Muzzle velocity** 945 m/s; **Rate of fire (cyclic)** 700-850 rpm; **Combat range** Up to 1,000 m (unconfirmed).

The Light Support Weapon was designed in conjunction with the original 4.85 mm Individual Weapon as the Light Support Weapon (LSW) XL65E4. It was designed to be the squad support weapon equivalent of the IW to the extent that in the original design 80 per cent of the parts fitted to the LSW could be interchanged with those on the IW. With the change to the 5.56 mm calibre a great deal of interchangeability can no doubt still take place, and in appearance the two designs have much in common. The LSW does have a heavier barrel than the IW and there is also a light bipod. The firing mechanism is designed to remain open after bursts of fire to prevent ammunition 'cook offs' occurring in a heated chamber but the weapon fires from a closed action for single shots. Normally, a 30-round magazine is used but the 20-round magazine of the IW can also be fitted.

With development concentrating on the IW at present, the LSW will enter production after IW production is well under way. When (and if) the LSW reaches the troops it will be used to add to the overall firepower of the infantry squad only, and it will not replace the heavier GPMG in either its heavy fire or tank machine-gun roles. The 'if' is inserted as it would appear that the future of the LSW is in even more doubt than that of the IW, mainly on cost grounds but also due to the fact that some tacticians doubt whether a small-calibre support weapon has any place on the modern battlefield. But in the meantime, development work on the 5.56 mm LSW XL73E2 continues at Enfield Lock.

7.62 mm Machine-gun L4A4

Calibre 7.62 mm; **Length** 1.133 m; **Length of barrel** 0.536 m; **Weight empty** 9.96 kg; **Weight loaded** 10.68 kg; **Muzzle velocity** 869 m/s; **Magazine capacity** 30 rounds*; **Rate of fire (cyclic)** 500-575 rpm; **Rate of fire (practical)** 120 rpm; **Rate of fire (single-shot)** 40 rpm; **Maximum effective range** 800 m.

*In an emergency the 20-round magazine of the L1A1 Rifle can be used.

The L4A4 is the 'modern' version of the well-known and well-tried Bren Gun which was in-

The XL73E2 Light Support Weapon. It is now known that the universally-available American M16 30-round magazine will be used for both the IW and LSW in the future.

Above *The L4A4 Machine Gun—the ancestry from the old 0.303 Bren Gun can be clearly seen* (MoD).

Left *The L7A2 GPMG on the L4A1 Buffered Tripod.*

Below *The L7A2 GPMG in its original 'British' production form* (MoD).

Below right *The L8A1 Chieftain co-axial machine-gun.*

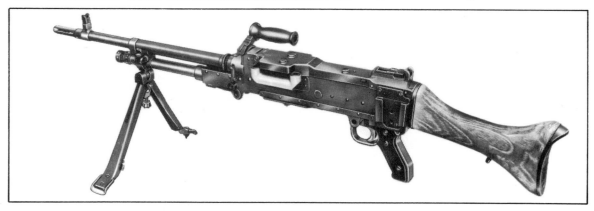

troduced into British Army service prior to World War 2. Originally chambered for the .303-in cartridge, the adoption of the NATO 7.62 × 51 mm round prompted a revision of the Bren Gun to accommodate the new calibre. The changes involved a new chromium-plated barrel which enabled barrel wear to be reduced to the extent that barrel changes in combat could be virtually ignored. Other alterations were to the breech block and the magazine. Originally the L4A4 was the basic infantry squad weapon, but it was gradually replaced by the GPMG, and it is now used mainly for local and anti-aircraft defence of vehicles belonging to the Royal Artillery, the Royal Engineers and other such units. It is also used by TA units intended for Home Defence only, and by the Ulster Defence Regiment.

7.62 mm General Purpose Machine-Gun L7A2

Calibre 7.62 mm; **Length as LMG** 1.232 m; **Length as HMG** 1.049 m; **Length of barrel** 0.629 m; **Weight empty (LMG role)** 10.9 kg; **Weight loaded (LMG role)** 13.85 kg; **Weight of tripod** 13.64 kg; **Muzzle velocity** 838 m/s; **Type of feed** 100-round belt; **Rate of fire (cyclic)** 625-750 rpm; **Rate of fire in LMG role** 100 rpm; **Rate of fire in HMG role** 200 rpm; **Maximum effective range (LMG)** 800 m; **Maximum effective range (HMG)** 1,800 m.

The General Purpose Machine-Gun (GPMG) concept was a German innovation that came into being during the Second World War, in that the old machine-gun divisions into light and heavy types were resolved into one design that could fulfil both roles. After 1945 there were numerous new designs along the same lines and in 1957 a series of trials were held to determine the future machine-gun for British service. The result was announced in June 1958 when the Belgian FN MAG was selected but further development was needed before British production began in 1963. The first production model was the L7A1 but further modifications resulted in the L7A2 which is the current version.

The L7A2 is a very well-made weapon that in many ways reverts to the old 'solid metal' designs of pre-1939. It cannot be said that it is a popular machine-gun for in its light role (with a bipod) it is really too heavy and awkward a load while in the heavy, or sustained fire role, it lacks the high fire volume that is often needed as the barrel tends to overheat too quickly. In the latter role the standard tripod is the Mounting Tripod L4A1 and in this configuration an indirect fire sight, the Sight Unit Trilux C2, can be fitted (this sight is the same as that used with the 81 mm mortar). Nevertheless, for all its unpopularity, the GPMG is the standard British machine-gun and is used not only as a squad weapon but also for anti-aircraft defence (on a variety of mountings), as a vehicle defence weapon, and for the sustained fire role. There are also a number of special purpose variants which are mentioned below.

L8A1: The Chieftain tank uses a special conversion of the L7A2 known as the L8A1 which has numerous design changes to suit its role in the confines of an AFV interior. It can be modified for normal ground use.

The L8A2 is a version produced for installation in the FV4030/4 Challenger.

L20A1: This variant features a solenoid-operated trigger as it is used in helicopter and aircraft pods, and is produced in right- and left-hand feed versions (the L7A2 uses a left-hand feed only).

L37A1: Machine-gun fire from APCs and other light armoured vehicles often involves the use of extra tracer rounds for sighting as direct vision of a target is not always possible. Thus a special barrel is fitted and the L37A1 is made up of a mixture of L7A2 and L8A1 components. Like the L8A1 it can be converted for the normal ground role.

The L37A2 is a version produced for installation on the cupola of the FV4030/4 Challenger.

L41A1: This is a drill or training version of the L8A1 and cannot be fired.

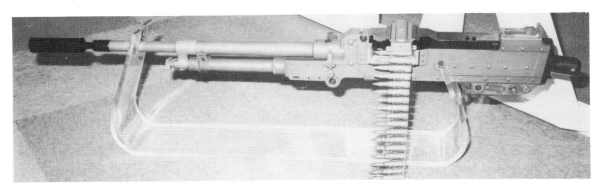

Below The L43A1 ranging machine-gun for the FV101 Scorpion.

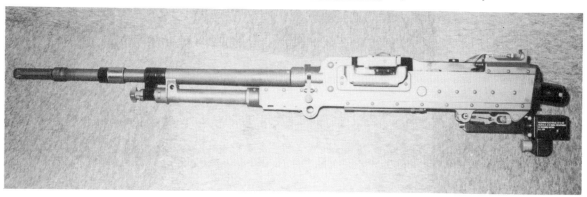

L43A1: The L43A1 is fitted as the ranging machine-gun for the Scorpion's 76 mm main armament, but is has a secondary role as a co-axial machine-gun.

L46A1: Another drill or training version, this is an inactive L7A2. It cannot be fired.

.30 Machine-Gun L3A3 and L3A4

Calibre 7.62 mm/.30 in; **Length** 1.044 m; **Length of barrel** 0.61 m; **Weight of gun** 14.1 kg; **Weight of tripod** 6.36 kg; **Muzzle velocity** 860 m/s; **Type of feed** 250-round belt; **Rate of fire (cyclic)** 400-550 rpm; **Rate of fire (practical)** 120 rpm; **Maximum effective range** 1,000 m.

Although the L3A3 and L3A4 are obsolescent it would be futile to suggest that they have yet to pass from British Army service. The two sub-variants are both based on the same American Browning design, the Model 1919A4 which first entered American service soon after the end of the Great War. In British service the L3A3 is a fixed vehicle version (and the most common) while the L3A4 is the same weapon mounted on a normal ground tripod. The L3A3 version is still used on such 'last generation' vehicles as the Saladin and the Saracen. It is also a possible weapon for the Shorland.

.50 Machine-Gun L40A1

Calibre 12.7 mm/.50 in; **Length** 1.094 m; **Length of barrel** 0.813 m; **Weight empty** 11.3 kg; **Weight loaded (approx)** 13.5 kg; **Muzzle velocity** 536 m/s; **Magazine capacity** 10 rounds; **Rate of fire** Single-shot; **Maximum effective range** 1,100 m.

Although it is classed as a machine-gun the L40A1 could perhaps be better classified as a spotting rifle for it is used in that role for the Wombat 120 mm anti-tank gun. L40A1 is the British designation for the American Rifle, Spotting Cal. .50 M8 and it is mounted over the barrel of the Wombat. When fired its projectile shows its path by tracer and if it hits its target it emits a small smoke marker. As the barrel of the Wombat is aligned with that of the L40A1 (their ballistics are very similar) it is then accurately aimed and can be fired.

Shotgun, Automatic, 12 Bore, L32A1

Calibre 12 bore/20.2 mm; **Length** 1.247 m; **Length of barrel** 0.752 m; **Weight** 3.83 kg;

Right *The L40A1 spotting rifle mounted over a Wombat barrel but minus its magazines.*

Below *The 40 mm M79 grenade launcher, used in small numbers only.*

Magazine capacity 5 rounds.

During the 1960s the Army had a requirement for fighting shotguns for specialised jungle and close-quarter warfare. Before that time shotguns had been 'unofficially' obtained from local sources but this led to a variety of types in use until the L32A1 was standardised in 1965. The L32A1 is a virtually unmodified Browning automatic shotgun produced by Fabriques Nationale in Belgium and has few changes, if any, from the widely-used commercial model. In service some changes might be introduced locally, such as shortened barrels and matt metal finishes, but these changes are few.

Today, fighting shotguns are little used by the Army and consequently many are now in store, along with smaller numbers of Remington Model 870 Wingmaster pump-action repeating shotguns,

another model obtained at about the same time as the L32A1. From time to time they are used on 'special missions' and for training purposes.

The ammunition used differs from commercial ammunition in having heavier loads. The Americans, who have long favoured the use of shotguns for short-range combats, use loads with only nine shot spheres or less (single ball loads have been reported but it is not known if these have ever been used by the British Army). The cartridge cases are usually plastic-coated, but all-brass cases are often used in combat.

40 mm Grenade Launcher M79
Calibre 40 mm; **Length** 0.737 m; **Length of barrel** 0.356 m; **Weight empty** 2.72 kg; **Weight loaded** 2.95 kg; **Muzzle velocity** 76 m/s; **Weight of**

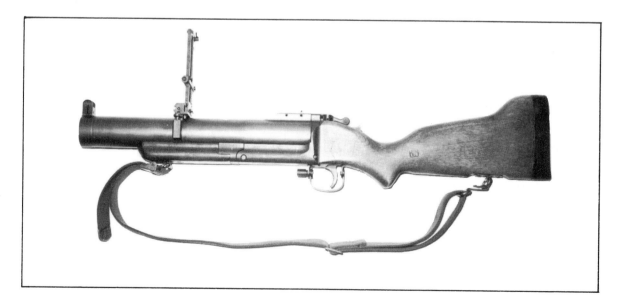

grenade (HE M406) 0.227 kg; **Magazine capacity** Single-shot only; **Rate of fire** 6-10 rpm; **Maximum effective range (area targets)** 400 m; **Maximum effective range (individual targets)** 150 m.

The M79 is an American weapon that can fire a wide range of 40 mm grenades. Its use in the British Army is at present confined to Northern Ireland where it is used for the point defence of buildings, and to a lesser extent, for crowd control when CS or dye marker grenades are fired, as well as smoke for screening. The normal offensive grenade contains high explosive. Considering that the M79 fires such a large calibre projectile it is a relatively small and light weapon. This has been brought about by the design of the grenade round in which the propellant is contained in an aluminium cartridge case. When fired the propellant gases expand in a small compartment at high pressure, and only when a predetermined pressure has been reached does the main propelling body of gas escape into the main case chamber at a much lower and more manageable pressure. The M79 is loaded in the same manner as a shotgun, ie, the barrel is broken

downwards and the grenade round is inserted directly into the barrel. Once in flight the grenade spins at a rate of over 600 revolutions per second to provide stabilisation for aiming, and the high spin rate also arms the fuze.

Grenade Discharger L1A1

Length 0.695 m; **Weight** 2.7 kg; **Weight of grenade (nominal)** 0.55 kg; **Maximum range** 100 m.

The L1A1 is mainly used to fire irritant CS grenades to break up rioting crowds or unlawful assemblies, but it can also fire smoke grenades for screening purposes. The discharger cup has an internal diameter of 66 mm and the power source for grenade propellant ignition consists of two U2 batteries housed in the section just forward of the padded butt. To fire the discharger the grenade is loaded from the muzzle. The cocking plunger just forward of the pistol grip is then pulled to the rear. The grenade is discharged by pulling the trigger at the same time as the safety button just behind the discharger cup is pressed. Thus both hands have to be used to fire the discharger which is a considerable safety factor in its favour. The grenades fired by the L1A1 discharger are as follows: Smoke Screening L5A1 and L5A2; Anti-riot Irritant L6; Smoke Screening L7 Green; Anti-riot Irritant L9; Anti-riot Irritant (Long Range) L11; Practice Anti-riot (Long Range) L14; and Drill Grenade (Discharger) Smoke L1—drill only, not fired. The L1A1 is manufactured by the Royal Small Arms Factory at Enfield Lock.

High explosive grenades

Grenade, Hand No. 36M: The 36M grenade is probably one of the oldest weapon designs still in Army use as it was first produced in 1915, and ever since then has been known as the 'Mills Bomb'. It has long been obsolescent but some still remain for training purposes. It weighs 0.774 kg and can be hand thrown to about 25 metres. Long overdue for replacement by the L2 series.

Grenade, Hand-Rifle, Anti-Personnel L2: Now the standard British hand grenade, the design of the L2 series is based on that of the American M26 but differs in having a separate fuze assembly (the Fuze L25A6). Produced by The Royal Ordnance Factory at Chorley, there are two versions, the L2A1 and L2A2, but they differ only in manufacturing expedients. The egg-shaped body is 77.5 mm long and has a filling of 170 grams of RDX/TNT. Although it was originally intended

Left *The L1A1 at the ready.*

that this grenade should be fired from a rifle as well as being thrown by hand, the rifle role no longer applies, and it is a hand grenade only. There are two practice grenades, both inert, the L3A1 and L4A1.

Grenade, Rifle M406: Fired from the 40 mm Grenade Launcher M79, this American grenade weighs 0.227 kg. It is employed only in Northern Ireland. At one time it was intended that the 40 mm grenades and their launcher would become a standard service issue for the Infantry, after trials held in 1972, but supply difficulties prevented this happening.

Smoke grenades

Grenade No. 80 WP: Although this grenade is scheduled to be replaced by the XL21E1, there are still considerable stocks available and they will continue to be used for some while yet. The design originated during World War 2 and as well as being thrown by hand, it was also intended to be fired from AFV smoke dischargers. Weight is approximately 0.55 kg.

Grenade, Hand No. 83 Smoke: Another World War 2 veteran, but still in production at the Royal Ordnance Factory at Glascoed, the No. 83 can emit red, blue, green or yellow smoke for marking purposes. The grenade is 140 mm high and has a diameter of 63.5 mm. Weight is about 0.5 kg. It is scheduled for replacement by the XL6E1.

Smoke Grenade XL21E1: Originally known as the XL5E1, this grenade will in time replace the No. 80. It is filled with red phosphorous and weighs about 0.45 kg.

Grenade, Hand, Coloured Smoke Marking XL6E1: Very similar to the XL21E1, this grenade will eventually replace the No. 83. Like the latter it can be issued with smoke of several colours.

Smoke Screening Grenade L5: Fired from the Grenade Discharger L1A1, this grenade exists in two versions, the L5A1 and the L5A2, which differ only in the filling. Both are 178 mm long and 63.5 mm in diameter. They can discharge white smoke for about 30-50 seconds and can be fired to a range of about 60 metres.

Smoke Screening Green Grenade L7A1: This is similar in appearance and performance to the L5 but emits green smoke.

Smoke Screening Grenade L34A1: While the above-mentioned grenades are all products of the Royal Ordnance Factory at Glascoed in Gwent, the L34A1 is a commercial product from Schermuly Limited of Salisbury. The L34A1 has a 'twist-and-pull' operated fuze, and weighs 0.308 kg. A hand-thrown grenade, it is 105 mm long and 55 mm in

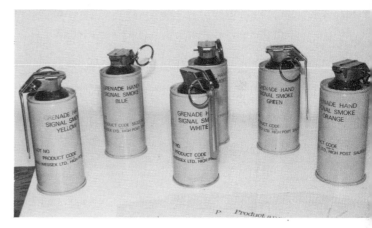

Top *L2A2 anti-personnel grenades. Fully assembled examples are on the left, while those on the right await their fuze assemblies.* **Above** *These smoke grenades are typical in shape and appearance to many types, including the various CS grenades.*

diameter. After a delay of 1-2 seconds it emits grey-white smoke for up to 45 seconds.

Smoke Screening Grenade L8A1: While the above grenades are all intended for use by Infantry, the L8 has been designed to be discharged from AFV and vehicle smoke dischargers. Electrically fired, the L8 is a cylindrical metal and rubber grenade filled with red phosphorous. When fired the casing breaks up and the smoke cloud then covers an area some 35 metres in diameter at a height of about six metres, and about 25 metres away from the vehicle. The 360 gram filling enables the cloud to last for about three minutes. The L8 weighs 0.68 kg, is 185 mm long and 66 mm in diameter.

Smoke Screening Grenade L27: The L27 grenade is the same size as the L8 but is lighter at 0.535 kg. It uses the 23-pellet system used by CS grenades but is intended to be fired from vehicle smoke dischargers. The grenade bursts about five metres from the ground and 25 metres from the vehicle, dispersing the 23 pellets which then produce green screening smoke. The smoke produced lasts for about 12 seconds before it breaks up, but this is usually sufficient for the firing vehicle to move to a fresh position, and the L27 has also been used for riot control. The area covered by the smoke cloud is about 20 metres in diameter.

Grenades, Hand, Signal Smoke: These grenades are a relatively new product from the Royal Ordnance Factory, Glascoed, and there are four different types in the range. They differ only in the colour of smoke they produce, and are the L46 (blue), L47 (green), L48 (red) and L49 (orange). These smoke grenades are used for a variety of purposes which include position indication, signals to aircraft or helicopters, target indication at short ranges, wind and speed indicators for helicopters and other aircraft and as a search and rescue marker. The grenades all have a prominent screw cap which, once removed, can be used to pull a lanyard to initiate the two- to four-second delay. Once the smoke is produced it lasts for at least 45 seconds. Each of these smoke grenades is 135 mm high, 55 mm in diameter, and the weight is 0.35 kg.

Irritant grenades

CS is perhaps better described as a disabling agent rather than an irritant but its effect on concentrations of personnel has much the same result. The term CS is a manageable term for ortho-chloro-benzalmalono-nitrile which in its stable form is a solid substance. Exposure to the atmosphere produces a vapour (usually white or light grey) that causes the disabling effect by inducing choking, eye tearing and a general difficulty in breathing. High concentrations can cause nausea and vomiting. The effects are usually not totally disabling but can persist, especially if droplets of the vapour adhere to clothing. CS has a general odour of pepper. It was first used by the British Army in 1959 when it began to replace CN which is conventional tear gas (alpha-chloroaceto-phenone).

Grenade Hand No. 91: Although it was declared obsolete in 1958, this tear-gas grenade is still used for training purposes, usually in giving troops confidence in their protective equipment. It weighs about 0.45 kg.

Grenade, CS Anti-riot, Irritant, L1A1 and L2A1: These two CS-filled grenades are the same size, being 114 mm long and 57 mm in body diameter. They differ in their action as the L1A1 emits CS smoke from holes drilled in an internal sleeve. This has the disadvantage that it can be smothered or even thrown back by a determined rioter. The L2A1 overcame this problem by the use of a small internal gunpowder charge which scattered 400 smoke-producing pellets over a wide area, but *this* had the disadvantage that the CS cloud was sometimes of insufficient density to produce any lasting effects. Both types have now been replaced by the L13 but they are still likely to be encountered.

Grenade, Hand, Anti-riot Irritant, L13A1: Although similar in appearance to the L1A1 and L2A1, the L13A1 is slightly larger as it is 175 mm long and 66 mm in diameter. It weighs 0.55 kg and can be thrown to about 25 metres. Once thrown there is a delay of 2 to 2.4 seconds before an internal charge detonates scattering 23 CS aluminium-encased pellets over a radius of seven to eight metres. Each pellet emits CS smoke for about 12 seconds. The Grenade, Anti-riot, Practice L16 is used for training and operates in exactly the same manner as the L13A1, but the pellets produce only harmless smoke.

Grenade, Hand, Anti-riot Irritant, L1A3: While the grenades mentioned above are Royal Ordnance Factory, Glascoed, products, the L1A3 is a Schermuly product. The L1A3 is 140 mm long, has a diameter of 64 mm, and weighs 0.454 kg. When thrown there is a delay of 1.5 seconds in order to enable the thrower to withdraw before the CS smoke cloud is emitted in such density that it cannot be thrown back without considerable risk to the would-be thrower. A training version producing orange smoke is available.

Grenade, Discharger, Anti-riot Irritant L6A1: Basically similar in appearance to the Smoke Screening Grenade L5, the L6A1 contains two pellets of irritating agent which are scattered by the detonation of a 2.6-gram charge of gunpowder. It is fired by the Grenade Discharger L1A1 to a range of about 60 metres. It has now been replaced by the L11 but may still be encountered.

Grenade, Discharger, Anti-riot Irritant L9A1: Designed to be fired from the Grenade Discharger L1A1, the L9A1 is now obsolescent and due to be replaced by the L11. In use the L9A1 scatters 400 CS pellets which, like the Hand Grenade L2A1, often proved unable to produce sufficient concentrations to disable determined rioters.

Grenade, Discharger, Anti-riot Irritant (Long Range) L11A1: This is now the 'standard' anti-riot grenade fired from the Grenade Discharger L1A1. It can be fired to a range of about 80 to 100 metres and when detonated, ideally about six metres above a rioting assembly, scatters 23 CS pellets over a 25-metre diameter circle. The L11A1 weighs about 0.56 kg and is 185 mm long with a diameter of 66 mm. Each CS pellet can emit gas for about 12 seconds. For training purposes, the Grenade, Discharger, Anti-riot Practice L14 operates in exactly the same way as the L11A1 but emits only harmless smoke.

Cartridge, 1.5-in, Anti-riot Irritant L3A1: Another Schermuly product, the L3A1 is fired from the various 1.5-in pistols and riot guns in service. It has replaced the earlier L2A2 cartridge which had a pressed-paper body, for the L3A1 has an aluminium case. Each cartridge is 120 mm long and weighs 0.2 kg, of which 0.098 kg is the CS element. Each CS filling can produce disabling smoke for up to 25 seconds, and can be fired up to 100 metres. The L4A1 is a practice version.

CS Hand Spray L1A1: Although it is not a grenade in any sense the CS Hand Spray L1A1 is included here as it does not fit readily into any other category. It is a small aerosol spray can intended for close-quarter use in order to disable or pacify an opponent at very short ranges (up to about one metre). It can thus be used in riot situations for self-protection or in arresting violent opponents. Each can, which resembles a conventional aerosol container apart from the markings, weighs only 0.12 kg and contains enough CS filling for 50 two-second bursts. The can is 123 mm long and 38.5 mm in diameter and can thus be easily concealed on the person. It is produced by Schermuly.

Baton rounds

Baton rounds were originally an American idea intended to assist in breaking up riotous assemblies. It had been discovered that conventional firearms were often worse than useless in some circumstances as they either produced only harmless noise when fired over heads, or deaths and serious injuries which provided not only political problems but often accentuated the situations, both long and short term, by producing martyrs. The baton round was introduced as it was designed to stun or disable rather than injure or maim. Properly handled, it could even be used to disable ringleaders or other individuals.

The first baton rounds were wood but they proved lethal under certain circumstances. They were replaced by the infamous 'rubber bullets', but experience and analysis in Northern Ireland indicated that rubber rounds still had a statistical risk of producing serious injury, even though no really serious wounds had been inflicted by their use. Thus the present baton round in British Army use is a blunt slug of PVC, which not only decreases the injury risk but is more accurate at ranges up to 30 metres. The PVC round in service is the Round, Anti-riot, 1.5-in Baton L5A1, and is fired from a variety of projectors. The complete round is 107 mm long with a diameter of 38 mm. Weight of the complete round is 0.199 kg of which the PVC projectile makes up 0.135 kg. The worst injury that the PVC baton round is expected to produce is severe bruising and the resultant shock.

While the L5A1 is produced by the Royal Ordnance Factories, the commercial concern of Schermuly also has two of its products in service as baton rounds. They are the L3A1 and the L5A2, both of which are slightly lighter than the L5A1 and can be fired to slightly longer ranges. The weight of both complete rounds is 0.17 kg and the baton component is 0.107 kg. The L3A1 has a longer range than the L5A2. Cartridges firing multiple baton projectiles are now coming into use.

51 mm Mortar L9A1

Calibre 51.25 mm; **Length of barrel overall** 0.75 m; **Outside barrel diameter** 55 mm; **Weight of barrel** 2.6 kg; **Weight of breech piece** 3.05 kg; **Weight complete (with sling)** 6.275 kg; **Maximum range** 750 m; **Minimum range** 50 m; **Bomb weight (HE L1A1)** 1.025 kg; **Bomb weight (smoke L2A1)** 0.95 kg; **Bomb weight (illuminating)** 0.825 kg; **Rate of fire (normal)** 3 rpm for five minutes; **Rate of fire (rapid)** 8 rpm for two minutes.

The 51 mm Mortar has had a very protracted development life ever since it was decided to introduce a lightweight weapon to replace the venerable 2-in mortar (which has now all but passed from use and is used only occasionally, if at all, as a flare or illuminating device launcher). To date the development period has extended to well over ten years. Much of the development work has been carried out by the Royal Armament Research and Development Establishment (RARDE) at Fort Halstead in Kent, and for much of its early life the 51 mm mortar featured a monopod leg which was a protracted source of design troubles, even though the Army had long since decided that such a nicety was not really required anyway. The ammunition was a further source of development delay for a while but by the late 1970s the 51 mm Mortar design was finally frozen and made ready for production. When production finally begins (it had not yet started when these words were written in early 1982) it will be carried out at the Royal Ordnance Factory at Nottingham.

The 51 mm Mortar at first sight appears to be a simple weapon as it is but a barrel placed on a spade-shaped breech-piece, a sight and a sling. In fact it is the result of a great deal of detail design work, and has been designed from the outset to be carried and used by one man, although in action the team would actually be two, with one carrying extra

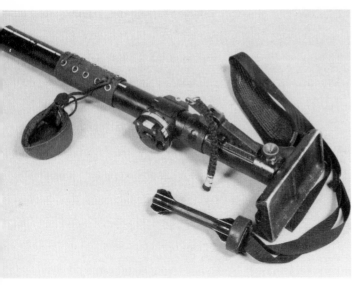

The 51 mm Mortar, showing the sight, short range insert, and sling (ROF).

ammunition. In action the bombs are introduced into the barrel from the muzzle and fired by a waterproof trigger mechanism at the base of the barrel. The spade breech piece absorbs the recoil. To aim the mortar the firer uses a line painted along the barrel for direction and range is then read off the Trilux sight—the barrel is held steady using a webbing gaiter around the barrel. For short range use a special insert (SRI) is placed in the barrel. This insert restricts the depth to which a bomb can fall inside the barrel and the resultant propellant gases can expand further than usual, thus forcing the bomb to a shorter range than normal. This feature is especially useful in close-quarter combat.

The ammunition used with the 51 mm Mortar consists of HE, smoke and illuninating bombs, the latter being intended for use with close-range anti-tank weapons such as the LAW, or even Milan. The HE bomb has its case interior serrated so that when the charge detonates a large number of lethal steel segments are produced to enhance its effectiveness. The bombs are carried in a webbing satchel, each holding six in waterproof tubes. Practice bombs are available for drill and training purposes, and the 51 mm Mortar can also fire existing stocks of old 2-in Mortar bombs that remain.

Rocket 66 mm HEAT L1A1

Calibre 66 mm; **Length extended** 0.893 m; **Length closed** 0.655 m; **Length of rocket** 0.508 m; **Weight complete** 2.37 kg; **Weight of rocket** 1 kg; **Muzzle velocity** 145 m/s; **Maximum effective**

range 300 m; **Armour penetration** Up to 300 mm steel plate.

The L1A1 is the British designation for the American M72A1 and M72A2 HEAT rocket (HEAT—High Explosive Anti-Tank). Designed originally as the successor to the large and cumbersome 3.5-in 'bazooka' rocket launchers, the L1A1 in some ways resembles the World War 2 German 'Panzerfaust' anti-tank weapon as it is intended to be a 'one-shot and throw away' device. Basically the L1A1 is a smoothbore tube containing the anti-tank rocket. In action the waterproof sealing caps on each end are removed and the tube is telescoped outwards to its full length. Simple sights are then raised and the rocket fired by percussion. Once fired a dangerous exhaust cone area extends to some 15 metres to the rear of the launcher tube and a further 25 metre 'caution zone' has to be left clear to avoid further hazards caused by the rocket exhaust. After firing the tube is discarded. The rocket has an armour penetration capability against most AFVs in service and the weapon is so light and handy that it can be carried by almost every member of an infantry squad. The L1A1 is American in origin but the British version is made under licence by Raufoss in Norway.

But for all its handiness and light weight, the L1A1 must now be regarded as, at the best, obsolescent. Its hollow-charge warhead is now too small to make any real effect on the armour protection of the latest Warsaw Pact MBTs and in future it will probably prove effective only on such MBTs as the T-54/55 and lighter tanks. It is for this reason that the Light Anti-armour weapon (LAW) has been developed.

LAW 80

Projectile calibre 94 mm; **Launcher length, extended** 1.5 m approx; **Launcher length, closed** 1 m approx; **Weight overall** 9.5 kg; **Weight of projectile** 4 kg; **Maximum range** 500 m; **Combat range** up to 300 m.

LAW 80 is the latest name for the British Army's new **L**ight **A**nti-armour **W**eapon. It has long been recognised that for the infantryman or front-line soldier to be able to tackle the increasing carapaces of armour that surround the modern and future main battle tanks, something better than the existing 66 mm L1A1 rocket and the 84 mm L14A1 gun was needed. The problem is that thick armour requires a large warhead to penetrate it, and that large warheads have required large launching systems, be they guns, rockets or whatever. For the average front-line soldier to be able to use such a large warhead, the launching system had to be portable and handy enough to be deployed efffectively without having manpower tied up with heavy weapon systems. The British Army answer is LAW 80.

LAW 80 is a rocket system that can be carried and used by one man. It is powerful enough for its rocket projectile to be able to have an armour penetration 'well in excess of that required to penetrate present and future MBT frontal armour'. Put into everyday terminology, that means armour well over 600 mm thick. To penetrate such an armour thickness the LAW 80 rocket projectile has a warhead diameter of 94 mm, but the warhead design is such that its performance produces results well in excess of what might be expected from a conventionally designed hollow-charge warhead. The internal features of the LAW 80 warhead are

Below *The L1A1 ready for firing.* **Bottom** *Mock-up of LAW 80. The figure on the right has the launcher ready for use, while the figure on the left has the telescoped launcher slung on its webbing sling.*

obviously very closely guarded secrets, but it is obvious that some form of anti-armour design breakthrough has been made.

The LAW 80 rocket has wrap-around folding fins to provide stability in flight and travels towards its target at a speed of nearly Mach 1. The LAW 80 launcher is a filament-wound Kevlar in epoxy resin tube which can be telescoped for storage and carrying. Just before it is required for action the tube is extended and the end covers removed. The launcher tube also carries the shoulder rest, firing grip and the x1 plastic optical sight. To back up the sight there is an integral aiming rifle under the launcher tube with its own six-round magazine. Once the target is in the sight the firer can select the aiming rifle to fire a spotting round. This not only accurately determines the aim but also the range. If the aiming round hits the target tank it produces an indicating flash, and the main projectile can then be selected and fired. If, for any reason, the main projectile is not fired, the tube can be once more telescoped for later re-use. The six aiming rounds are considered to be enough for two possible engagements. Once fired, the launcher tube is discarded.

LAW 80 can be handled and stored exactly as a conventional round of ammunition. The tube is weatherproof and has a shelf life of about ten years. Using the weapon in enclosed areas, however, produces its own hazards as the rocket uses a fair amount of propellant and an area to the rear of about 20 metres could be dangerous to personnel and equipment. Once fired, the rocket warhead will not be armed until it has travelled about 10 to 20 metres.

LAW 80 is still under development although troop trials are continuing. The production and general involvement of various concerns in the production programme is quite a list. The prime contractor, Hunting Engineering, is dealing with the launcher, sights and various types of training equipment. The Royal Ordnance Factory at Blackburn (among others) will produce the projectile, and the Royal Small Arms Factory at Enfield Lock will produce the spotting rifle. Other Royal Ordnance Factories or facilities will produce the rocket motor and general technical advice and design detail. Miltrain Limited and Hendry Electronics will be involved in some quite involved indoor training systems, and EPS (Research and Development) Limited will be responsible for the important packaging. This list of companies involved is included to give some idea of the scope of manufacturing and other skills involved in a modern weapons programme, even one as compact as LAW 80.

The introduction into service of LAW 80 is expected to be some time in the mid-1980s. In the meantime considerable efforts are being made to interest other NATO nations in its potential. When it gets into service the front-line soldier will have the ability to destroy virtually any armour that is set against him. It will be issued widely, not only to the front-line but to troops on supply routes and in rear areas. In time it will no doubt be issued to soft-skin and armoured vehicle crews as a standard issue item. It will be a formidable weapon.

Ordnance Muzzle-Loading 81 mm L16A1

Calibre 81 mm; **Length of barrel overall** 1.28 m; **Weight of barrel** 12.28 kg; **Weight of mounting** 11.8 kg; **Weight of sight unit** 1.25 kg; **Weight of base plate** 11.8 kg; **Weight complete in action** 36.7 kg; **Muzzle velocity (maximum)** 255 m/s; **Maximum range** 5,650 m; **Maximum range (HE L31E3)** 5,800 m plus; **Minimum range** 200 m; **Elevation** 45° to 80°; **Traverse** 5° left/right at 45°; **Bomb weight (HE L15A3)** 4.47 kg; **Bomb weight (Smoke L19A4)** 4.49 kg; **Rate of fire** 15 rpm.

The 81 mm Mortar entered service in 1961, only four years after a design study was initiated at the

Loading the 81 mm Mortar from an FV432 mortar carrier.

Royal Armament Research and Development Establishment at Fort Halstead. The Canadian equivalent establishment was also involved and produced two components of the overall equipment in the shape of the sight unit and the base plate (this has a diameter of 0.546 metre, can allow a 360° manual traverse without re-bedding, and can also accommodate the American 81 mm mortar barrel). The mounting used is the Mounting 81 mm Mortar L5A2 and is known as a 'K' mount, an arrangement that enables levelling to be effected using only one of the mounting legs. The mortar barrel itself has several advanced features, one of which is the use of fins around the bottom half to dissipate the heat produced by firing. The barrel itself it constructed from forged steel. Detail design points are the provision of a slight muzzle taper internally to ease loading, and a removable breech plug to facilitate a variety of possible mountings (and also for easy replacement of the fixed firing pin).

The ammunition used with the 81 mm Mortar is of an advanced design and is still the subject of considerable development. The standard HE bomb is the L15A3 which has a ductile cast iron body which ensures that over 40 per cent of the bomb provides lethal fragments on detonation. A system of one primary and up to eight separate charges can be used to cover ranges from 200 to 5,650 metres. A new HE bomb with a cast iron body providing even more fragmentation is now in service. This is the XL31E2 which uses a revised charge system using only six possible charges. The standard smoke bomb is the L19A4 which produces the white phosphorous smoke. An illuminating bomb is still under development by the French Thompson-Brandt concern based on their Mark 68 bomb. A version of the French design is already in Army use, but lacks the range of the new bomb which is said to be 'in excess of 5,000 metres', and the new design produces 20 per cent more illumination to boot. A practice bomb, already in service, is the inert L27A1 which is fired to a maximum range of only some 80 metres. As the 81 mm calibre is the standard NATO choice, ammunition produced in other NATO states can also be fired.

The normal Infantry carrier for the 81 mm Mortar is the adapted FV432 which has a 360° mounting for the barrel fitted to the rear compartment floor. In the mortar role the FV432 can carry 160 bombs in racks ready for use. The other Infantry carrier is the Land Rover, in all its three basic versions, but for really basic use the 81 mm Mortar can be broken down into three man-pack loads, two of 11.35 kg and one of 12.28 kg—more men would be needed to carry the ammunition.

At present the British Army uses the well-tried and trusted method of plotting board and range tables to determine firing data, but with the advent of the microprocessor this seems very likely to change soon. Already there is a Marconi-designed mortar firing control system ready and proved in the shape of MORCOS (Mortar Data Computing System) which can store and display all the information needed to deal with up to ten separate targets. The information involved can be entered and displayed in a fashion very similar to that used on the everyday pocket calculator. Early versions used a hand-held unit with 24 keys and an eight-digit display, but the eventual Service version may well incorporate some differences. The power supply comes from a normal 9-volt battery. At the time of writing it is not certain whether or not MORCOS has been accepted for service use, but something very like it will no doubt be introduced very soon.

Apart from the microprocessor, the introduction of such devices as MORCOS has been made possible by the use of a new design of obturating (sealing) ring fitted around the body diameter of most modern mortar projectiles. These rings are made from a variety of plastic which lays almost flush with the sides of the bomb when it is introduced into the mortar barrel. As the bomb propellant is detonated the rings spread outwards and effectively seal the space between the bomb and the sides of the barrel. This reduces the 'windage' which has always been a random influence on the bombs' external ballistic behaviour, and removing this variable has rendered the use of electronic calculators possible.

Gun, 84 mm Infantry L14A1

Calibre 84 mm; **Length of barrel** 1.13 m; **Weight complete** 16 kg; **Muzzle velocity** 160 m/s; **Weight of HEAT round L40A4** 2.59 kg; **Weight of HEAT projectile** 1.7 kg; **Range, anti-tank (mobile)** 400 m; **Range, anti-tank (stationary)** 500 m; **Range, HE and smoke** 1,000 m; **Rate of fire** 6 rpm; **Armour penetration (HEAT at 60°)** 228 mm.

The usual name given to the L14A1 is 'Carl Gustav' as the origins of this shoulder-fired recoilless gun are Swedish. Designed and produced by the Förenade Fabriksverken (FFV) at Eskilstuna, the Carl Gustav is now the usual squad anti-tank weapon although it can be used for other tasks. Although it can be loaded and fired by one man, two usually make up the gun team with one loading and the other aiming and firing. As with all recoilless weapons, a considerable amount of dangerous (and visible) back-blast is produced on firing, but this is more than made up for by the armour penetration capabilities of the large HEAT

An 84 mm 'Carl Gustav' ready for firing.

projectile which can penetrate up to 228 mm of armour. 84 mm rounds are manufactured in the United Kingdom, and HEAT practice and drill rounds are all produced by the Royal Ordnance Factories. High explosive and smoke rounds can also be fired from the Carl Gustav. For training on indoor ranges a 6.5 mm or .22 sub-calibre device can be fitted into a specially converted round which is then loaded into the barrel in the normal way. Although it is intended as a man-portable weapon, the Carl Gustav can be fired from open-topped vehicles, and the FV432 can be fitted with a special resting bar across the top hatch.

Gun, 120 mm BAT L6 Wombat

Calibre 120 mm; **Length overall** 3.86 m; **Length of bore** 2.34 m; **Weight in action (approx)** 308 kg; **Traverse** 360°; **Elevation** −8° to +17°; **Muzzle velocity** 463 m/s; **Round weight** 27.3 kg; **Projectile weight (HESH)** 12.8 kg; **Maximum effective range** 1,100 m; **Rate of fire** 4 rpm.

The development of the Wombat can be traced back to the immediate post-war years when it was decided to produce a 120 mm recoilless gun to replace existing anti-tank guns. The first of these was the 120 mm BAT L1 (BAT—Battalion Anti-Tank gun) which was almost as heavy as the weapon it was supposed to replace, namely the well-tried 17 pr. The L1 did enter service but further development led to the lighter and handier 120 mm BAT L4, the Mobat. In time the L4 replaced the L1 in service but it was felt that there was room for improvement, both in weight and performance, so further development at the Royal Armament Research and Development Establishment at Fort Halstead

produced the 120 mm BAT L6, soon named the Wombat. The Wombat is less than half the weight of its predecessor and also has a better range, mainly due to the use of a .50 Machine-Gun L40A1 for aiming purposes (the Mobat used a Bren Gun for the same purpose). There are several other improvements over the earlier gun, especially in the sighting unit which can accommodate both light intensifier and infra-red devices.

Normally the Wombat is served by two or three men, one of whom acts as loader and another as layer. Laying the Wombat involves the use of a rather complex sighting telescope which is first used

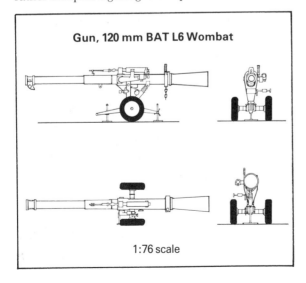

Gun, 120 mm BAT L6 Wombat

1:76 scale

to direct the single-round fire of the .50 spotting rifle. The round fired by the rifle emits a stream of tracer which clearly shows its trajectory, and if a hard target is hit a small burst of marker smoke is emitted. As the barrel of the rifle and the gun are aligned the main projectile can be fired—the trajectories of the .50 and 120 mm projectiles are ballistically matched out to about 1,100 m. The accurate laying of the main barrel is most important for firing the Wombat produces two unfortunate effects: not only an alarmingly loud report, but the considerable back-blast kicks up a very large cloud of dust and debris, both of which can combine to reveal the firing position. Not surprisingly, many soldiers refer to the Wombat as the 'VC Gun', but it has already been recognised as obsolescent and is now being replaced by Milan. Nevertheless, it seems likely that the Wombat will remain in service for some years to come, especially with TA and other reserve units.

The round used with the Wombat is still that used on the very first BAT, namely the L1. The projectile used against tanks has a HESH (High Explosive Squash Head) warhead, and is stated to be effective against any known AFV, but exact figures cannot be quoted.

Having only small pneumatic wheels, the Wombat is not designed for other than hand-towing over short distances. Normally it is intended for carriage inside or on a vehicle. In mechanised formations the FV432 is the main type used. Small ramps enable the gun to be wheeled into the '432 but it is possible to mount the gun so that it has a

Left *The L6 Wombat* (MoD).

Right *The 30 mm Rarden Gun in cut-away. The handle at the breech is the charging/cocking handle.*

Below right *Cross-section of the HE/T L8A2 and L5A2 APSE projectiles* (Oerlikon).

270° traverse out of the top hatch. Each '432 so employed can carry 14 of the bulky 120 mm rounds. The other main portee vehicle is the Land Rover which can be quickly fitted with a special small winch and ramp kit, along with racks for six rounds. Although it is not intended for other than a tactical emergency, the Wombat can be fired from the back of the modified Land Rover. Trials have been carried out in mounting it on the rear of a Lightweight Land Rover, while another carrier that can be equipped to carry it is the Bv 202 Over Snow vehicle. On this vehicle the Wombat is carried in the rear section.

Ordnance

Cannon, 30 mm Rarden L21

Calibre 30 mm; **Length overall** 2.959 m; **Length of barrel** 2.44 m; **Weight complete** 110 kg; **Muzzle velocity (British ammunition)** 1,070 m/s; **Muzzle velocity (Hispano ammunition)** 1,080 m/s; **Round weight (APSE L5A2)** 0.9044 kg; **Round weight (HE/T L8A2)** 0.9039 kg; **Shell weight (APSE L5A2)** 0.3574 kg; **Shell weight (HE/T L8A2)** 0.3569 kg; **Maximum effective range** 4,000 m plus; **Rate of fire (cyclic)** 80-90 rpm.

One of the more interesting aspects of the Rarden is its original design philosophy which was evolved during the early 1960s. At that time it was decided to produce a light AFV gun that could perforate the armour expected to be carried by a new generation of APCs, and which would be capable of this task at ranges of over 1,000 metres. It was envisaged that the new gun would be fitted into relatively light vehicles and thus the trunnion forces exerted had to be fairly light as well, while to add an extra stricture to the design specification the gun had to take up as little space as possible. Other requirements were a useful HE shell performance and the ability to be used against slow low-flying aircraft and helicopters. Of all these specifications the most restricting was the low trunnion loading but it could be met if a low rate of fire was accepted, and this was subsequently agreed. The end result was a 30 mm gun with a rate of fire of 80-90 rpm. The only design

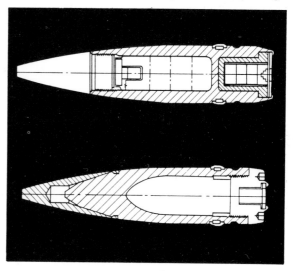

Right *Ammunition for the 76 mm L23A1. From left to right: Drill; L29A3 HESH; Smoke (BE) L32A5; HE L24A4; HE/PRAC L25A4 and Canister L33A1.*

specification that was not met was the anti-aircraft and helicopter capability as such a low rate of fire would be fairly ineffective against such targets, but all the other requirements were achieved.

The design was a combined effort by the Royal Armament Research and Development Establishment at Fort Halstead, and the Royal Small Arms Factory at Enfield Lock, so hence the designation 'Rarden'. Two basic types of ammunition were developed for the gun, one an armour-piercing shell with secondary effects (APSE—this type of projectile is designed to explode only after the armour has been penetrated), and a high explosive shell with tracer (HE/T). One logistic advantage which was incorporated into the ammunition design was that the Rarden could also fire the existing and readily available Hispano-Suiza 831 L 30 mm rounds—the HE round is the UIAT and the AP the RINT. In the United Kingdom a considerable amount of time and effort was put into the development of an armour piercing/discarding sabot round (APDS) with a muzzle velocity of over 1,200 m/s, but in the end the technical difficulties involved were too great and the project was terminated only to be re-introduced later. The warheads of the HE/T shell contain 0.256 kg of explosive and the APSE shell contains 0.16 kg. For practice purposes there is the L7A4 practice shell.

The rounds are loaded into the Rarden in clips of three, and the gun can hold up to six rounds ready to fire. Only 0.43 metres of the gun's total length protrudes into a vehicle's turret, and the only exter-

nal part of the gun mechanism handled by the crew is the cocking handle—the rest is sealed off and no fumes can escape into the turret itself. Two rather unusual features of the operation are that the Rarden uses the little-encountered 'long recoil' system of operation, and an automatic sliding breech block. The low rate of fire has the real advantage that it makes the Rarden very accurate; target groupings of one metre at 1,000 metres have been quoted.

To date the Rarden is fitted to only two service vehicles, the FV107 Scimitar and the FV721 Fox, both of which are employed as light reconnaissance vehicles. Both have essentially similar turrets but the Scimitar carries 165 rounds and the Fox 99. A turret derived from that fitted to the Fox was at one time intended for use on the FV432 but that programme was terminated in 1976 after only 13 had been produced. One early project that came to naught was the mounting of a Rarden on a small and light wheeled mounting, but only one or two prototypes were made. Designs for mounting Rardens on small patrol boats have been produced.

Gun 76 mm L23A1

Calibre 76.2 mm; **Length overall** 2.156 m; **Weight complete** 150.59 kg; **Muzzle velocity (HESH)** 533 m/s; **Muzzle velocity (HE)** 514 m/s; **Muzzle velocity (smoke)** 290 m/s; **Round weight (HESH L29A3)** 7.4 kg; **Round weight (HE L24A4)** 7.33 kg; **Round weight (smoke L32A5)** 10.2 kg; **Shell weight (HESH L29A3)** 5.39 kg; **Shell weight (HE L24A4)** 5.36 kg; **Shell weight**

(smoke L32A5) 8.51 kg; **Maximum direct range (HESH, HE)** 2,200 m; **Maximum indirect range (HESH, HE)** 5,000 m; **Maximum range (smoke)** 3,700 m.

The L23A1 is a lightened version of the earlier L5A1 fitted to the FV601 Saladin, and uses much the same ammunition. To date, only one British Army vehicle is fitted with the L23A1 and that is the FV101 Scorpion which can carry 40 rounds. Rounds available which are not mentioned in the above table are SH/Prac L40A1 (Squash Head/ Practice), HE/Prac L25A4 (High Explosive/ Practice), Illuminating L32A5 and Canister L33A1. The latter is an anti-personnel round intended for use against infantry tank-hunter squads or massed infantry at ranges up to about 100 metres (it is also a reversion to an ancient artillery practice). The Canister projectile is a thin-walled container packed with steel balls—the container breaks up as the projectile leaves the muzzle and the lethal balls are scattered in a wide cone. The weight of the L33A1 round is 7.76 kg.

The L23A1 is an entirely conventional gun using a falling-block breech. The recoil length is approximately 0.28 metres.

Ordnance, QF, 25 pr Marks 2/1, 3/1 and 4

Calibre 87.6 mm; **Length of bore** 2.346 m; **Length of rifling (Mark 3/1)** 1.877 m; **Length overall** 4.65 m; **Width overall** 2.134 m; **Track width** 1.79 m; **Height travelling** 1.65 m; **Weight in action** 1,801 kg; **Traverse on carriage** 8°; **Traverse on platform** 360°; **Elevation** -5° to +40°; **Muzzle velocity (HE)** 518 m/s; **Shell weight (HE)** 11.34 kg; **Shell weight (smoke)** 9.93 kg; **Maximum range** 12,253 m; **Rate of fire** 10 rpm.

Although the 25 pr has long been out of service as a front-line artillery piece it is still in use today, although its duties are confined to saluting and ceremonial purposes. Some are also used by various Cadet units for training, while others continue firing for various trials and experiments.

The 25 pr has had a long and respected service life as it entered service in 1940 and was not withdrawn from front-line use until 1967 when the last example was ceremoniously retired by 14 Field Regiment RA. Even then it served on with the TA, and it still remains a front-line weapon with many other armies. One of the main reasons for this longevity is the robust and compact construction, but perhaps the real reason so many remain around is that the gun (actually a gun-howitzer) gained so many laurels in the years between 1940 and 1945. The full story of the 25 pr has no place here, but it was replaced by the 105 mm Pack Howitzer L5 which, in its turn, has been replaced by the 105 mm Light Gun L118. But still the 25 pr remains, and its future status seems to be that it will be around for a long while, even if its role is purely symbolic. The Royal Regiment of Artillery uses its guns as its colours, and this means that the present missile batteries are somewhat at a loss for colours when on

ceremonial parades. Therefore it has been suggested that a 25 pr should be issued to each missile battery to fulfil this task, and this might well happen. In the meantime, 25 prs are used at many locations as 'clock' guns (as at Edinburgh Castle) and as saluting batteries (as at Gibraltar). Many more act as gate guardians. Some cadet units continue to fire live ammunition but this is now in short supply, and any future stocks will have to come from other nations such as India, where the 25 pr is still a front-line weapon. But the 25 pr is still used to at least partially equip a few TA batteries and it is used by at least five OTUs. The Honorable Artillery Company still uses a small number.

Gun Equipment, 105 mm L5

Calibre 105 mm; **Length of barrel with muzzle brake** 1.716 m; **Length of barrel** 1.478 m; **Length of rifling** 1.074 m; **Length overall (three-section trail)** 4.8 m; **Length overall (two-section trail)** 4.2 m; **Width** 1.45 m; **Height (normal)** 1.93 m; **Height (anti-tank)** 1.55 m; **Weight in action (three-section trail)** 1,310 kg; **Weight in action (two-section trail)** 1,270 kg; **Traverse (normal)** 36°; **Traverse (anti-tank)** 56°; **Elevation** −5° to +65°; **Muzzle velocity (max)** 424 m/s; **Shell weight (HE M1)** 19.05 kg; **Shell weight (HEAT M67)** 16.81 kg; **Maximum range** 10,575 m; **Rate of fire (normal)** 3-4 rpm; **Rate of fire (rapid)** 8 rpm.

The British Army knew the Gun Equipment, 105 mm L5 as the Pack Howitzer since its full title was rather too cumbersome to trip off the tongue—it was Howitzer, Pack 105 mm L10A1 on Carriage 105 mm Howitzer L3A1. It was procured from Italy as the towed artillery replacement for the old 25 pr and its use spread to nearly all the various field and specialist Royal Artillery batteries other than those based in BAOR. The Pack Howitzer was an Italian design, the 105/14 Model 56, produced by OtO Melara SpA at La Spezia in Northern Italy. Despite the fact that the Pack Howitzer had less range than the piece it was replacing it had the advantage of firing a heavier shell and the howitzer itself was mounted on a carriage that possessed considerable versatility. The carriage could be fired from a normal field configuration or the axles could be reversed to lower the height and at the same time increase the traverse for anti-tank firing. Being designed from the outset for pack transportation, the

Top left *Senior instructors manning a 25 pr during a Larkhill rapid-fire competition.* **Above left** *Men of the Gibraltar Regiment firing a salute from one of the 25 prs held at the Devil's Gap battery.* **Left** *The 105 mm Pack Howitzer ready for towing.* **Right** *One of the last active service Pack Howitzers being fired by the Gibraltar Regiment at sea targets off Europa Point.*

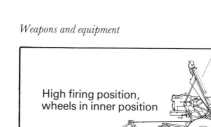

High firing position,
wheels in inner position

Low firing position,
wheels in outer position

Shield omitted for clarity

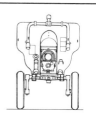

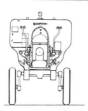

Road travelling position

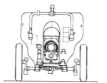

Gun Equipment, 105 mm L5

1:76 scale

carriage and the main components of the howitzer could be rapidly stripped down for all manner of transport from basic manpower to mule conveyance (the last British Army mule unit was disbanded in Hong Kong at the end of 1975). To reduce weight the howitzer could be taken into action with the shield removed and the number of trail sections reduced from the normal three to two. The usual British towing vehicle was the ¾-tonne Land Rover which also carried the six-man crew, and other Land Rovers carried the ammunition, along with 4-tonne trucks.

With the advent of the new 105 mm Light Gun the Pack Howitzer was gradually withdrawn from front-line service but it is still in use today with training units (such as the Junior Leaders Regiment, Royal Artillery) and a few specialist units such as the Gibraltar Regiment. Others are

kept in reserve against some likely future role. As the Pack Howitzer fires the widely available 105 mm American ammunition, supply is not likely to prove difficult for many years to come.

Ordnance, BL, 105 mm Field L13A1

Calibre 105 mm; **Length of barrel** 3.25 m; **Muzzle velocity (maximum)** 708 m/s; **Shell weight (HE L31)** 15.1 kg; **Projectile weight (HESH L42)** 10.49 kg; **Shell weight (smoke L51)** 15.98 kg; **Shell weight (HE M1)** 14.9 kg; **Propellant weight (HE and smoke)** 2.4 kg; **Propellant weight (HESH)** 3.52 kg; **Maximum range** 17,200 m; **Maximum range (American M1)** 15,000 m; **Rate of fire** 12 rpm.

The 105 mm L13 gun is at present fitted to only one vehicle, namely the FV433 Abbot, and is thus the main armament of the field regiments based in

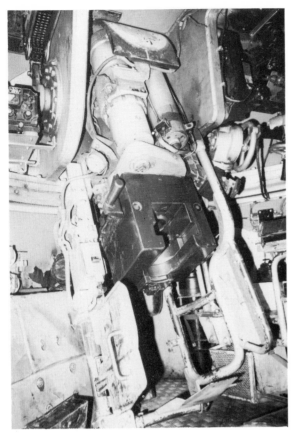

Above *The breech of a 105 mm L13A1 gun. This photograph was taken inside one of the Value-engineered Abbots used at BATUS, Suffield, and thus it lacks the power rammer of the normal version.*

Germany. It is yet another product of the Royal Armament Research and Development Establishment at Fort Halstead in Kent. It came into service in 1965 and from then onwards has been the main close-support weapon of the Royal Artillery. When it first came into service the Abbot with its L13 gun was a considerable advance on the 25 pr it was replacing, both in range and shell weight, but by the late 1970s it was seen to be approaching obsolescence as 105 mm fire has been proved to be incapable of inflicting sufficient damage on the massed AFV attacks expected in any future European conflict. However, it still has a considerable capability against 'softer' targets, and is expected to remain in service for many years yet.

The L13 gun has considerable range for its calibre, while the varieties of ammunition developed for it have many advantages in performance over the American 105 mm M1 types in use before the advent of L13. Unfortunately this has the logistic disadvantage within NATO that the British ammunition is non-standard with other 105 mm weapons. To some extent this incompatability can be reduced by the ability of the L13 to fire American projectiles with British charges, but the range is then reduced to 15,000 metres (this is still far greater than any other NATO 105 mm artillery piece can achieve). Another factor is that the ammunition is also used by the British L118 Light Gun. The main offensive projectile is the Shell, 105 mm, Field, High Explosive L31, but for anti-tank use a High Explosive Squash Head (HESH) round is available but no longer in production. Other projectiles in service include Illuminating L43. The basic smoke round is the L45 but there is a red (the L37) and an orange smoke round (the L38).

Gun, 105 mm L118

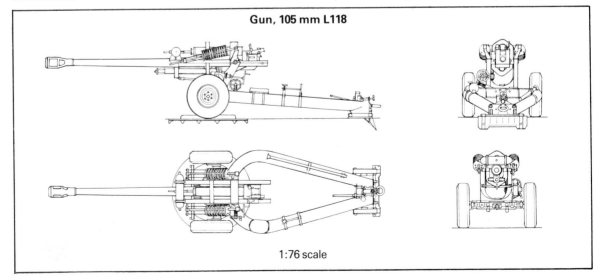

1:76 scale

The L13A1 has a vertical sliding breech block, and the ammunition is loaded separately with brass cases holding the propellant charges. Up to eight separate charges can be selected. When using American M1 ammunition a shorter cartridge case is used. The gun has a prominent muzzle brake and a bore evacuator is fitted to eliminate propellant fumes in the Abbot turret. Barrel life is stated to be well over 10,000 rounds.

Gun, 105 mm Field L118

Calibre 105 mm; **Length of barrel** 3.17 m; **Length overall (firing at 0°)** 7.01 m; **Length overall (folded)** 4.8 m; **Width overall** 1.78 m; **Track width** 1.42 m; **Height travelling** 1.22 m; **Weight in action (approx)** 1,858 kg; **Traverse on carriage** 11°; **Traverse on platform** 360°; **Elevation** −5.5° to +70°; **Muzzle velocity (maximum)** 708 m/s; **Shell weight (HE L31)** 15.1 kg; **Shell weight (HESH L42)** 10.49 kg; **Shell weight (smoke L51)** 15.98 kg; **Maximum range (HE)** 17,200 m; **Minimum range (HE)** 2,500 m; **Maximum range against AFVs (HESH)** 800 m; **Rate of fire** 6 rpm.

Usually known as the Light Gun, the L118 is now the standard equipment of field regiments based in the United Kingdom, having replaced the last of the 105 mm Pack Howitzers L5 at the end of 1978. The Light Gun has had an extended development time scale as the first design studies were begun during the mid-1960s and the gun was accepted for service in 1971. Like so many other British weapons the Light Gun was a design product of the Royal Armament Research and Development Establishment at Fort Halstead but the production lines are at the Royal Ordnance Factory at Nottingham, from which the first production examples were delivered in 1974.

Designed from the outset to provide as much range as possible with a high degree of portability, the Light Gun fires the same ammunition as that used with the 105 mm gun fitted to the FV433 Abbot. With this ammunition it has a range of 17,200 metres which is well in excess of that of any comparable gun, but the price paid for this performance is that the gun is now heavier than earlier design estimates indicated. Nevertheless, it is light enough to be carried in a C-130 Hercules transport aircraft, and it can be carried into action slung beneath a helicopter. The only current RAF helicopter capable of carrying the Light Gun underslung in one load is the Puma—the older Wessex can carry a single gun in two underslung loads and reassembling the gun takes about ten minutes. On the ground the normal towing vehicle is the 1-tonne Land Rover which carries the crew of six and a limited number of rounds, while a second 1-tonne Land Rover acts as a limber vehicle carrying 28 rounds. Normally the Light Gun is towed with its barrel turned through 180° and clamped over the curved tubular box trails. Getting the gun into action thus involves the removal and refitting of one of the wheels but this can be accomplished by a trained crew within a very short time. This towing configuration is used because, with the gun in the normal 'action' position, the towed load is very long when compared with the tyre track, and the gun is then likely to turn over rather easily. Reversing the barrel over the trails lowers the centre of gravity considerably making it much more stable and

Below *The full gun detachment of a Light Gun ready for firing.*

Top *The normal towing configuration for a Light Gun with the covers fitted.* **Above** *The 105 mm Light Gun fitted with the L119 barrel for firing American ammunition* (Gunner Magazine).

capable of an excellent cross-country performance.

The ammunition used with the Light Gun is separate and there are seven propellant charges available. This number of charges along with a very wide elevation arc (−5.5° to +70°) makes the Light Gun an extremely flexible weapon, and to reduce the range down to 2,500 metres at high angles of elevation, spoiler rings can be added to the noses of the projectiles to degrade their performance. In addition to the Shell, 105 mm, Field, High Explosive L31, there are available smoke, High Explosive Squash Head, illuminating and various practice rounds. But there are still considerable stocks of the American M1 105 mm ammunition on hand so in order to use these up for training purposes a separate gun barrel and breech can be fitted on to the Light Gun carriage. This new ordnance is designated L119 and is shorter and lighter than the

L118, and with a different muzzle brake. The changeover takes about two hours, and the range is reduced to 11,400 metres.

The Light Gun has many modern features, not the least of which is the general method of construction in order to keep down weight, but it does have one rather obvious 'throw-back' to an earlier era. This is the 360° traverse platform which is normally carried over the trails. In action this is placed on the ground and the gun wheels are placed on it. One man can then make very rapid traverse changes using the trail handspike which can be a valuable asset when fighting tanks and other AFVs at short ranges. As it is expected that the Light Gun will encounter tanks in any future conflict the platform has been retained and the gun can thus fire HESH projectiles at combat ranges up to about 800 metres. HESH is now no longer in production.

The Light Gun proved its value in the Falklands where, during the final siege of Port Stanley, up to 400 rounds per gun per day were being fired.

Ordnance, BL, 120 mm Tank L11A5

Calibre 120 mm; **Length of bore (approx)** 6.6 m; **Muzzle velocity (HESH L31A7)** 670 m/s; **Muzzle velocity (APDS L15A4)** 1,370 m/s; **Projectile weight (HESH L31A7)** 17.08 kg; **Projectile weight (APDS L15A4)** 10.36 kg; **Projectile weight (smoke L34A1)** 17.5 kg; **Propellant weight (HESH and smoke)** 3.03 kg; **Propellant weight (APDS)** 8.845 kg; **Maximum effective range (HESH)** 8,000 m; **Maximum effective range (APDS)** 3,000 m plus; **Rate of fire (normal)** 6 rpm.

The 120 mm tank gun fitted to the FV4201 Chieftain is regarded as one of the most powerful tank guns in service anywhere, and is capable of defeating any tank armour likely to be pitted against it—even the latest Soviet AFVs are regarded as being vulnerable at long ranges. There are several versions in service including the L11A3 and the L11A7 in addition to the L11A5, but all are basically similar. Where the L11 series differs from other contemporary tank guns is that it uses separate ammunition and the propellant is totally combustible when ignited. This bagged combustible propellant is stowed inside the tank in water-surrounded compartments, a system which has been chosen as not only does it save weight, but as there is no sizeable cartridge case to dispose of, there is a substantial saving in stowage space, and the risk of fumes within the turret is greatly reduced. The gun has a sliding breech block which also holds a ten-tube magazine holding the electrical vent firing tubes.

To ensure that accuracy is kept to a high order,

Above *A 120 mm L11A5 gun just off the production line at the Royal Ordnance Factory, Nottingham, clearly showing the massive breech block* (ROF Nottingham). **Below** *Ammunition for the 120 mm L11 tank gun. From left to right: Propelling charges; Smoke; DS/PRAC; APDS; PRAC/SH and HESH* (MoD).

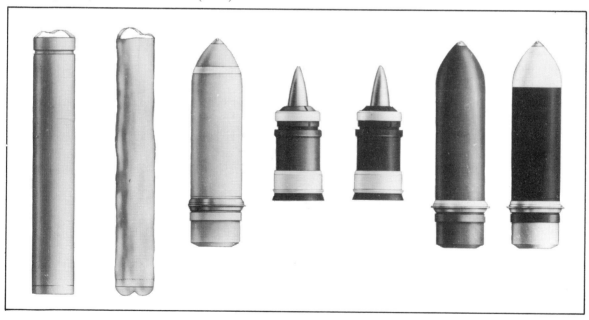

Prototype of a new 120 mm tank gun on a proofing stand on the Shoeburyness Ranges (MoD P & E. E. Shoeburyness, via Simon Dunstan).

the L11 series have an advanced form of fire control (IFCS), and one of the factors that this system has to compensate for is the degree of barrel warping induced by external heating effects. Even under moderate climatic conditions the barrel is so long that even a slight side breeze can induce warping due to a difference in temperature from one side of the barrel to another. These slight warpings can make a difference to long-range accuracy, so they are almost entirely eliminated by the use of insulating thermal sleeves wrapped around the whole length of the barrel. Another feature of the L11 barrel is the fitting of a fume evacuator half way along the bore to prevent propellant fumes from entering the turret.

The main offensive projectiles fired by the L11 series are HESH. Other projectiles used are smoke and illuminating, and special training projectiles (inert projectiles so designed that barrel wear is greatly reduced when compared to live projectiles) have been developed for HESH and APDS—they are SH/Prac L32A5 and DS/T L20A1 respectively. A canister projectile weighing some 14.63 kg has been under development for some time but its service future is uncertain.

While the L11 series are still very powerful weapons the technology that produced them (at the Royal Ordnance Factory in Nottingham) has been further advanced to a new family of 120 mm guns. Known provisionally as the 'Modern Technology' gun, the new weapon has an even better perfor-

mance than the L11 as it is manufactured from a special steel known as Electro-slag Refined (ESR) which can cater with greatly increased internal pressures compared with other materials. The use of separate charges will continue although the propellant will no longer be bagged but manufactured in solid pieces that are totally combustible. While it is not possible to quote comparable technical data for the L11 series, it can be quoted that a prototype of the 'Modern Technology' gun weighs 2,000 kg—the barrel alone being 1,248 kg. Overall length is 5.68 metres of which the barrel takes up 5.41 metres. A new range of ammunition has been developed for this gun, which has a barrel life of about 550 rounds. All the projectiles are of the order of 20-25 kg. Both HESH and APDS are retained but much improved in performance, as is the new smoke shell. Three new rounds have been introduced. The first of these is an APFSDS (Armour Piercing Fin Stabilised Discarding Sabot) which will be fired at a muzzle velocity of around 1,500 metres per second. As the new gun is rifled, a slipping ring is introduced to the sabot component to prevent this finned projectile from rotating. The second new projectile is a finned HEAT shell, while the third item is a canister round for close-in anti-personnel use.

Trials are continuing with the 'Modern Technology' gun and it seems certain that in one form or another it will be the main armament of the next generation of British Main Battle Tanks.

Howitzer, 155 mm L121 (FH70)

Calibre 155 mm; **Length of bore** 6.037 m; **Length overall (firing)** 12.43 m; **Length overall (travelling)** 9.45 m; **Width over wheels** 2.58 m; **Height travelling** 2.64 m; **Weight in action (approx)** 9,144 kg; **Traverse** 52°; **Elevation** −5.5° to +70°; **Muzzle velocity (HE, max)** 827 m/s; **Shell weight (HE M107)** 43.5 kg; **Maximum range (HE normal)** 24,000 m; **Maximum range (rocket-assisted M549 (L15))** 30,000 m; **Rate of fire** 6 rpm.

FH70 is rather rare within NATO as it is an example of a completed collaborative project carried out by NATO members alone. The United Kingdom was one of the two founder members of the FH70 project which began with an agreement between the United Kingdom and West Germany to develop and produce a new 155 mm towed howitzer. That agreement was signed in August 1968, and Italy became a participating member in 1970 (the USA were invited to take part but declined). All three interested states wanted the new 155 mm to replace existing field equipment. The United Kingdom needed it to replenish their medium field regiments which used the venerable 5.5-in gun-howitzers, not only on the grounds of age but as the result of collected battle evidence that the 155 mm calibre was the smallest-sized projectile capable of breaking up massed tank attacks while the tanks themselves were in the forming-up phase, and after.

The new howitzer was given the development designation FH70 and this has been continued. All three nations took over a part of the total design and development, and later, production. The British share was divided between the Royal Armament Research and Development Establishment (which was involved in the early design stages), Vickers-Armstrong (much of the carriage design and construction) and various Royal Ordnance Factories which became involved with the ammunition. The West German firm of Rheinmetall carried out much of the work on the ordnance itself and got involved in such items as the sights the auxiliary power unit (APU), and also in ammunition design. Italy contributed by developing various cradle components and other sub-assemblies, and again were involved in ammunition design and development.

The first trials battery was a three-nation unit and had six guns. It was formed in 1975, in Germany, and was responsible for many of the early development trials. The first FH70s differed in several respects from the production models, the most noticeable of these features being the recuperator cylinder over the barrel—later models had this under the barrel. But the overall layout of FH70 was basically the same as it is today. The gun has a long barrel with a prominent muzzle brake which is reported to be 23 per cent efficient). The carriage has long split trails with large spades. Forward of the main cradle is an auxiliary power unit which is used to drive the FH70 over short distances; this is a Volkswagen 4-stroke petrol engine of 1,795 cc capacity which can deliver 76 bhp. The APU is necessary as the FH70 is a bulky and heavy artillery piece and man-handling, even over short distances, is a considerable task. Power is directed to both the main gun wheels and two dolly wheels can be unfolded from their position just forward of the trail spades.

In action the howitzer rests on a firing platform

Right *Maintenance on a FH 70 after firing on the range at Larkhill.*

Left *A FH 70 covered and ready for towing.*

Below *The FH70* (Vickers).

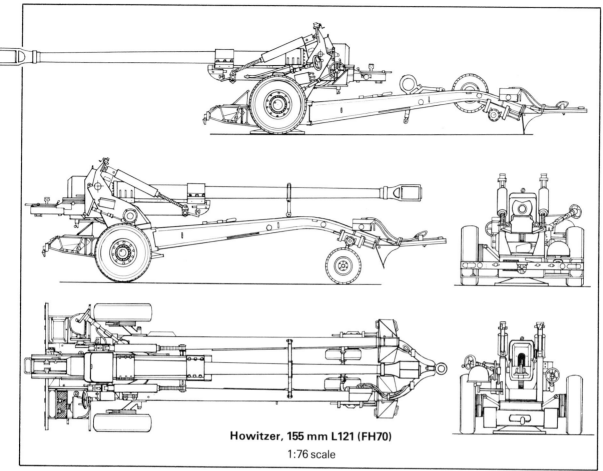

Howitzer, 155 mm L121 (FH70)

1:76 scale

under the main axle. The sighting mechanism is rather complex and is on the left of the cradle. While the barrel is a conventional monobloc component it incorporates modern metallurgical practices and is thus lighter than older designs of the same nature. The buffer and recuperator are situated below the barrel, and the breech block is similar in concept to that used on the Rheinmetall-designed 155 mm howitzer fitted to the American M109G self-propelled howitzer. Thus it has upward-opening, sliding breech block with the added feature of an automatic ignition tube loader holding 10 or 11 tubes.

Although trials and development of much of the ammunition intended for the FH70 continue, the first production examples of the gun came off the lines in early 1978—the main United Kingdom production centre is at the Vickers-Armstrong works at Barrow-in-Furness. The first Royal Artillery unit to receive FH70 was B Battery, 1 RHA, which was fully equipped by October 1978. Produc-

tion total for the United Kingdom is reported to be 71.

As stated above, the ammunition trials continue. FH70 can fire existing American 155 mm projectiles but all three user nations will use ammunition developed during the FH70 programme. Already available are HE and smoke shells, both of which can be fired to a range of 24,000 metres. Still under development is a rocket-assisted shell (the L15) which is reported to be capable of ranges up to about 30,000 metres, and sub-calibre projectiles are another longer-range alternative. Up to eight propellant charges can be selected. The FH70 ordnance is simillar to that intended for use on the self-propelled SP70, and the ammunition fired is the same.

The tractor and limber vehicles selected for United Kingdom Army use are the Foden FH70 6x6 tractor and limber. Like the 105 mm Light Gun, the FH70 is towed with the barrel over the trails.

Cannon, 155 mm Howitzer M185; Mount, Howitzer, 155 mm M127

Calibre 155 mm; **Length of barrel** 6.045 m; **Weight (approx)** 1,700 kg; **Muzzle velocity (HE, smoke)** 684.3 m/s; **Shell weight (HE M107)** 42.91 kg; **Shell weight (smoke M116)** 42.22 kg; **Shell weight (illuminating M485)** 41.73 kg; **Maximum range (HE, smoke)** 18,000 m; **Rate of fire (rapid)** 3 rpm; **Rate of fire (normal)** 2 rpm.

The M185 is an American howitzer with a development history that can be traced back to 1952. In that year it was projected as a 156 mm howitzer intended for a self-propelled mounting, but in time the calibre reverted to the more conventional 155 mm as the T255E5. In 1961 this was standardised by the US Army as the M126 with an overall length of 4.598 metres (the barrel length was L/23.4) and a range of 14,700 metres. It was fitted to only one self-propelled mounting, the M109. In time the M126 was further developed and lengthened to L/39 which increased its range to over 18,000 metres. The new lengthened barrel became the M185 and vehicles fitted with the new barrel became the M109A1.

The M109, with the early M126 barrel, first entered British Army service in 1965 and from then onwards it became the standard equipment for the Royal Artillery's medium self-propelled batteries. It was intended that they would be replaced by the SP70, but this equipment has had such a prolonged development period that it was decided to retrofit the M185 into the existing M109s. With this in mind, two M109A1s were delivered to the Royal Artillery for trials that began in 1975. As a result of these, a major retrofitting programme was completed by late 1978. The first formation to receive their new howitzers was 39 Field Regiment, Royal Artillery, and they had the unusual experience of proof firing their new pieces themselves, on the artillery ranges near Munster, in West Germany.

The M185 is a rather complex piece of artillery with a very prominent muzzle brake and a bore evacuator. The breech mechanism is a large semi-automatic screw arrangement which tends to produce a rather slow rate of fire, even though a power rammer is fitted. Even with the rammer, the normal rate of fire is still only some two rounds per minute. Separate loading ammunition is used, and the same projectiles as those used with the M126 are fired. But the propellant charges have been increased in number and variety to make full use of the longer barrel with its advantages in projectile range. The number of propellant charge combinations gives the M185 a wide choice of elevation angles to suit particular fire tasks. To illustrate this, one of the Larkhill Open Day 'party pieces' is an M109A1 (and before it, an M109) firing its howitzer at maximum elevation and near minimum elevation—the two shells arrive on the same target simultaneously.

To give an idea of the costs of modern warfare, it was announced during 1979 that a further 150,000 rounds of 155 mm ammunition had been procured from the United States. The cost was $28.7m.

The length of the 155 mm M185 Howitzer can be appreciated from this photograph when the length of the 105 mm L13A1 gun alongside is compared.

Cannon, 175 mm Gun M113; Mount, Gun-Howitzer M158

Calibre 175 mm; **Length overall** 10.87 m; **Length of barrel** 10.49 m; **Length of rifling** 8.87 m; **Weight** 6,259.5 kg; **Muzzle velocity** 914 m/s; **Shell weight (HE M437)** 66.78 kg; **Maximum range** 32,700 m; **Rate of fire (rapid)** 2 rpm; **Rate of fire (normal)** 1 rpm.

The development of this American long-range gun began at the Watervliet Arsenal, New York, during the late 1950s. It entered British Army service during 1965 and 1966, and ever since then has been the Army's 'long-range rifle'. The M113, originally known as the T256E3, is a very long-barrelled gun, but it does have an extremely long range to match, and it is thus used mainly in the long-range harassing and interdiction role. Only high explosive projectiles are fired. The use of such a long barrel does have the constraint that con-

The great length of the 175 mm Gun M113 can be seen from this side-on view.

siderable internal pressures are reached and these have the effect of reducing the barrel life to about 1,200 rounds. The early guns had an even shorter life of some 400 rounds but the weapon was modified to the M113E1 standard and the expected life was trebled. The M113 will be replaced in its long-range role by the MLRS rocket system.

Cannon, 8-in Howitzer M201; Mount, Gun-Howitzer M158

Calibre 203 mm/8 in; **Length overall** 7.85 m; **Weight (approx)** 6,400 kg; **Muzzle velocity (HE charge 8)** 711 m/s; **Shell weight (HE M106)** 92.53 kg; **Maximum range** 21,300 m; **Rate of fire (normal)** 1 round every 2 minutes.

The 8-in howitzer used by the Royal Artillery is an American piece with a British provenance. The US Army adopted the 8-in howitzer from the British in 1917 and ever since then they have retained the weapon in some form or another. The early British model was followed in 1940 by a updated and improved American version, the M1 which, in its turn, was replaced by the M2 in 1945. The M2 was a towed weapon which was redesignated the M115 in 1961, the same year in which it was decided to adapt the barrel for mounting on the new self-propelled carriage M110—the same as that used for the 175 mm Gun M113. The British Army used the self-propelled M2 for many years on the M110, but as always, the gunners called for more range and a longer version emerged.

The 8-in M201 is virtually a longer version of the earlier M2, and was originally produced for the US Army. The British Army decided to adapt their existing 8-in self-propelled carriages to take the new barrels and the changeover was made during 1981. The longer barrel enables a larger charge to be used and the increased muzzle velocity increases the range by a substantial margin.

In all its forms the 8-in howitzer has gained for itself an enviable reputation for accuracy, and the heavy shell has a devastating effect over its target. The usual conventional projectile is the American HE M106 but in the British Army the M201 will fire nuclear shells. A nuclear shell has been under development for the 8-in howitzer for some years at the Atomic Weapons Establishment at Aldermaston, and is now probably ready for use, but there is an existing American nuclear shell, the M422, with the XM753 under development.

The M201 has a Welin-type breech mechanism little changed from the British original, although the whole piece has benefited from gradual metallurgical and other improvements over the years. The M201 can employ up to eight separate bag charges. It is expected that, as the 175 mm M107 guns and carriages are phased out in favour of MLRS during the mid-1980s, the carriages will be converted to take new 8-in barrels and thus increase the nuclear potential of the Army.

Rockets and missiles

Multiple Launch Rocket System

Rocket body diameter 227 mm; **Rocket length** 3.96 m; **Rocket weight** 272 kg; **Rocket range** at least 30,000 m.
Vehicle: Crew 3 or 4; **Length (travelling)** 6.97 m; **Height (travelling)** 2.59 m; **Width (travelling)** 2.97 m; **Track width** 0.533 m; **Ground clearance** 0.43 m; **Maximum speed** 64 km/h; **Range** 483 km; **Engine type** Cummins VTA-903 turbocharged diesel; **Engine power** 500 hp at 2,400 rpm; **Fuel capacity** 617 litres.

In 1976 the US Army issued a requirement, and development contracts, for a long-range rocket system that was intended to provide some form of counter to the expected disparity between the

NATO armies and the Warsaw Pact forces in artillery strengths—on some European fronts this is expected to be of the order of at least 2.7 to 1 against NATO. The new system was expected to be both powerful and flexible, and was initially known as the General Support Rocket System (GSRS), but by 1978 the programme became an international

one with the added involvement of the United Kingdom, France and West Germany. The programme then became known as the Multiple Launch Rocket System, or MLRS, with plans being made for production lines to be set up in both Europe and the USA. Italy has now joined the group.

There were two prime contractors bidding for the

MLRS

1:76 scale

MLRS contract initially, Boeing and the Vought Corporation. Following an involved 'shoot-out' on the White Sands Missile Range, Vought was awarded the contract in May 1980.

The Vought MLRS system is based on a much-modified M2 Bradley Infantry Fighting Vehicle chassis and consists of an armoured crew cab forward with the launcher assembly to the rear. The long rockets are carried in pallets each taking six rockets, and the missiles are loaded into the vehicle launcher on their pallets. Once loaded the pallets act as the launcher frames. Each pallet weighs about 1,800 kg, and the loading sequence is mechanical from a power-assisted limber vehicle. Each loading sequence takes about five minutes. The launcher can be traversed and elevated from within the vehicle cab and laying is assisted by the vehicle's inertial navigation system.

The first batch of rockets will have a warhead payload consisting of over 600 M42 scatterable minelets, each weighing 0.23 kg and with a small hollow-charge warhead capable of penetrating up to 100 mm of armour. Later rockets will use the West German AT-11 anti-tank mines and future developments include binary chemical warheads and terminally-guided anti-armour submunitions.

The British Army is expected to get its first MLRS equipments during the mid-1980s. They will then replace the 175 mm M107 self-propelled guns and at least partially supplement (but not replace) the 8-in Howitzer M110, which will retain its nuclear role. In the British Army, the full crew of the MLRS is expected to be about six men, three with the launcher and three with the limber vehicle and acting as ammunition numbers. There is, however, a snag for the Army regarding MLRS. At the present time the Army is unable to take full

advantage of the 30,000-metre range of MLRS as it simply has no form of long-range target acquisition system suitable for use with such a weapon system. The Midge drone system is both too limited and too slow in use to be of any immediate assistance to find and pinpoint long-range targets and the only answer seems to be some form of long-range target acquisition radar such as the American Hughes 'Firefinder' system. As always this will present a problem as such radars are both large, expensive and demanding in manpower and signal communication facilities. With defence spending restrictions as they are at present, funding such a programme seems to be a very long-term project but without some form of target acquisition, the full potential of MLRS cannot be realised.

Top, left to right *The MLRS with loading boom extended; the launcher vehicle ready to fire; elevating the launcher; ready to move* (Vought). **Below** *Cutaway drawing of a MLRS rocket* (Vought).

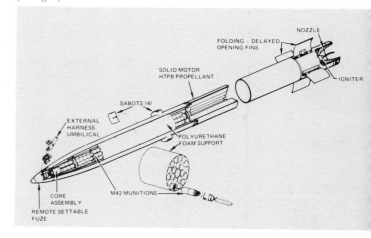

Lance

Weight at launch 1,285.47 kg; **Length of rocket** 6.146 m; **Diameter of body** 557 mm; **Weight of warhead (M234)** 210.92 kg; **Maximum speed** Mach 3 plus; **Maximum altitude reached** 45,720 m; **Range limits** 4.8 to 121 km; **Maximum flight time** 200 seconds.

Lance is the main artillery 'punch' of the British Army as it is a ballistic artillery rocket fitted with a nuclear warhead. It is an American design produced by a bevy of contractors under the aegis of the LTV Aerospace Corporation, Michigan. Known originally as the Missile B, Lance eventually obtained the service designation of MGM-52C. The development of Lance started in 1962 and firing trials commenced during 1965 but it was not until 1971 that the first production examples were issued to the US Army. It was then offered to NATO nations and the United Kingdom was one

customer, with the first equipments being issued for Army service during 1976, when they replaced the obsolete Honest John rockets then in use.

Lance is a free-flight missile, ie, it does not have any form of external guidance once it has been launched. This does not mean that Lance is unguided, for it is, but all the guidance is fed into the missile before launch. The Lance missiles are carried to the firing point in a tracked carrier known as the M752 Self-Propelled Launcher, or SPL. This carrier is used as the missile launcher and also carries the crew of six men—two in the driver's cab and four alongside the Lance missile. The M752 SPL is based on the suspension and power train of the American M113 APC, as is the other carrier associated with the Lance missile. This other vehicle is the Loader-Transporter, or LT, with the designation M688. The LT carries a crew of two men and two Lance missiles minus their fins which

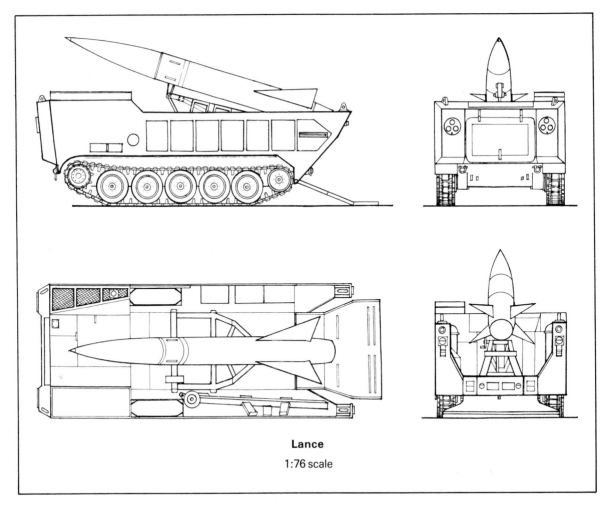

Lance

1:76 scale

are stowed along the insides of the carrier. The LT also has a small crane to load the missiles on to the SPL. Both vehicles have the same dimensions but differ in their battle weights. The data for both vehicles is as follows. **Length** 6.568 m; **Width** 2.709 m; **Height to top of cab** 2.715 m; **Weight in action (SPL)** 9,075.02 kg; **Weight in action (LT)** 10,691.63 kg; **Engine type** GMC Model 6V53; **Engine power** 215 bhp; **Maximum speed (road)** 64 km/h.

The SPL carries the Lance missile and its launcher, and once in the firing position the missile is aligned to its target using normal artillery techniques. As this is being carried out the flight information is fed into the missile inertial guidance system from a solid state programmer (the AN/GJM-24(XO-2)) which then goes to monitor and control the launch while also supplying all the necessary pre-flight electrical power supplies. On firing, a rocket boost motor provides the main launch power for a period of 1.5 to 6 seconds, depending on the range required, after which a smaller rocket motor takes over. Flight stabilisation is provided by the spin initiated by inclined jets tapped off from the main booster motor. The inertial guidance system, using the pre-programmed directions and data, determines when the motor should switch off, and Lance then completes its journey in free flight.

The British Army uses only nuclear warheads in its Lance missiles, taking the view that to launch and maintain such an expensive missile system is not worth the cost and effort involved if conventional warheads alone are involved. However, other NATO forces are equipped with conventional Lance warheads, usually the M188 with a weight of 453.59 kg, and some interchange of such warheads may take place.

At present, the Royal Artillery has only one Lance regiment in the shape of 50 Missile Regiment, Royal Artillery. It is under the direct control of HQ 1 (Br) Corps, and consists of the following four batteries; 15 Missile Battery, RA; 19 Missile Battery, RA; 36 Missile Battery, RA; and 51 Missile Battery, RA. Each battery has three launcher sections equipped with SPLs, two assembly sections equipped with LTs, and a single reconnaissance/survey section.

Blowpipe

Weight complete 19.39 kg; **Weight with IFF** 21.2 kg; **Length of missile** 1.349 m; **Body diameter** 76.2 mm; **Fin span** 0.274 m; **Maximum range** 3,000 m plus.

The Blowpipe ground-to-air missile was originally a private venture developed by Short Brothers and Harland of Belfast, who incorporated

Above *Preparing a Lance for launch from its SPL.* **Below** *Blowpipe* (Short Brothers and Harland).

Cutaway example of a Blowpipe missile head in its launcher, showing the aiming unit and the missile guidance fins.

into the missile much of the know-how gleaned from their Seacat and Tigercat missile systems. The choice of the Short Brothers missile came from the results of a programme undertaken by the Royal Radar Establishment starting in 1966, which was meant to investigate the possibility of providing a one-man missile for defence against low-flying attack aircraft. Blowpipe was the missile chosen as a result of that study and it is now in service with the Royal Artillery Blowpipe batteries in 1 (Br) Corps, and three TA air defence regiments.

Blowpipe is a small light missile contained in a sealed canister which can be taken from store into the field without any prior preparation. In the field it is prepared for use by clipping-on the aiming unit, which takes only a few seconds. The system is then ready for use. Once a target is seen, if IFF (Identification Friend or Foe) is fitted the target is immediately challenged. If the result is hostile the missile can be fired. As the trigger is pulled a primary rocket motor propels the missile out of the canister. The secondary motor then cuts in and carries the missile towards its target. Using a monocular graticuled sight the firer can guide the missile with a small thumb-controlled joystick—to assist him the missile has small flares in its tail. When at its target the warhead is detonated by either an impact or a proximity fuze. If it misses it is automatically destroyed by a self-destruct mechanism. After firing, the aiming unit is removed from the empty canister and clipped on to a fresh round, ready for re-use. In use Blowpipe has proved to be a very accurate system, mainly due to the manoeuvreability which is made possible by the small canard wings around the warhead being able to swivel independent of the rest of the missile body. All guidance commands are transmitted by radio via the transmitting aerials in the canister walls.

Blowpipe is backed up by simple test equipment and for training a simulator mounted on a test stand is available. Also available are training rounds which use only the primary firing rocket and inert missiles. It is also possible to use the simulator against live targets without firing a missile.

At present the Blowpipe is used by one Blowpipe battery attached to one close support regiment of the Artillery group in each armoured division of 1 (Br) Corps. The Blowpipe teams will be carried in FV103 Spartan APCs although some Land Rovers have been converted to carry Blowpipes by the addition of suitable racks and towed trailers. For some time there have been rumours of multiple Blowpipe launchers fitted to vehicles and the FV4333 Stormer has been mentioned as one possible mounting. At the time of writing, however, such projects are still unconfirmed.

Rapier

Weight at launch 42.6 kg; **Length of missile** 2.235 m; **Body diameter** 0.133 m; **Wing span** 0.381 m; **Maximum range** 6,800 m; **Maximum operational height** 3,000 m; **Maximum speed** Mach 2 plus; **Fire unit weight** 1,227 kg; **Fire unit length** 4.064 m; **Fire unit height** 2.134 m; **Fire unit width** 1.778 m; **Radar weight** 1,186 kg; **Radar length** 4.14 m; **Radar height (in action)** 3.378 m; **Radar height (travelling)** 2.032 m; **Radar width** 1.753 m; **Optical tracker weight** 119 kg; **Optical tracker height** 1.549 m; **Tripod diameter** 1.828 m; **Generator weight** 243 kg; **Generator length** 0.991 m; **Generator height** 0.914 m; **Generator width** 0.832 m.

The early development story of Rapier is a rather involved one which began in the early 1960s when it was decided to develop a point-defence anti-aircraft guided missile for Army use known as the PT 428. Early studies revealed that PT428 would be an expensive proposition so in 1962 it was decided to drop the project and adopt the American Mauler system. The choice was unfortunate for early tests of

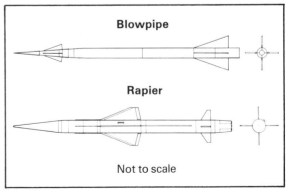

Left *The Rapier Fire Unit.* **Right** *The DN181 'Blindfire' radar used with the Rapier system* (Marconi SDS).

the Mauler soon showed that it would be even more expensive, and that the Army would be able to purchase only a small number of the units it felt it required. As a cheap back-up it was decided during 1963 that a new system, soon to be known as the ET.316, should be developed by the British Aircraft Corporation (now part of British Aerospace). BAC had already been working since 1961 on a private venture known as Sightline, and this formed the basis of the ET.316 which in time became known as Rapier. The first test firings were made during 1965 and in the same year the American Mauler programme was cancelled, so the Rapier system then stood alone.

Progress with Rapier was steady and generally successful. In 1968 a production contract was issued, and by 1971 the first units were being issued to the Army and the Royal Air Force Regiment.

In its basic form the Rapier system consists of three parts—the fire unit, the optical tracker, and the generator—but the addition of a 'Blindfire' (DN181) radar unit makes the Rapier system into an all-weather weapon. The complete system can be deployed in the field by seven men with no recourse

to mechanical handling equipment. Once in position the complete system covers an area of about 30 metres in diameter. The fire unit is loaded with four missiles and then receives no further attention once the connections to the other units have been made. The time-into-action is usually about 15 minutes, but once ready the radar unit commences a constant 360° scan out to about 12 kilometres. Any aerial target approaching is automatically interrogated by an IFF query signal, and if the result is hostile the operator on the tracking unit is warned. The operator then searches for the target, as does the fire unit radar head. If both find the target the operator has a choice of either a visual or a radar engagement. If radar is selected the sequence is automatic. If a visual engagement is chosen, the operator uses the tracker head and a control joystick to guide the missile. The radar proved to have limitations during the Falklands fighting, possibly due to damage incurred during the long sea voyage.

When it is considered that each fire unit can cover an area of sky about 100 square kilometres in area up to a height of some 3,000 metres, the full defence capability of Rapier can be appreciated. One of the more important features of Rapier's performance is its reaction time. From acquiring a target to firing the missile the time lapse can be as little as six seconds, and the time to engage another target can be as little as a further three seconds. Once the fire unit has expended all four of its missiles, two men can reload in about 2½ minutes.

The Royal Artillery has three Light Air Defence Regiments equipped with Rapier. They are 12 and 22 with 1 (Br) Corps, and 16 with the UKLF. There are also three TA units so equipped. Each regiment is made up of three batteries, each with three troops. Each troop has four fire units, each of which can be further broken down as follows. The fire unit is towed by a 1-tonne Land Rover which carries the optical tracker and three of the detachment—who can visually engage a target by themselves if necessary as the vehicle carries four missiles. A second 1-tonne Land Rover tows the radar unit and carries four more missiles, plus another two men. A ¾-tonne Land Rover carries the remaining two men of the detachment and all the remaining stores, while at the same time towing a trailer carrying a further nine missiles. This trailer is the FV2412 1-tonne Cargo Trailer (Specialist) which has the following dimensions: **Weight empty** 534 kg; **Length** 3.632 m; **Height** 1.346 m; **Width** 1.752

Swingfire
Weight of missile 37 kg; **Length** 1.067 m;

FV102 Striker with missile bins raised.

Maximum body diameter 0.17 m; **Wing span** 0.373 m; **Maximum effective range** 4,000 m; **Minimum range** 150 m; **Arc of fire (traverse)** 90°; **Arc of fire (elevation)** ± 20°.

Swingfire is an anti-tank missile that can trace its origins back to the late 1950s and a Fairey missile venture code-named Orange William. When Fairey was taken under the umbrella of the British Aircraft Corporation, the design was taken over and developed to the stage where it became Swingfire and accepted for service by the British Army. That was during 1969 and once in service Swingfire replaced the large and cumbersome Malkara missile in the anti-tank role.

Swingfire derives its name from the fact that it can be launched at an angle from its target, ie, it can 'swing' round corners. The missile is wire-guided which produces the definite battlefield advantage that once launched, enemy electronic or other counter measures cannot affect its guidance. Due to its size and weight, Swingfire is carried into action on a vehicle, and two Army vehicles now in service have been adapted for this role. They are the FV438, an adaptation of the FV432 APC, and the FV102 Striker. (The earlier FV712 Ferret Mark 5 was an interim vehicle only, and was withdrawn by the end of 1978.) The FV438 has two missile launchers and can be reloaded from inside the vehicle, while the FV102 Striker has five launchers but has to be reloaded from outside. Both these vehicles have the advantage that they need not launch missiles using the internal sighting and firing systems. If required, they can be hidden behind cover with the firing unit/sight remote from the vehicle and up to 100 metres away.

The missiles are delivered in sealed containers. As soon as it is launched the Swingfire missile is pre-programmed to fly into the centre of the line-of-sight of the sight in use. It can then be controlled by the operator's thumb joystick on the sight unit. On most occasions the guidance changes need only be minor for the angle of the sight from the angle of launch is computed constantly with corrections being passed along the guidance wires. In-flight corrections are usually allowances for side-winds and variations in wind strength. If it hits its target, the warhead is said to be capable of destroying or severely disabling any known MBT.

As Swingfire is the most important anti-tank missile in service, its distribution is fairly lavish. Each armoured division of 1 (Br) Corps has one anti-tank battery as part of its artillery group. Each of these batteries has five or six troops, one of which is composed of six FV102 Strikers. The other four or five troops are equipped with FV438s; two troops with six vehicles and the other two or three with four vehicles. UKLF formations are equipped in a different fashion as each Royal Artillery regiment has one battery with two troops of six vehicles each—the third troop of the battery uses Blowpipe.

Swingfire has a considerable re-supply and repair back-up, and for training each Swingfire has its own integral simulator for practice in the handling of the rather tricky guidance controls. Swingfire is unique in having this training aid.

There is an Infantry version of Swingfire which can be mounted on simple frame launchers suitable for light wheeled vehicles or static ground positions. Known as Beeswing, this version was acquired by the Army in small numbers but the resultant trials did not result in adoption for service. A helicopter-launched version known as Hawkswing was one of the competing missiles considered for arming the Lynxes of the Army Air Corps, but with the eventual choice of the TOW missile for this role, further development of Hawkswing was terminated. A thermal-imaging night sight for Swingfire is known to be under development. One source has stated that this is the IR17, developed by Barr and Stroud.

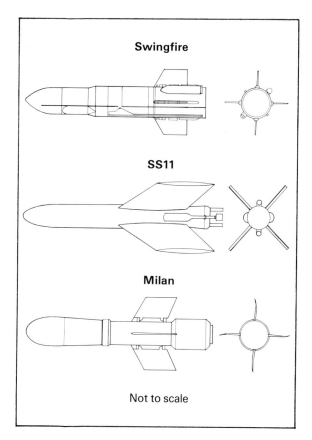

Swingfire

SS11

Milan

Not to scale

SS11

Weight of missile 29.9 kg; **Length overall** 1.201 m; **Body diameter** 0.164 m; **Wingspan** 0.495 m; **Body length** 1.08 m; **Speed** 100 to 190 m/s; **Maximum range** 3,000 m; **Minimum range** 350 m; **Armour penetration (60°)** 342 mm.

The SS11 is a French anti-tank missile which has been in production by Aerospatiale since 1956. Considering the date at which it was introduced into production, the SS11 is an advanced design of wire-guided anti-tank missile which has proved itself to be very successful and has been widely exported. Aiming and guiding is simple line-of-sight with manual control through an optical sight unit, and on the ground the launchers are either simple zero-length launching frames or even just the lid of the carrying box.

Within the British Army the SS11 is used by the Army Air Corps as the main anti-tank armament for their Scout helicopters. Up to four SS11s are carried by each Scout with the aimer/firer sitting in the front left-hand seat. A sight is mounted in a stabilised mount in the roof.

Milan

Weight of missile 6.65 kg; **Weight of missile and container** 11.5 kg; **Weight of launch unit** 15.5 kg; **Length of missile** 0.769 m; **Body diameter (minimum)** 90 mm; **Wing span** 0.225 m; **Weight of warhead** 2.98 kg; **Weight of warhead charge** 1.45 kg; **Velocity** 75 to 200 m/s; **Maximum range** 2,000 m; **Minimum range** 25 m; **Rate of fire (maximum range)** 3-4 rpm; **Time of flight to 2,000 m** Up to 13 seconds; **Armour penetration** Up to 352 mm.

Milan is the acronym for 'Missile d'Infantrie Leger Anti-Char', and is a second generation wire-guided anti-tank missile which has been in production since 1972 from a French-West German consortium known as Euromissile (formed by Aerospatiale and Messerschmitt-Bölkow-Blohm). The first major production batches for French and West German Army service were made by 1975. In that same year the first contacts to negotiate the procurement of Milan for the British Army Infantry battalions were made, but the subsequent negotiations dragged on until 1978, and became the subject of considerable political acrimony within the United Kingdom. Some small trial batches were obtained before 1978 but in that year it was announced that Milan would be procured in quantity and would be in full-scale service by the early 1980s.

Milan is a one-man weapon, but in action it would be served by two or three men with the 'extras' carrying additional missiles. The missiles

Top *SS11 anti-tank missiles fitted to a Scout pylon.* **Above** *The Milan launcher* (MoD).

to allow another container tube to be clipped on to the launcher. When the missile has 'coasted' far enough forward to prevent the rocket motor exhaust from harming the firer (and also preventing the launch position being given away by the exhaust 'signature'), the main motor ignites. Once in flight four fins spring outwards into position ready to provide flight stabilisation, and the guidance wire unwinds from a bobbin (the wire is less than 0.4 mm in diameter). Small flares around the missile tail enable the firer to track it towards its target, but the actual guidance is automatic once the firer has pin-pointed the target using an illuminated graticule in the sight.

The Milans used by the British Army are licence-produced in the United Kingdom by the Dynamics Group of British Aerospace. Unfortunately, a Treasury 'leak' that emerged during early 1979 revealed that this arrangement cost the nation some £40 million more than if the missiles had been pur-chased direct, and not surprisingly this revelation added yet more acrimony to the existing political wrangles involving Milan. But the introduction of Milan into service has been much more smooth. The introductory training for the weapon is carried out at Netheravon and lasts five weeks. The course involves live firing and the use of a simulator produced by the French firm of Giravions Dorand.

The initial Milan organisation is at present based on a mix of 1-tonne and ½-tonne Land Rovers organised into a Milan platoon within each Infantry battalion. In time similar platoons will emerge based on the FV432 within the mechanised battalions. The Milan platoon at present has 57 men and 13 vehicles. These are divided into four sections, each with two detachments, and each detachment has two two-man teams with one launcher (or 'firing post') each. Thus the platoon has 16 launchers and a carrying capacity of some 200 missiles. In time Milan will replace the unloved L6 Wombat 120 mm recoilless gun. The 1980 Defence White Paper disclosed the interesting fact that each Milan missile costs £7,000.

The introduction of Milan will no doubt lead to some revisions of anti-tank defence tactics and in time its performance will no doubt be enhanced by technological advances. Already a thermal-imaging sight for use at night or in poor visibility is under development. This is the Mira 2, a joint design by the West German Siemens concern and the French TRT. It will be capable of detecting the presence of a target at 3,200 metres and identifying it at about 1,500 metres. Another innovation, this time a British one, is the introduction of a 'Simfire' simulator known as SIMLAN which exactly reproduces the use of Milan on the battlefield.

themselves are issued in sealed container tubes which are clipped on to the launching unit. The launcher unit is fairly bulky and is either used on a low tripod mounting, mounted on to a monopod support, or mounted on a light vehicle. The firer/aimer uses a periscopic optical sight with the eyepiece behind the launcher front which also acts as a shield. When the missile is fired it is pushed for-ward out of the tube by a gas generator at the base of the container tube—the pressures involved also propel the empty tube to the rear about three metres

TOW

Weight of missile (approx) 24 kg; **Length of missile** 1.168 m; **Body diameter** 0.152 m; **Minimum range** 65 m; **Maximum range** 3,750 m; **Length of launch tube** 2.2 m; **Speed** 200 m/s plus; **Armour penetration (60°)** 408 mm.

The designation TOW is yet another acronym, this time an American one for Tube-launched, Optically-tracked, Wire-guided. During 1978 it was announced that the contest for the next generation of helicopter-launched anti-tank missiles was to be between the British Hawkswing (a variant of Swingfire), the Franco-German HOT and the American TOW. TOW emerged as the final choice and will enter service during the early 1980s as the main anti-tank armament of the Lynx.

TOW has been in service for some years with the American services (the first firing trials were made during 1965) and it has long been an American ground and helicopter-launched missile. The American design designation is BGM-71A, while the service designation is M151E2. Only the helicopter version will be obtained by the British Army. The usual launch configuration on American helicopters is four tubes on each side of the aircraft, but the Army Air Corps uses only three a side. As mentioned in the acronym, TOW is wire-guided and optically tracked, but where TOW scores over other systems is its relatively high missile velocity and the ease with which it can be guided. All the firer has to do is fire the missile and keep the optical sight graticules on the target—the rest is done automatically.

In the USA, TOW is produced by several con-cerns but the main contractor is the Hughes Aircraft Company of Culver City, California. For the British contract, some degree of sub-contracting was expected but in early 1979 it was announced that initially only the helicopter racks would be manufactured in the United Kingdom, along with some electronic components.

Midge

Length with booster 3.73 m; **Length in flight** 2.6 m; **Wing span** 0.94 m; **Body diameter** 0.33 m; **Engine type** Williams WR 2-6 single-stage turbo-jet; **Booster type** Bristol Aerojet Wagtail; **Operational speed (maximum)** 740 km/h; **Operational altitude** 300 to 1,200 m; **Range** 155 to 160 km.

Midge is the general-use British Army term for the Canadair AN/USD-501 reconnaissance drone system. Based on what was originally a Canadian development known as the CL-89, the system is now an international one with Canada, West Germany and the United Kingdom all being involved.

Within the British Army, Midge is used by the Royal Artillery locating regiments, but they are under the control of divisional intelligence (G Int). When tasked for a mission the Midge drone is pre-programmed and zero-length launched from a specially equipped Bedford 4-tonne truck. Initial propulsion comes from a rocket booster motor which burns for two seconds after which a small jet engine takes over. The drone then follows its programmed course and fires its cameras or infra-red sensors at preset intervals. The cameras used are Zeiss stereoscopic tri-lens devices which can give overlapping negatives for eventual stereoscopic

Left *TOW launching tubes as fitted to Lynx helicopters.* **Right** *A Midge ready for launching.*

examination to show up detail. If fitted, the infra-red sensors produce a visual record on to film through mist, darkness and conventional camouflage of any heat-emitting objects. As an alternative for night photography, flares can be discharged from the drone tail to illuminate ground targets.

The flight path is usually a circular or elliptical one as the drone must end up somewhere near its launch site for rapid recovery (it is theoretically possible to preset a straight unit-to-unit course but for operational reasons this is rarely carried out). As the drone nears its launch site it is homed-in by radio beacons up to the point where the engine shuts down and parachutes open to lower the drone to the ground. Air bags in the nose are inflated to reduce the shock of landing. Once recovered, the camera or infra-red pack is removed and hurriedly taken for processing at a special high-speed processing station near the Midge command section. As a rough guide the time interval between a launch request and the examination of dried negatives is about one hour, although for night missions it is longer. As the Midge sections are rarely used in the forward battle areas this limits their operational ranges to about 55 kilometres for a there-and-back mission beyond the front line. Each drone can be re-used.

In BAOR Midge is operated by three troops of 94 Locating Regiment. Each troop has three officers and 99 Other Ranks (not all of them Royal Artillery). Their equipment consists of about 35 vehicles of which only two are launchers, but there are six limber vehicles carrying a total of 20 drones. In the United Kingdom, one troop of 22 Locating Battery is in support of the 6th Field Force.

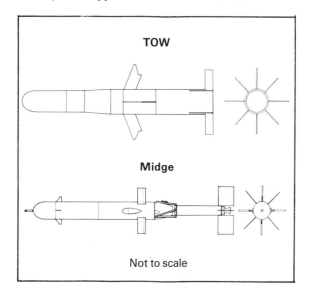

TOW

Midge

Not to scale

Special equipment

Heli-Telly & Nitesun

One of the off-shoots from the Army's enforced investment of resources in Northern Ireland has been the detailed operational experience gained from the use of airborne vision devices. There are several of these in use, of which only two have been revealed publicly—these are Heli-Telly and Nitesun. Of these, Heli-Telly has perhaps the greatest operational interest as it consists of an airborne television system with a role to play outside that which it has in Northern Ireland. The system, at present installed in Scout helicopters but likely to be used also by the Lynx, was developed by Marconi Elliott Avionics Systems.

The airborne component of Heli-Telly consists of a television camera weighing some 150 kg. In service with the British Army, an all-colour system is employed but monochrome can also be used. Once airborne the camera can give ground-based commanders an excellent idea of the ground to be covered in an operation and prevents them having to spend a portion of their valuable time in operational reconnaissance of specific areas. In the close confines of the type of operations carried out in Northern Ireland, Heli-Telly is invaluable. In town areas it enables commanders to see exactly what is happening in streets several blocks away, and in country areas a single Heli-Telly can be used to cover a wide area or several road blocks or other specific points. The camera itself can be focused into a 1° beam enabling the operator to pick out individuals at ranges of up to 1.5 kilometres. The signals picked up can be transmitted to mobile or temporary ground stations which in their turn can retransmit to permanent stations—a permanent ground station can receive signals from up to 40 kilometres away. As a general rule, all transmissions are video recorded. The mobile ground stations are housed in specially equipped Land Rovers.

The airborne equipment is mounted on a stabilised platform on the helicopter to ensure the transmitted pictures are as free from vibration blurs as is possible. The camera itself is operated by a joystick and can be pointed in almost any direction from the rear cabin out to one side. Image intensifiers may be fitted to the camera enabling Heli-Telly to be used under poor visibility or starlight conditions—the operational value of such a system can be readily imagined.

In contrast, Nitesun is a more specialised device with specific applications for the internal and

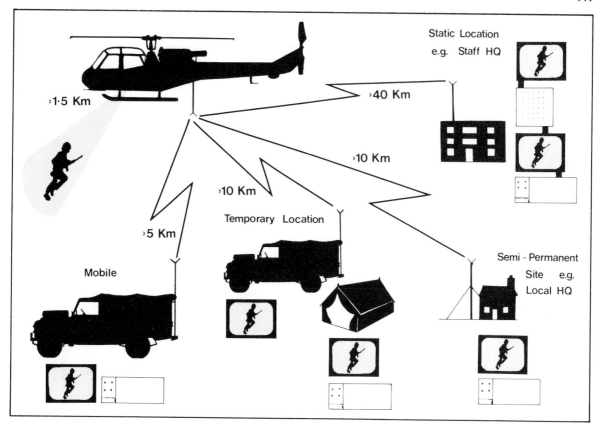

security type of operation carried out in Northern Ireland. Nitesun consists of a small and powerful searchlight suspended under a helicopter. Its value lies in that the beam can be accurately concentrated to pin-point any particular area, so that a location such as a suspected ambush point can be suddenly illuminated. The beam is so powerful that the helicopter can fly above normal small-arms retaliatory fire and from a height it also has the advantage that the beam can be widened to sweep larger areas.

The searchlight itself weighs 11.34 kg and is usually used suspended from Scout helicopters. It is pointed by means of a small remote control unit (weighing 0.85 kg) carried within the cabin. Apart from the usual powerful light beam, an infra-red filter may be fitted for less obvious surveillance. In use as a conventional searchlight the beam can give an illumination intensity fifty times brighter than clear moonlight up to 1,000 metres away (with a beam some 100 metres in diameter). Nitesun is an American product and it was developed by the Spectrolab concern at Symlar in California. Their design designation was SX-16.

Night vision devices

Night vision devices fall into two main categories, infra-red (IR) and image intensifiers (II). Of the two, the image intensifiers are now the more widely used as the infra-red devices not only need large and bulky power supplies, but can be relatively easily detected on the battlefield. The image intensifiers have the advantage that they are 'passive' and emit no easily-detected radiation. They rely entirely on the amplification of available light, for even on the darkest night there is still sufficient light to be amplified electronically to make it visible to the human eye—some image intensifiers are capable of amplifications up to 50,000 times and more. Image intensifiers can also be relatively small and light as they are often powered by little more than torch batteries (some of the larger instruments do have larger power sources), and they can double as weapon sights or surveillance devices.

Some infra-red devices are still used by the Army, the main users now being Chieftain tank crews. Image intensifiers are now used by nearly every arm of the Services and a wide range of models and devices is now in use. The accompanying table

shows only the main types at present in service or under development. Many trials have been made with various image intensifier devices from within the United Kingdom and elsewhere and some of these (such as the Scotos weapon night sights) may be encountered, but they have, to date, been obtained in small numbers only.

Infra-red devices	Magnification	Field of view (mils)	Weight (kg)
Commander's IR periscope	× 3	250	19
Gunner's IR sight	× 3	250	13

These are both fitted to the FV4201 Chieftain.

Yet another night vision system that is now coming into more general use is the thermal imager. This system uses infra-red, but in a passive form in that it converts infra-red sources into visible images. Thus a vehicle or human form that is constantly emitting infra-red radiations in the form of heat can be rendered visible. The radiations can be detected and seen even when cover from vision or camouflage is used by the 'target'. Thermal imaging sights are now under development for a variety of weapons and vehicles, and one application being in area surveillance. Use of such a sight can enable troops to detect when an infra-red emitting source moves into

Top left *The infra-red/white light searchlight fitted to Chieftain and used in conjunction with the commander's and gunner's IR sights.* **Top right** *The Crew Served Weapon Sight fitted to a 'winterised' Wombat.* **Above** *A NOD (Night Observation Device) in use by the Royal Artillery in Northern Ireland (Army PR Northern Ireland).* **Below right** *Concealing a Classic sensor unit (Racal-SES).*

Image Intensifiers

	Magnification	Field of view (mils)	Weight (kg)	Remarks
Pocketscope	× 1.15	711	0.9	Hand-held
Individual Weapon Sight (IWS)L1A2	× 3.75	180	2.78	SLR, Carl Gustav, etc
Telescope Straight II L1E1 (Twiggy)	× 5	129	11	Tripod-mounted
Crew Served Weapon Sight (CSWS)	× 5.7	108	8.54	Wombat
Night Observation Device	—		—	
Sight Unit II L3A1	× 1.4	380	5	Spartan Chieftain ARV
Night Sight L2E1	× 5.8 or × 1.6	142 or 498	59	Fox
Night Sight L2E1	× 5.8 or × 1.6	142 or 498	57	Scorpion, Scimitar
Driver's Periscope L4A1	× 1	890	10.34	Chieftain
Commander's II Sight	× 1	—	56	For Chieftain, still under development.

a covered area, when a visual or aural signal can then be given. Known as the thermal pointer, one version is under development for the Chieftain commander's image intensifier periscope.

Classic

Classic is an entirely new piece of detection equipment for the British Army, although it has used similar American equipments in Northern Ireland and elsewhere. The system uses seismic detectors that can reveal the movement of men and vehicles in areas of 'dead' or unseen ground up to a range of about seven kilometres.

Classic is the acronym for Covert Local Area Sensor System for Intruder Classification. It is designed to be emplaced in front of defence or other positions and consists of a number of sensors transmitting information to a central monitor. Each sensor has a small aerial that transmits short burst radio signals whenever movement occurs near its position. Each sensor may be buried or hidden in undergrowth or trees and it can discriminate between personnel on foot, wheeled vehicles or tracked vehicles. Each sensor weighs 1.2 kg and is 230 mm high, 95 mm wide and has a depth of 42 mm. They transmit their information to a hand-held monitor unit, if necessary via a relay unit which may be emplaced at some convenient point. The monitor unit can handle up to eight sensors and the information is displayed on a series of LED displays in a coded form. A rough sketch map showing the layout and position of the sensors may be drawn on the monitor unit panel.

The Classic system is battery-powered and includes a number of ancilliary units such as battery chargers, carrying harnesses and even a 'hard copy' paper printer to provide a log of events. Extra sensors such as infra-red or trip-wires can be employed if required.

Classic is produced by Racal-SES Limited of

Windsor, Berkshire, and is one outcome of development work carried out in conjunction with the Royal Signals Research Establishment, and more involved and advanced systems along the same lines can be expected over the next few years. The first examples of Classic were delivered during 1982.

Mines and mine detectors

Anti-Personnel Mine M18A1 (Claymore)

Weight 1.58 kg; **Length** 0.216 m; **Height** 0.083 m; **Width** 0.035 m; **Weight of charge** 0.68 kg.

The Claymore mine is an American anti-personnel device of undoubted lethality and unpleasantness. It is a small curved and innocuous box supported by four scissor-type metal legs which is set up, usually hidden in long grass or undergrowth, covering a path or route it is expected that an enemy will take. As the enemy approaches, the Claymore mine can be fired, either remotely or by a trip wire. As it fires the curved face of the mine faces towards the enemy and the main bursting charge (0.68 kg of C-4 plastic explosive) projects 700 small steel balls forward in a 60° arc. The arc ranges out to about 50 metres and upwards about one metre. Any personnel caught in this fan of steel projectiles cannot escape injury. In the mine the steel balls are held ready for firing in a plastic matrix. Not all of the blast is projected forwards for an area up to 16 metres to the rear of the mine is also a danger area.

The Claymore mine is carried in a bandolier which also holds the firing cap fitted to the mine, the firing device, and a small test set.

Ranger mine system

Weight loaded 630 kg; **Weight of loaded magazine** 14 kg; **Tube capacity** 18 mines; **Height above platform** 1.295 m; **Width** 2.21 m; **Length** 1.473 m; **Range (approx)** 100 m; **Rate of fire** 1 tube (18 mines) per second; **Total capacity** 1,296 mines; **Elevation** +5° to +35°; **Traverse** 180°.

The Ranger anti-personnel system is a joint development by the Royal Armament Research and Development Establishment at Fort Halstead and EMI Electronics Limited of Hayes, Middlesex. It was developed specifically to meet the mine-laying needs of modern mobile warfare when anti-personnel minefields will have to be laid rapidly and with none of the careful planning and patterned layout of past conflicts. With Ranger, minefields can be laid as and when the situation demands. Existing anti-tank minefields can be sown with anti-personnel mines to delay clearing by the enemy, river crossing approaches can be sown from the other side of the river, tracks can be denied to enemy infantry, and so on.

Left *Loading a Ranger launcher.* **Right** *A fully-loaded Ranger Mine system fitted to an FV432.*

The main reason for the rapid laying ability of the Ranger system is a multi-barreled projector which can be mounted on the back of a truck or on the roof of a mobile tracked vehicle—in the British Army the usual carrying vehicle is the FV432. The projector carries 72 disposable tubes, each of which contain 18 anti-personnel mines. The tubes are issued in magazines of four, so the total projector capacity is 18 magazines. In use the projector is loaded and the traverse and elevation are pre-set. As the carrying vehicle moves the projector is fired, one tube at a time at the rate of a tube every second. As each tube fires the 18 mines contained are distributed to a range of up to 100 metres. As they fly through the air they are dispersed in a random pattern, and 20 seconds after they are fired each mine becomes armed automatically. The dimensions of the mine are 34 mm deep with a diameter of 62 mm. Each mine, which is usually coloured green, contains a 10 gram charge of RDX/Wax which is pressure detonated. The charge is sufficient to inflict sufficient damage to disable, but not to inflict a fatal wound.

Once the projector is fired and empty, it can be reloaded by two men with fresh magazines in about six minutes. Normally, the Ranger system is used in conjunction with the Bar Mine Layer, so sizeable tracts of country can be rendered impassable to advancing forces in a very short space of time. In this way, an enemy can be channelled to any direction that suits the defender, unless of course they are willing to give up the momentum of an advance and spend time in mine-clearing. Even here the Ranger mine does not lend itself to rapid clearing, for apart from landing in random patterns, the body is plastic

and difficult to detect using conventional mine detectors.

Although the Ranger system is usually mounted on FV432s, other vehicles can be adapted to carry the projector. One vehicle that has been seen so adapted is the FV622 Stalwart. For training purposes special magazines are issued, each of which fires compressed peat 'mines' which do not require clearing after use, but inert plastic mines are also available.

Bar Mine system

Mine layer weight 1,240 kg; **Length** 1.22 m; **Height** 0.84 m; **Width over wheel cages** 1.02 m; **Mine weight** 11 kg; **Length** 1.2 m; **Width** 0.108 m; **Depth** 0.081 m; **Weight of explosive** 8.4 kg.

The Bar Mine system was developed for the same reasons that gave rise to the Ranger anti-personnel mine system, and enables the Army to sow anti-tank minefields rapidly as and when they are required. As with so many other weapon systems, the Bar Mine and its layer are design products of the Royal Armament Research and Development Establishment at Fort Halstead in Kent. Production is carried out at Royal Ordnance factories, the mine itself at Chorley and the layer at Nottingham.

The Bar Mine itself is capable of disabling any tank by blowing off one or more of its tracks. To assist in the speed of the laying operation, the mine is issued with its fuze already installed, and for storage and transport the mines are packed in palletised loads of 72 ready for easy handling by mechanised means such as the Eager Beaver. The load weighs 855 kg and can be quickly unpacked for use. For use on a small scale, packs of four mines are available. Once laid the Bar Mine is not easy to detect as it has few metal components.

The Bar Mine Layer is normally towed behind an FV432 although other vehicles can be used—the main advantage of the FV432 is that the crew can operate under cover. Vehicles that can be used include the various versions of the Land Rover, any 4-ton truck (including GMC trucks at the Suffield Training Ground in Canada), and the FV622 Stalwart. The layer is towed behind the vehicle with its conveyor projecting over the tailboard, or into the towing vehicle. As the layer progresses a plough blade cuts a furrow. The Bar Mines are then placed on the conveyor and as they pass through the layer body the fuze is activated automatically. Once the mine has been placed in the ploughed furrow, two disc wheels bury it and smooth down the earth surface. In a remarkably short time the furrow soon blends with the surrounding surface and the mines remain well hidden. Up to 600 or 700 mines can be sown in an hour using one vehicle and a three man crew, but logistic back-up is needed for this rate to be usefully maintained. (Land Rovers can only lay Bar Mines on the surface as they lack the power needed to pull the digging ploughshare. The Bv202 Over-Snow vehicle has been mentioned in some sources as another possible tractor.)

Normally the Bar Mines are laid in conjunction with the Ranger anti-personnel mines. A Bar Mine minefield, once laid, presents a formidable obstacle to attacking armour and unless time is spent clearing it, attacking forces can be usefully 'channelled' along the routes the defenders dictate. The shape of the Bar Mine also has the effect that fewer are needed to cover any given area than the conventional dish mines, and as they are capable of being laid at greater speed as and when the tactical situation dictates, they are far more cost-effective than the older mine systems.

The Bar Mine system has one additional cost-effectiveness advantage. When the mines are newly sown the channel furrows are highly visible, but due to the random method used when laying the mines, crossing the channels is a risky business. As a result time-consuming clearing methods have to be employed, or a way round discovered. This gives rise to the possibility of laying 'false' minefields by simply ploughing tracts of ground, without sowing any mines at all.

One of the most common methods of mine-clearing is the use of mechanised flails (now little used) or mine rollers, a method much favoured by Warsaw Pact armies, no doubt because of its efficiency and ease of fitting to any MBT. The Bar Mine is already ahead of this counter-measure as a double-impulse fuze is an alternative fitting. It works on the principle that the first impulse (the mine roller) will not fire the mine but arm it ready for the second impulse (the pushing MBT).

Horizontal Action Anti-tank Mine

Weight 12 kg; **Length** 0.26 m; **Body diameter** 0.2 m.

The Horizontal Action Anti-tank Mine is a French device used to cover tracks and other likely points used by AFVs. The original French designation is MIACAH, or Mine Antichar à Action Horizontale, and consists of a drum-shaped charge mounted on a circular frame. In use it is placed close to the probable path of an AFV and a wire is stretched across the path. The front of the mine is pointed towards the wire and the mine itself is concealed or camouflaged. As an AFV crosses the wire the charge is detonated and the shaped charge forms a projectile which is fired against the side of the target. Depending on the angle of impact the mine can penetrate up to 70 mm of armour and as it is likely to be fired at the sides of AFVs this is often

A Bar Mine Layer ready for use behind a M135 on the Suffield Ranges in Canada.

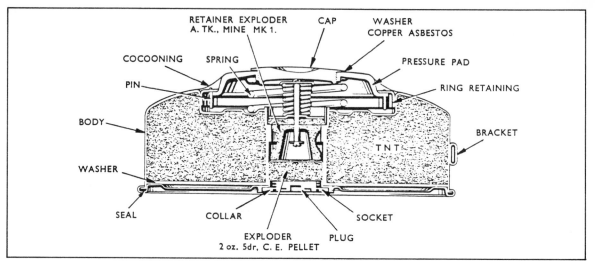

RETAINER EXPLODER
A. TK., MINE MK 1.

CAP

WASHER
COPPER ASBESTOS

COCOONING   SPRING

PRESSURE PAD

PIN

RING RETAINING

BODY

BRACKET

T N T

WASHER

SEAL   COLLAR

SOCKET

EXPLODER   PLUG
2 oz. 5dr, C. E. PELLET

Above Cross-section of a Mark 7 anti-tank mine (ROF).

Left A Horizontal Action Anti-tank Mine, also known as the Off-Route Mine.

Right Giant Viper on tow behind a Centurion AVRE.

sufficient to cause extensive damage. The mine is effective up to about 80 metres. The mines in British Army use are filled in the United Kingdom.

Anti-Tank Mine Mark 7

Weight 13.6 kg; **Diameter** 0.325 m; **Depth** 0.13 m; **Weight of charge** 8.89 kg.

Although it is now being replaced by the Bar Mine system, the Mark 7 mine is still likely to be used in any future conflict, mainly because there are still large stocks to hand. As they are still sown by time-honoured manual methods, the Mark 7 minefields are more likely to be static and pre-planned affairs.

The Mark 7 mine is disc-shaped with the conventional domed top. The actuating pressure is 275 kg which means it can be crossed by walking infantry

but will detonate when a vehicle passes over. Anti-handling devices can be fitted to slow down clearance.

There is a mechanical system for sowing large Mark 7 minefields but it is not likely to be seen in use today. The method involves the Mark 3 Minelayer, a 4-ton truck to carry the mines ready for loading into the layer, and a tracked tractor to tow the truck and the layer. With the advent of the Bar Mine Layer it is not likely that this method of minelaying will be used in the future, but small Mark 7 minefields may still be laid by hand.

Giant Viper L3A1

Weight complete with trailer 4,483 kg; **Weight of Giant Viper complete** 2,880 kg; **Weight of hose** 2,136 kg; **Length of hose** 229 m; **Diameter of hose**

68 mm; **Trailer weight (unloaded)** 1,651 kg; **Trailer length** 5.867 m; **Trailer height** 1.829 m; **Trailer width** 2.489 m; **Wheel track** 2.159 m.

While the Giant Viper minefield clearing equipment is intended rapidly to clear all types of minefield, its prime function is the clearing of anti-tank minefields. The equipment is used by the Royal Engineers and consists of several parts, the main component of which is a 229 metre-long hose filled with plastic explosive. The hose is fired from a special carrying trailer towed behind an FV4003 Centurion AVRE, an FV180 CET or an FV432. To fire the hose a cluster of eight rockets is used, stabilised in flight by three parachutes. The sequence is as follows. Once the edge of the minefield has been located, the towing vehicle approaches within about 45 metres of its edge. The rockets are then aligned to the path required through the mine field and the rockets are fired from within the towing vehicle. When fired the rockets make a very impressive roar, and the hose unfurls from its special packing case as they progress. Once on the ground the plastic explosive contents are fired, again from the towing vehicle. The path cleared is up to 7.28 metres wide and up to 189 metres long. Up to 80 per cent of the mines along this strip will have been detonated, and often more.

The trailer used to carry the Giant Viper is a special one, the FV3705 Trailer, Mine Clearance Equipment Giant Viper, No. 2 Mark 3. Normally the Giant Viper parts are carried in a 4-tonne truck but only the hose box requires mechanical handling.

During 1979 the first examples of a new Giant Viper trailer were seen. They consist of converted Medium Girder Bridge FV2842 trailers, altered by the addition of an extra axle. The conversion work is carried out by the Royal Ordnance factories, and the idea seems to be to provide a cost-saving exercise in order to increase the number of Giant Vipers available for mine-clearing.

Mine Detector No. 4C

Weight in use 9.15 kg; **Weight in transit box** 14.4 kg; **Search head length** 0.286 m; **Search head height** 0.108 m; **Search head width** 0.184 m; **Amplifier depth** 0.216 m; **Amplifier height** 0.108 m; **Amplifier width** 0.108 m; **Handle extended** 0.127 m; **Handle collapsed** 0.38 m; **Detection depth (soil)** 0.51 m; **Detection depth (pavé)** 0.305 m.

The Mine Detector No. 4C is the standard metal mine detector in service with the British Army and has been in use since 1968. Developed from the earlier No. 4 and 4A, the No. 4C is produced by United Scientific Instruments Limited, based in London. It works on the principle that two wire coils produce a mutually balanced inductance. When a metal object comes within their electrical field an imbalance is caused which produces an amplified tone in the user's headset. In operation the search head can be used in two configurations. The more usual is with the handle extended and the search head parallel to the ground. In some exposed

positions the prone configuration can be adopted where the handle is collapsed and the head is adjusted to lay along the ground. In either configuration there are two degrees of sensitivity that can be selected. The normal can detect metal objects up to 51 cm below the surface, but some soils contain ferrite particles and are known as pavé, so the second degree of sensitivity can be selected. This facility can also be used when the anti-sweep ploy of spreading minute steel needles or filings across minefields is encountered.

P6/2 Sweep Metal Detector
Weight complete 4.5 kg; **Length of long probe** 1.016 m; **Length of short probe** 0.4 m; **Length of open loop probe** 1.143 m; **Length of personnel probe** 0.4 m; **Dimensions of electronic unit** 0.25 × 0.08 × 0.25 m.

The P6/2 Sweep metal and mine detector has been in Army service since 1975 and is a militarised version of the Plessey P6 pulse induction metal detector. In Army use the Sweep is issued with four different probes which can be used to fulfil almost any mine or metal detection role from conventional mine detection to personnel body searches. The probes are an open loop probe for normal ground searches, a ferrite rod for searching foliage and water locations, a short probe and the personnel search probe. Using the ferrite probe an object the size of an automatic pistol can be detected up to 0.28 metres away. Any metal or mines detected indicate their presence by aural signals from a small loudspeaker or through headphones. The main electronic unit is carried in a shoulder-slung haversack. Needless to say the Sweep has been put to good use in Northern Ireland and has been instrumental in many weapon finds.

Wheelbarrow
Weight in action 195 kg; **Length** 1.22 m; **Height (minimum operational)** 0.82 m; **Width** 0.69 m; **Maximum speed** 33.5 m/min; **Range (standard)** 100 m; **Endurance (approx)** 2 hours.

Wheelbarrow is a remotely controlled EOD vehicle, specifically designed to meet the operational need which has arisen from the large scale escalation in terrorist and urban guerrilla activity over the last decade. The current version in service is the Mark 7, and the data above refers to this version.

The original Wheelbarrow was designed and produced in just over one month in early 1972 in response to an urgent request from the EOD per-

Above right *A Mine Detector Mark 4C in use* (United Service Instruments). **Right** *A P6/2 'Sweep' in use with the probe head fitted* (Plessey Radar).

sonnel in Northern Ireland, and went into service immediately. The first version had three wheels and was in fact based on an electrically powered garden wheelbarrow—hence its name. The name has been retained ever since despite the adoption of tracks and numerous modifications to the extent that the present Mark 7 bears little resemblance to its precursor. Over the years the Wheelbarrows have been drastically improved both in performance and versatility until today they are very advanced devices, and have proved so successful in their dangerous role that they have joined the long list of British defence exports to all parts of the world. The Mark 7 Wheelbarrow is a remotely-operated device which can be used in a range of circumstances where the use of a human investigator would prove hazardous or lethal. In service a number have been destroyed in circumstances that would have caused death or serious injuries in conventional search and clearing operations.

Wheelbarrow is electrically driven by two battery-operated motors. Commands are made on a hand-held control box and transmitted through a 100 metre-long 18-core cable. The commands are given to a wide variety of fixtures on the Wheelbarrow vehicle, most of which are on a moving and extendible boom mounted over the vehicle itself. This boom can carry a variety of accessories but an almost universal fitting is a small television camera feeding a nine-inch monitor viewed by the operator. The boom also mounts a five-round automatic shotgun which can be fired to blast open suspect packages or even force an entry into doors or vehicle windows, but for smashing open windows there is another special device available. Handling devices and grabs can also be fitted and there is even a device for placing a car-towing hook in position. To give an example of the degree of sophistication that has been reached by Wheelbarrow there is the now almost universal fitting of downward-firing nail guns that fire nails into the floor once a Wheelbarrow enters a doorway. The nails prevent the door closing and blocking the vital exit. Other and more recent attachments and weapons fitted to Wheelbarrow are still subject to security restrictions.

As the various forms of terrorist bomb and explosive devices proliferate, more and more experience is being gained in handling and neutralising them. Wheelbarrow has proved invaluable in this essential and unpleasant form of warfare and as the years go by the Wheelbarrow type of vehicle will become even more complex and sophisticated. Already Marauder has been developed and no doubt even more specialised variants will emerge in time. Many lives (and a great deal of property) have already been saved by their use and no doubt many more will be saved in the future, but Wheelbarrows and their ilk are relatively expensive items and should not be hazarded wantonly. Whenever possible they are withdrawn from disruptive or controlled explosions and are not used in such a fashion that they are liable to be blown up without good cause. If for no other reason than that their operators become quite attached to their own particular vehicles, Wheelbarrows are used carefully with as little risk as possible.

The Wheelbarrow Mark 7 is manufactured by Morfax Limited of Mitcham, Surrey. It and other EOD equipments utilised by British bomb disposal teams are carried in specially modified and armoured Ford Transit vans.

Marauder

No data can be quoted regarding Marauder and few details have yet been released other than general outlines. It is an advanced explosive handling vehicle that has been developed using the considerable fund of experience gained from the use of Wheelbarrow. As a result it is more mobile, versatile and complex. From what little has been released it can be seen that Marauder has a much more advanced set of remotely-controlled booms and handling devices than Wheelbarrow—the track system is also much more complex and is obviously capable of operating in a wide range of confined and restricted situations. It is understood that the final service form of Marauder has yet to be defined but the present configuration of two flexible arms and one boom is to be retained. Each arm has its own miniature television camera and the ends of the arms can be fitted with all manner of handling devices, including some that can be used to open packages without disturbing the contents. The usual shotgun, nail gun and charge-planting fixtures are retained but the arm flexibility and delicacy of operation make them much more versatile than the Wheelbarrow components. Marauder is another product of Morfax Limited and is manufactured at Mitcham, Surrey.

Radar
Radar, GS No. 14 Mark 1 ZB298
Weight complete with tripod 40.16 kg; **Weight less tripod** 30.16 kg; **Head dimensions** 508 × 483 × 178 mm; **Minimum range** 50 m; **Maximum range** 10,000 m.

The Radar, GS No. 14 Mark 1 is often referred to by its commercial designation of ZB298. It is a Marconi-Elliott product that was developed to a

Government contract issued in 1964—the first prototypes were completed in 1966. It is now the standard Infantry surveillance radar and is used mounted on a tripod for field use or on a vehicle such as the FV432 or FV103 Spartan—the FV701(H) Ferret Mark 2/3 was at one time a ZB298 vehicle.

The ZB298 operates on a slight modification of the Doppler effect in which moving objects appear to produce different frequencies as they move, with the differing frequencies being relative to a fixed position. With the ZB298 a fixed frequency beam is transmitted over a sector and any moving object is detected and displayed on a console as a series of blips, the size of the blips being used to determine the speed and range of the moving object. With the minimum of training an operator can determine the size and nature of the object so displayed. Men moving, whether they are running, walking or crawling, can be easily detected and the range from the radar head can be determined down to five metres. Vehicles produce their own pulse 'signature', as do such static objects as waving tree branches. An aural signal in headphones assists in the discrimination.

The primary role of the ZB298 is night surveillance but it can also be used in fog and other poor visibility conditions, or for artillery and mortar fire control.

Note the large and distinctive ZB298 fitted to the roof of this FV103 Spartan. This vehicle/radar combination is used within the RAC Armoured Reconnaissance Regiments.

Radar FA No. 15 (Cymbeline)

Weight of equipment 390 kg; **Weight of complete trailer** 980 kg; **Length of trailer** 1.5 m; **Height of trailer (in action)** 2.29 m; **Height of trailer (folded)** 1.07 m; **Width** 1.68 m; **Minimum range** 1,000 m; **Maximum displayed range** 20,000 m; **Scanned sector** 40°30′; **Elevation** −5° to +20°15′.

The mortar took such a toll of casualties during World War 2 that after 1945 a great deal of effort was expended in finding a method of locating mortars in the field. The method finally chosen has been used on several location radars and is still in use on the present locating radar, namely Cymbeline. Very simply, when a mortar is fired its bomb rises at a steep angle. If the bomb can be detected on a radar beam, the detecting radar can then be automatically switched to a higher angle when the bomb trajectory will be once more intercepted. Using a rapid calculator the path of the bomb can be quickly traced back to its firing point and counter-fire can be directed in a very short time.

The first mortar locating radar in Army service on a large scale was the Radar, FA No. 8, or Green Archer. It has now been replaced by the Radar FA No. 15 Marks 1 and 2, known as Cymbeline. Cym-beline is much smaller and lighter than its predecessor and much easier to use. A product of EMI Industries, the first examples were delivered to the Army in 1973. There are two marks, the Mark 1 being mounted on a towed trailer and the Mark 2 mounted on an FV432.

Both marks operate on the same principle which has been outlined above. Cymbeline does have one refinement in that its beam is switched electronically across its 40°30′ sector 16 times a second—an alert beam angle can be selected if required so that the two detection beams can be used with great accuracy. The detection range will vary with the calibre of the mortar bomb being detected. An 81 mm bomb can be detected up to 10,000 metres away, while a 120 mm bomb can be detected at ranges of up to 14,000 metres—the maximum range of Cymbeline is 20,000 metres.

Cymbeline is self-contained and has its own power generator driven by a Wankel engine. On the Mark 2 version the radar aerial is levelled independently of the vehicle, but the Mark 1 trailer version is lifted off its trailer and then levelled—the aerial unit can be lifted by four men. With the Mark 1 the display unit is set up about 15 metres from the aerial—with the Mark 2 the unit is inside the FV432. The normal crew for a Cymbeline is four men, with another two in a forward area to give aural warning of mortars firing and in roughly what sector.

There are other roles that Cymbeline can fulfil

apart from mortar detection. It can be used in a coastal or ground surveillance role, it can be used to control helicopters or light aircraft in its detection area, it has a limited artillery control and survey capability, and as well as detecting mortar fire it can also detect rocket firing locations.

To back up the Cymbeline sets in the field a special field repair workshop container can be loaded on to a 4-tonne truck, which is also used to tow the workshop's power generator. A training simulator is also in service.

Each 105 mm field regiment in 1 (Br) Corps and elsewhere has a Cymbeline troop. Its make-up can vary but it usually comprises four tracked Cymbeline sets, or three towed.

The trailer used to carry the Mark 1 Cymbeline is a rather complex one known as the FV2425 Trailer, 1-tonne, Lightweight Field Artillery Radar No. 2. Its dimensions are as follows: **Weight unladen** 447

Left *Cymbeline aerial extended on a FV432.* **Above** *The Radar No. 17 Mark 1 (Mobile) used at Gibraltar by 8 Surveillance Troop RA.*

kg; **Length** 3.353 m; **Height** 0.711 m; **Width** 1.778 m; **Wheel track** 1.499 m.

It was announced during 1977 that a new trailer-mounted rocket and mortar location radar was under development with the code-name Cervantes. Cervantes follows the same general operating lines as Cymbeline but has an extra detection beam that increases the general accuracy and efficiency of the system. Troop trials were carried out during 1981 and it is expected that the first equipments will be issued during 1982 or 1983.

Radar No. 17 Mark 1

The Radar No. 17 Mark 1 is the Army version of the widely-used Decca Marine Radar, but only a relative handful are in British Army service. The first examples were procured during 1971 and were sent to Gibraltar where they were used (and still are) by 8 Surveillance Troop, RA. Since then more have been obtained and they are currently in service in Belize and Northern Ireland, as well as being used for range safety in the Hebrides.

The Army version of the Decca Marine Radar is carried in a specially-equipped version of the Land Rover with the rotating aerial very prominent on the special body roof. In this form the radar is designated Radar No. 17 Mark 1 (Mobile). As such the radar is completely self-contained and powered by a 24 volt generator towed by the vehicle. Each unit has a crew of six men who operate in three-man shifts.

The rotating aerial feeds signals into the equipment which has a visual PPI (Planned Position Indicator) display giving an indication of the position and range of any target relative to the radar. The maximum range of the equipment is some 24 nautical miles but boats about 50 metres long can be picked up out to a range of about 20,000 metres. At shorter ranges (the equipment has eight range 'bands') the radar can be quite discriminating as small 10-metre craft can be detected up to 5,000 metres away, and even swimmers can be detected up to 750 metres away. This discrimination is invaluable for coast or harbour surveillance and the Radar No.17 Mark 1 has many applications.

Radar, GS No. 18 Mark 1 (Prowler)
Weight of radar head 3.5 kg; **Weight of tripod** 3.5 kg; **Weight of battery** 3.5 or 1.1 kg; **Range (men)** 900-1,500 m; **Range (vehicles)** 3,000 m; **Minimum range** 75 m.

Prowler is a product of Marconi Radar Systems Limited, and is intended for general battlefield surveillance at Infantry company level. It can be carried and operated by only one man, and its operation has designed to be as simple and rugged as possible (there are only four controls). Prowler is operated in two modes—Search and Range. In the Search mode the equipment acts as a conventional doppler radar, but in the Range mode the doppler pulses are generated to determine the range of any particular target using an LED display marked in 25 metre graticules. Two batteries can be used with Prowler and differ only in their operational life. A tripod can be used with Prowler for static 'sentry' duties. The radar head is 0.28 metres high, 0.3 metres wide and 0.095 metres deep.

Radar, GS No. 20 Mark 1 (Claribel)
It is not possible to quote very much data regarding Claribel as it has not long been in service. Developed to an Army requirement and using experience gained the hard way in Northern Ireland, Claribel is used to detect incoming sniper fire from hidden positions. In the past mobile patrols or fixed installations have been fired on but it has not often proved possible to gain an aural fix on the firing point. Very often follow-up search patrols have been misdirected or even random with no idea of the correct area to search. Claribel is a simple light radar system that can be mounted on the roof of a vehicle or a fixed installation to detect incoming fire and visually indicate the appropriate sector from which it came. When a round is fired at a vehicle it is immediately detected and an aural warning signal is given. At the same time the appropriate sector is visually displayed on a small indicator—up to two firing points can be detected at any one time.

The installation of Claribel takes up very little space and it can even be hidden in vehicle bodywork if so desired. The detector elements are four small box aerials, one at the front and rear and one on each side. They all feed into the main control box which then feeds the indicator and warning device. As mentioned above, not only vehicles are equipped for such locations as guard posts and the like are fitted with Claribel, and in some fixed installations remote display units are used. The aerials can detect incoming rounds of all calibres and velocities from 5.56 mm up to 120 mm, and even slow-moving projectiles such as rockets can be detected. Claribel is manufactured by Microwave and Electronic Systems Limited of Newbridge, Midlothian, now part of the Racal Group.

Armoured Fighting Vehicles
FV4201 Chieftain
Armament 1 × 120 mm L11A5 Gun, 1 × 7.62 mm L8A1 Machine-Gun, 1 × 7.62 mm L37A1 Machine-Gun and 2 × 6-barrel smoke dischargers; **Crew** 4; **Weight in action** 55,000 kg; **Length (gun forward)** 10.795 m; **Length (gun clamped)** 9.73 m; **Length of hull** 7.52 m; **Height (top of cupola)** 2.82 m; **Width (with searchlight)** 3.62 m; **Width (over skirts)** 3.504 m; **Width (over tracks)** 3.33 m; **Track width** 0.61 m; **Ground clearance** 0.508 m; **Maximum road speed** 48 km/h; **Range (roads)** 400-500 km; **Range (cross-country)** 200-300 km; **Engine type** L60 No. 4 Mark 8A; **Engine power** 750 bhp at 2,250 rpm; **Engine capacity** 19 litres; **Fuel capacity** 950 litres; **Ammunition capacity** 120 mm—64 rounds, 7.62 mm—6,000 rounds; **Main armament elevation** -10° to +20°; **Main armament traverse** 360°.

Chieftain is the Main Battle Tank (MBT) of the British Army and as such forms the central striking force of the armoured divisions of 1 (Br) Corps in West Germany. Despite the fact that it has been in front-line service since 1967, it is still widely regarded as one of the most powerful fighting tanks in the world, and progressive improvements and modifications to the basic design and equipment seem to ensure that it will remain so for many years.

Top right *An early mark of Chieftain, probably a Mark 1 or 2 (MoD).* **Above right** *The classic side-on shot of Chieftain showing its low lines and prominent 120 mm gun with bore evacuator and thermal sleeve.* **Right** *Despite its bulk, Chieftain is quite low and with even a minimum of camouflage, it can be made to blend itself with the background.*

The FV4201 Chieftain had its origins in the early 1950s. The basic design concept was born in an era when the General Staff was acutely aware that up to the advent of the Centurion, British tank designs were either under-armoured or under-gunned, and in many cases both criticisms applied. As the Centurion had amply proved its battle value during the Korean War it was decided to procure a follow-on design which was formulated under the general designation of Medium Gun Tank No. 2. Initial design studies envisaged a low hull, low-slung suspension and a 105 mm gun, but the design specifications were constantly being improved and upgraded so it was not until 1954 that the first 'paper' designs approached the stage where hardware could be considered. Even then there was a brief interlude of collaboration on various component interchanges between the United Kingdom and the USA, but that eventually came to naught and the General Staff specification was finally issued in August 1958. It called for an effective gun-to-armour combination, combined with agility and the ability to stay in action for prolonged periods. The main armament was to be capable of engaging armour at very long ranges, but the armour carapace had to be capable of withstanding enemy artillery fire from medium calibres.

Already the main engine had been selected, as had several of the new tank's design features. To save on the all-important height the driver was to be in a reclining position, which would greatly reduce the hull depth, and the main armament was to be mounted in a sloping turret front without a mantlet. Both these features, and several others, were tested in the experimental FV4202 during 1956. Leyland built the FV4202 and were also given the overall design leadership. They had already selected their L60 engine pack as the main powerplant, and if hindsight can be introduced to pinpoint the main weakness of the Chieftain design, it must be stated that this has not proved to be a happy choice.

The L60 was originally designed as one of the various multi-fuel engines sought after by the Army in the years following the 1939-1945 war. Time was to show that the multi-fuel concept was an engineering blind alley which left the L60 with several unfortunate shortfalls, not the least of which was that the early examples proved to be incapable of delivering more than 650 bhp instead of the required 700 bhp. While the output was later increased to the proper figure (and even beyond to 750 bhp), it proved to be of no avail for, by the time it was attained, Chieftain was overweight. Numerous teething troubles with the gearbox, suspension and engine cooling had all added their

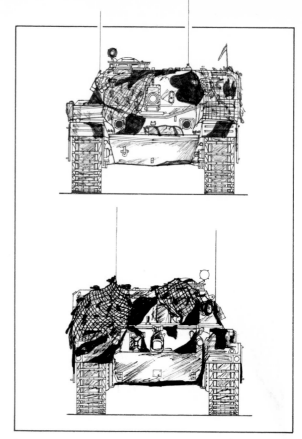

individual weight penalties to the extent that the suspension had to be strengthened, adding yet more weight. Consequently, Chieftain is still far less agile than many of its contemporaries, and the added load on the main engine (plus the unfortunate design faults) has generally rendered the L60 engine pack prone to constant troubles.

The first Chieftain prototype was ready in September 1959, and a series of six prototypes were delivered by the end of 1962. The resultant troop trials revealed the many problems mentioned above, but production finally got underway at two separate locations, the Vickers-Armstrong works at Elswick and the Royal Ordnance Factory at Leeds. The first examples were issued in May 1963 but it was not until early 1967 that the first full service versions were ready. To date there have been eight main marks and several sub-marks (and doubtless there are more to come), but the main versions are as follows: **Mark 1** 40 built with 585 bhp engines and used only for training and trials; **Mark 2** First service version with 650 bhp engine, issued in 1967; **Mark 3** Much revised Mark 2 with new cupola,

Right *Chieftains on parade, Sennelager 7.7.77.*

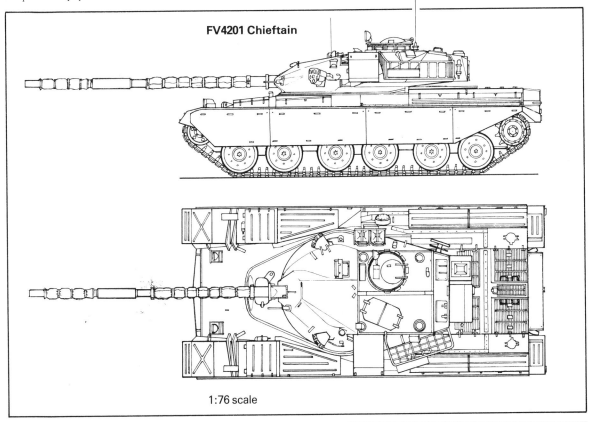

FV4201 Chieftain

1:76 scale

new suspension and many other detail alterations, in service from 1969; **Mark 4** Development model only; **Mark 5** Revised Mark 3 with new engine and gearbox, improved ventilation and improved exhaust system; **Mark 6** Improved Mark 2; **Mark 7** Revised Mark 3 with engine improvements; and **Mark 8** Mark 3 with full complement of modifications.

The above remarks give only a rough outline of the main versions, and in addition to them there are several sub-marks with varying modification states. It is quite possible that there will be more variants in the future as the Chieftain is still the subject of a considerable amount of development work covering all facets of tank technology and its associated equipment.

Chieftain production for the British Army ceased several years ago after some 700 to 800 examples had been delivered. Early versions, apart from the low-powered Mark 1, are all being gradually updated to Mark 8 standards by the addition of several innovations. One of these is the Improved Fire Control System (IFCS). Prior to the introduction of this, the main 120 mm armament was aimed and ranged by the use of a .50-in spotting machine-gun (the L21A1) mounted co-axially above the main gun barrel. When fired the machine-gun emitted three-round bursts of tracer. Observing their trajectory through the main gun sight the gunner could correct his aim accordingly. While this method had the advantage of simplicity, the early Chieftains had their offensive range restricted by the limitations of the machine-gun which had a range of only some 1,500 metres, although with the Mark 3 this was considerably improved to around 2,500 metres. Even with this improvement it was felt that something better was needed and that came with IFCS. Very basically, IFCS uses a GEC-Marconi 12-12P computer which handles all the variables likely to affect the projectile of the gun once it is fired. The computer is coupled with the tank laser sight (of which there have been four marks to date), which incorporates a laser range-finder with an accuracy of ±10 metres out to a range of 10,000 metres. The gunner and the tank commander both have sighting telescopes which contain aiming marks, and the control of the IFCS and the gun are both achieved by employing a small joystick operated by the left hand. Aiming is carried out by placing one aiming graticule on to the selected target, and the computer automatically moves the main gun to the correct elevation and 'aim-off' to obtain a hit. This usually takes but a few seconds, even with moving targets. Just about every variable possible is taken into consideration by the IFCS. For example, if the target is moving the movement rate is at once calculated by

measuring the traverse rate of the Chieftain turret and the elevation movement of the gun barrel. Crosswinds and headwinds are taken into account by a roof-mounted sensor which also measures temperature. The angle of gun trunnion tilt is noted by another sensor. Thus with IFCS, Chieftain has a very good chance of obtaining that 'first round kill' that is so vital in tank warfare.

At the time of writing, IFCS is not yet in full service. Early trials, held at Kirkcudbright, revealed some problems which delayed the first full-scale service acceptance trials, held in Germany, until February 1979—troop trials were scheduled for late 1979. It is hoped that the full scale into-service date will be early 1981. In the interim the ranging machine-guns have been withdrawn from use although many remained fitted until balancing counter-weights could be retrofitted in their place. Reliance was then placed on the laser rangefinders with extra references being made to other factors including the Muzzle Reference System (a device which quickly and accurately aligns the bore with the sight).

Both the gunner and commander can obtain target information, but the commander has a manual override control for target selection. The gunner has control of the co-axial L8A1 machine-gun, while the commander controls the L37A1 machine-gun mounted on his cupola. To provide some small measure of anti-aircraft defence this cupola machine-gun can be elevated and fired at angles up to 90° from within the turret. The interior of the Chieftain turret is crammed with all manner of gear apart from the IFCS and fire control apparatus. Apart from the commander and the gunner to the right of the gun, the loader on the left combines his task with that of radio operator, utilising two Clansman VRC 353 sets. Around the loader are the various ammunition stowage points and bins, and to the rear of the turret is the NBC ventilation equipment. On the early marks the NBC system was an over-pressure version, but eventually this will be replaced by the Mark 6 system which uses full filtration. At the front, the driver normally drives the tank with his front hatch open, but once in action the hatch is closed and the driver then assumes the fully reclining position using vision periscopes. Full night driving facilities are provided, and for night fighting a combined white light/infra-red searchlight is fitted to the left-hand side of the turret.

It has not proved possible to quote the armour thickness of the Chieftain but even a cursory glance will reveal the extra protection provided by the curved front glacis plate and the sloping turret.

The Chieftain L60 engine pack.

The side skirting plates provide some measure of protection against light hollow-charge missiles and also double as dust deflectors to keep the all-important vision devices and weapon sights clear.

The engine compartment at the rear is so designed that the L60 engine pack can be removed in one piece in a relatively short time—which, in view of its general reliability record, is just as well. At one point the L60 reliability history came under Parliamentary scrutiny (1977) and as a result a series of trials, known under the code-name 'Sundance', was undertaken to improve matters. As a result of these the main sources of troubles were eliminated and steps taken to introduce modifications to retrofit to all L60 packs. The main improvements were made by fitting new piston liners, but many other changes were added. The end result should substantially improve the reliability of the L60 engine pack, and a slight increase of power from 750 to 800 bhp may be possible. Meanwhile, the transmission and many other automotive components continue to be the subjects of continued development. In parentheses it should be noted that the main engine compartment also houses a 37 bhp auxiliary engine which is used for various purposes, one of them being recharging the batteries situated in the driver's compartment.

Chieftain can wade through up to one metre of water—an early attempt to provide a method of sealing the hull and turret for really deep obstacles did not pass beyond the acceptance stage (a high schnorkel tower was a prominent feature of the kit). A more widely-issued 'bolt-on' kit consists of a dozer blade that can be fitted to the front of the tank in about six to nine hours. Once fitted, Chieftain can then be used to excavate firing positions or remove obstacles, and at least one vehicle per troop is usually so equipped. The blade, once fitted, is hydraulically powered and controlled by the driver.

Chieftain continues to be the basis for a number of 'mid-life' improvements. Apart from the all-important IFCS mentioned above, the commander's cupola will continue to be the subject of a number of improvements. New sights will be fitted, among which will be a new image intensifier sight and a thermal imaging sight. The internal ammunition stowage is the subject of another modification and there will be many other minor and detailed changes to all parts of the tank. The intention is to keep Chieftain as the Army's MBT until the end of the 1980s, by which time its successor should be ready to enter service.

Major variants of the Chieftain are the FV4204 Armoured Recovery vehicle and the FV4205 Bridgelayer.

FV4030/4 Challenger

Armament 1 × 120 mm L11A5 gun, 1 × 7.62 mm L8A2 machine-gun, 1 × 7.62 mm L37A2 machine-gun, 2 × 5-barrel smoke dischargers; **Crew** 4; **Weight in action** 62,000 kg; **Length (gun forward)** 11.55 m; **Length (gun to rear)** 9.87 m; **Length (hull)** 8.39 m; **Height (overall)** 3.04 m; **Height (top of commander's sight)** 2.89 m; **Width (overall)** 3.518 m; **Width (over tracks)** 3.42 m; **Ground clearance** 0.5 m; **Maximum road speed** 56 km/h; **Engine type** Rolls-Royce CV12 TCA diesel; **Engine power** 1,200 bhp at 2,300 rpm; **Engine capacity** 26.1 litres; **Ammunition capacity** 120 mm—48 to 52 rounds according to mix; 7.62 mm—4,000 rounds.

While the FV4201 Chieftain is still one of the most powerful tanks in the world, development work on its successor began many years ago, as far back as the late 1960s. The story of its successor is a long and complicated one which at one time involved an international programme but eventually that period passed and work concentrated on a new project, the MBT-80. MBT-80 involved a considerable amount of time and resources during its early project definition period but as time went on it began to become apparent that not only would MBT-80 be a very expensive project but the time

Above *A pre-production FV4030/4 Challenger. Later versions will be equipped with a variant of the Modern Technology Gun.*

Left *The Rolls-Royce CV12TCA engine.*

factor began to weigh against it as a replacement for Chieftain would be needed by the mid-1980s at the latest, and it was very possible that new and powerful Warsaw Pact tanks would be in service even before then. Something was needed quickly, and thus MBT-80 came to an abrupt end in the middle of 1980.

It was replaced in the planning sequence by a new vehicle, the FV4030/4 Challenger. Challenger is a

development of the Chieftain line, a line that grew from the British Army's Chieftain design via a string of export and development models. The Chieftain was awarded several export contracts during its production life, many of which were able to benefit from the experience gained with Chieftain in British Army service. One of these export orders was made by the Shah of Iran who obtained large numbers of the Shir Iran 1, based on Chieftain but with an uprated engine. Then came the Shir Iran 2 with the new Chobham armour, an armour formed of layers of ceramics, aluminium and other, as yet, unannounced materials. But the Shah was toppled in the Iran Revolution leaving numbers of developed and completed Shir Iran 2s still on the production lines of the Royal Ordnance Factories, and with all manner of long-dated parts and equipment ordered and paid for. The Shir Iran series was designated FV4030 and by 1980 the FV4030/3 prototypes were running and on trials. From these the FV4030/4 was projected for British Army service, and the initial order was announced for 240 during July 1980. The cost was reported as some £300 million.

The first FV4030/4 examples were produced during late 1981 but their first public appearance did not take place until summer 1982, when the accompanying photograph was taken. The Challenger tank retains the main armament of the Chieftain in the shape of the 120 mm L11A5 rifled gun but it is expected that eventually some form of revised 120 mm rifled gun will be introduced. New and improved ammunition for the L11A5 will be used, including a new FSAPDS armour-penetrating shot. In time the Hughes Chain Gun might replace the L7A2 co-axial machine-gun but for the present the orthodox 7.62 mm machine-guns will be retained. The IFCS fire control system will also be used in its fully developed form, and generally, the overall shape and feel of the Chieftain series will be retained.

The main changes come with the new engine and the armour. The new 1,200 hp engine is a Rolls-Royce Motors product contained in an engine pack weighing 5.49 tonnes. It will provide Challenger with a far more lively performance than the generally underpowered Chieftain. The main engine is backed up by a Coventry Climax auxiliary engine for general battery-charging and stand-by use for systems.

The armour is of the Chobham type but is of the latest version. One source states that it might consist of several layers of nylon micro-mesh bonded on both sides by sheets of titanium alloy, and this might well be in addition to layers of ceramics and other exotic armour. It is stated to be virtually immune to nearly all types of modern anti-armour projectiles, and it gives Challenger a slab-sided appearance with the armour being obviously very chunky and thick. The vehicle uses a bolt-on hydro-pneumatic suspension system that can be easily replaced in the field. Clansman radio communications equipment will be used throughout. Thermal imaging sights will be provided as standard.

The FV4030/4 Challenger will be produced at the Royal Ordnance Factory, Leeds, with the first examples being produced in 1984 ready for service use in 1985. The initial order was understood to be sufficient to equip one armoured division but subsequent statements have been made to the effect that the order for 240 will equip four armoured regiments under the latest reorganisation round. Allowing for the usual quota for training and development use, it would appear that there will be enough for three armoured regiments at the current rate of issue. This will be enough for one of the three armoured divisions, with a useful war reserve.

Challenger will be the recipient of a great deal of development work over the next decade, and much of the long-term work that was intended for MBT-80 will now be diverted to Challenger.

FV4204 Armoured Recovery Vehicle

Armament 1 × 7.62 mm L37A1 Machine-Gun, 2 × 6-barrel smoke dischargers, 2 × 4-barrel smoke dischargers; **Crew** 4 + 1; **Weight in action (with crane)** 56,000 kg; **Length (travelling with blade)** 8.57 m; **Height** 2.79 m; **Width (over blade)** 3.53 m; **Width (over tracks)** 3.33 m; **Track width** 0.61 m; **Ground clearance (approx)** 0.5 m; **Maximum road speed** 42.4 km/h; **Range (roads)** 400-500 km; **Range (cross country)** 200-300 km; **Engine type** Leyland L60 No.4 Mark 8A; **Engine power** 750 bhp; **Engine capacity** 19 litres; **Ammunition capacity** 7.62 mm—1,600 rounds; **Smoke grenades** —20.

While the FV4006 Centurion Mark 2 ARV has given good service, the idea of using a new ARV compatible with the FV4201 Chieftain MBT has

The Chieftain ARV at work (Simon Dunstan).

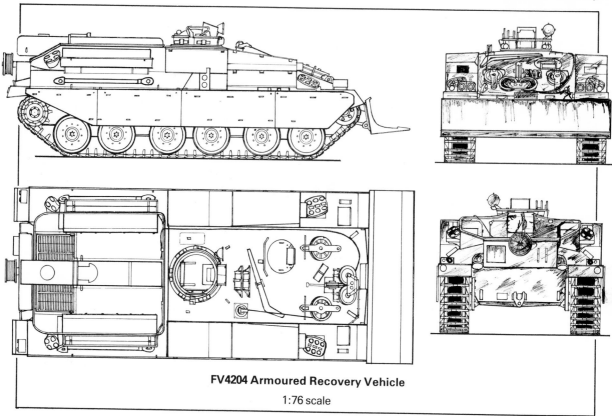

FV4204 Armoured Recovery Vehicle

1:76 scale

obvious attractions, so starting in 1964 the development began of a Chieftain ARV. The first prototypes were ready in 1971 and full production of the new vehicle began in 1974 at the Vickers Works at Elswick, Newcastle-upon-Tyne. It was not until 1976 that the first examples were issued for full service, when they were issued to REME recovery units.

The FV4204 ARV is based on the hull and suspension of the FV4201 Chieftain Mark 5. Numerous changes have been made to the Chieftain layout to enable it to carry out the ARV role. Starting at the front of the vehicle a large dozer blade has been fitted which is not intended primarily for the clearance of earth or obstacles (although it can be used for those purposes), but for stabilisation when the towing winches are in use. The driver's position has been shifted to the left to make room for the main winch. Behind him is the commander's hatch with a 360° swivelling cupola and a machine-gun and behind this is the main compartment with space for the other two or three crew members. The main winch has a pulling capacity of 30,000 kg, but with the dozer blade dug in this can be increased up to 90,000 kg—the dozer blade is operated by

hydraulic rams. Inside the same compartment is a second, smaller winch with a towing capacity of 3,000 kg. The length of towing cable for this second winch is 259 metres, while the main winch is provided with 122 metres. Both winches are driven via a power take-off from the main engine, but the smaller winch is hydraulically driven and controlled, and has an infinitely variable speed control. The winch controls are in the main crew compartment. Scattered in various stowage points are brackets, towing eyes, cables, special tools and all the varied paraphernalia required by the REME in the ARV role.

Some Chieftain ARVs have been fitted with a side-mounted crane which is fitted as standard to the Mark 2 export models.

FV4205 Chieftain Bridgelayer

Armament 2 × 7.62 mm L7A2 Machine-Guns, 2 × 6-barrel smoke dischargers; **Crew** 3; **Weight in action** 53,300 kg; **Length with bridge** 13.741 m; **Length of hull** 7.52 m; **Height with bridge** 3.923 m; **Width (with bridge)** 4.165 m; **Width (over skirts)** 3.504 m; **Width (over tracks)** 3.33 m;

A Chieftain Bridgelayer in the process of laying a No. 8 Bridge.

Track width 0.61 m; **Ground clearance** 0.5 m; **Maximum road speed** 43 km/h; **Range (roads)** 400 km; **Engine type** L60 No. 4 Mark 7A; **Engine power** 730 bhp; **Engine capacity** 19 litres; **Fuel capacity** 886 litres; **Ammunition capacity** 7.62 mm—3,200 rounds; **Bridge length (No. 8)** 24.384 m; **Bridge width (No. 8)** 4.165 m; **Bridge weight (No. 8)** 12,200 kg.

The Chieftain Bridgelayer, or FV4205 AVLB, was a joint effort with the design work being shared by the MVEE at Chobham, Tubes (Birmingham) and Lockheed Precision Products. The project was initiated in 1962 but requirement changes and the necessary re-designs delayed production until 1974 when the first examples were delivered to the Army. Once in service they soon replaced the earlier Centurion bridging variants, the FV4002 AVLB and FV4016 ARK. Stripped of their bridges, these two vehicles may still be encountered in use for driver training.

The Chieftain Bridgelayer can be used to lay two different bridges. The one usually carried is the No. 8 Tank Bridge which is folded into two halves over the vehicle. Once in the location that requires to be bridged the No. 8 bridge is laid in three stages. Power for the operation comes from a hydraulic pump located within the hull and driven by a take-off from the main engine. Five cylinders are driven by the pump for the actual bridging operation, two for each of the first two stages and one for the third and final stage. The complete launch operation usually lasts from three to five minutes. Once completed, the parent vehicle can disengage and either cross the bridge or withdraw to allow other vehicles to cross. If required, the bridgelayer can cross and recover the bridge ready for another crossing elsewhere—the recovery operation lasts about ten minutes. Once laid, the bridge has two trackways, each track with a width of 1.62 metres which enables small vehicles to cross on one track. The No. 8 bridge, like the No. 9 can be recovered from either end. Overall length is 24.4 metres and weight is some 12,700 kg.

The No. 9 Tank Bridge is part of the AVLB equipment and is usually carried on a semi-trailer. It is a one-piece bridge, 13.411 metres long and 4.165 metres wide. When in use with the Chieftain Bridgelayer it is operated in a straightforward up-

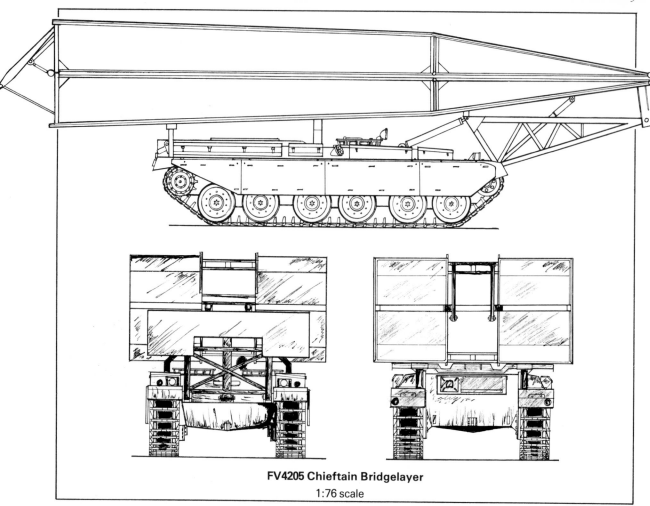

FV4205 Chieftain Bridgelayer
1:76 scale

Left *A Chieftain Bridgelayer minus the bridge but showing the hydraulic laying rams.*

and-over sequence in from three to five minutes. Weight of the No. 9 bridge is 9,144 kg, and it is produced by Laird (Anglesey) Limited.

The widths that can be bridged by the two bridges are from 22.25 metres to 22.86 metres for the No. 8, dependent on the state of the banks, and 12.2 metres for the No. 9.

Production of the Chieftain Bridgelayer is carried out at the Royal Ordnance Factory, Leeds, with final production taking place at Nottingham.

A possible future use for the Chieftain Bridgelayer is as the British carrier of what will one day be the next generation of military bridges. At present, the United Kingdom, the USA and West Germany are planning and developing a new bridging system that can be used as the basis of an assault bridge, a dry gap support bridge and a water gap support bridge. Already the form of the future system has been decided but a great deal of development work remains to be completed before any hardware gets into service. The time into service is stated to be mid-1988. The bridge to be used is an American design that can be adapted readily to suit the three main roles, but its final form has yet to be decided. From what little has been released it can be seen that the future Chieftain Bridgelayer will be involved in the assault role. A 30-metre bridge will be used for this, while the other tasks will be covered by a new 10 × 10 wheeled vehicle. It is planned that the assault bridge will be laid in about three to five minutes.

FV101 Scorpion

Armament 1 × 76 mm L23A1 Gun, 1 × 7.62 mm L43A1 Machine-Gun and 2 × 3- or 4-barrel smoke dischargers; **Crew** 3; **Weight in action** 7,938 kg; **Length overall** 4.788 m; **Length of hull** 4.572 m; **Height** 2.102 m; **Width (overall)** 2.235 m; **Width (over tracks)** 2.134 m; **Track width** 0.432 m; **Ground clearance (approx)** 0.356 m; **Maximum road speed** 80.5 km/h; **Range (roads)** 644 km; **Engine type** Jaguar J60 No. 1 Mark 100B; **Engine power** 190 bhp; **Engine capacity** 4.235 litres; **Fuel capacity** 423 litres; **Ammunition capacity** 76 mm —40 rounds, 7.62 mm—3,000 rounds; **Main armament elevation** −10° to +35°; **Main armament traverse** 360°.

By 1960 it was becoming apparent that the time was approaching when consideration would have to be given to replacing the then current family of reconnaissance vehicles which included the FV701 Ferret, FV601 Saladin and FV603 Saracen. As always, it was decided that the new vehicle was to be lighter, faster and air-portable. The early specification called for a weight limitation of 8,200 kg which made the new vehicle about one-third

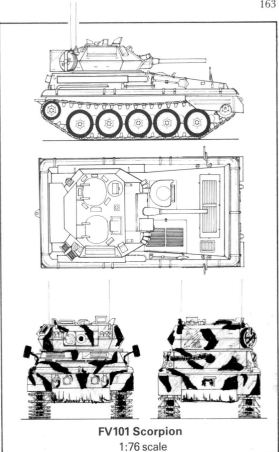

FV101 Scorpion
1:76 scale

lighter than any existing comparable type. To make the specification more difficult it was requested that the one vehicle should be capable of three major tasks—reconnaissance, fire support and anti-tank fire. Several design studies were made, one of which was the Armoured Vehicle Reconnaissance armed with a 76 mm or 105 mm gun. All these early studies had one major weakness in that they were too heavy. The end result was that it was decided to produce a family of tracked vehicles able to specialise in the various roles, since no one vehicle could combine all the requirements and still meet the air-portability strictures.

By 1963 the first hardware of the new project was produced as the TV15000 test vehicle. Much of the early work was carried out at the Fighting Vehicle Research and Development Establishment at Chobham in Surrey. The early results with the TV15000 led to the Mobile Test Rig which embodied nearly all the main motive and suspension details which were to become production features of what was by then known as the Combat Vehicle

Left *An FV101 Scorpion, unusual in that the turret hatches are open but the driver's hatch is closed down. This example is owned by the 17th/21st Lancers, but still has the wading screens fitted.* **Right** *An FV102 Striker fresh from the factory (Alvis Ltd).*

Reconnaissance (Tracked), or CVR(T).

In September 1967, Alvis Limited of Coventry were awarded the initial contract for 17 prototypes of what was eventually labelled FV101 Scorpion. Alvis rolled out the first prototype in January 1969, and by just over one year later all the prototypes had been delivered. Following extensive trials in all variations of terrain and climate, Alvis were awarded the full production contract for over 2,000 vehicles for the British Army—that was in May 1970 and the first full production model was completed in early 1972.

FV101 Scorpion was able to meet its stringent weight limits by the lavish use of welded aluminium armour which resulted in a much lighter hull and turret than the conventional steel. The thickness of the aluminium plates involved also allowed the main construction to be accomplished without the use of internal frames and stringers which enabled the weight to be reduced still further. The early weight restrictions were based on the carrying capacity of the Hawker Siddeley HS681 military transport project but that aircraft was one of the many victims of Government defence spending cuts and was never built. The aircraft now most likely to carry the Scorpion is the C-130 Hercules which can take two vehicles at one loading.

The general layout of Scorpion places the engine forward and the turret at the rear. The power plant is a de-rated version of the famous Jaguar 4.2-litre engine, but even in this form it gives Scorpion a very high power-to-weight ratio with all its subsequent advantages in agility and cross-country performance, which can be said to be limited by what the crew can physically stand. The turret accommodates two of the three crew members—the com-

mander is on the left with the gunner on the right. Forward of the turret, the driver sits on the left. All the crew members are furnished with vision devices, and night vision devices can be added for all positions. The gunner controls not only the 76 mm main gun but also the L43A1 Machine-Gun which doubles as a ranging device and co-axial weapon. Water obstacles present no problems for Scorpion, as it is able to ford about 1 metre without preparation. For deeper obstacles an integral wading screen can be raised by the crew in about five minutes, and the vehicle can then float using the tracks as the propulsion components, but a propeller kit has been developed which raises the water-crossing speed from 6.4 km/h to 9.65 km/h.

FV101 Scorpion is now used by the four armoured reconnaissance regiments of 1 (Br) Corps in West Germany. It has also been a considerable export success and has been sold to many nations, but within NATO the most important of these is Belgium, who ordered some 700 examples of the Scorpion family in October 1970. In late 1979 it was reported that the cost of a fully-equipped Scorpion was about £120,000.

While the Scorpion has emerged as a highly successful and useful reconnaissance vehicle it cannot be said to be capable of fulfilling all the roles required of it—for one thing its 76 mm gun, while useful as a support weapon and capable of defeating light armour, cannot deal with heavy main battle tanks. From this has grown the family of Scorpion variants which are described later.

During 1978 it was announced that the ranging machine-gun used with the Scorpion's 76 mm gun would be replaced by a laser rangefinder. The rangefinder involved is the LV10 produced by

United Scientific Instruments. The new rangefinder will eventually be only one part of a more general improvements package to be applied to all Scorpions and other vehicles in the CVR range, and which is planned for completion by about 1983-1984. For the Scorpion the main changes will be a new thermal imager sight for the commander, an improved anti-aircraft gun sight, improved external stowage, and powered traverse for the turret (some of these improvements will also apply to the FV107 Scimitar and the FV721 Fox). Other alterations will be made to the suspension and track to increase the track life, and some modifications will be made to the engine exhaust and ventilation systems to reduce the vehicle's 'thermal signature' detectable by infra-red and thermal imaging devices. For the crew, some changes will be made to internal ventilation and various crew stations to make the interior more habitable when the vehicle has to operate closed down over extended periods. Well before the planned completion date the flotation screens will have been removed from the Scorpion range of vehicles as it has now been assumed that their use in Europe will be limited—this will apply only to CVR(T)s used by the armoured divisions, and similar vehicles used by other arms of the service may retain them.

FV102 Striker

Armament 10 × Swingfire missiles, 1 × 7.62 mm L37A1 Machine-Gun and 2 × 4-barrel smoke dischargers; **Crew** 3; **Weight in action** 8,346 kg;

Length overall 4.826 m; **Height (overall)** 2.21 m; **Height (top of hull)** 1.727 m; **Width overall** 2.242 m; **Track width** 0.432 m; **Ground clearance (approx)** 0.356 m; **Maximum road speed** 80.5 km/h; **Range (roads)** 483 km; **Engine type** Jaguar J60 No. 1 Mark 100B; **Engine power** 190 bhp; **Engine capacity** 4.235 litres; **Fuel capacity** 350 litres; **Ammunition capacity** 10 × Swingfire missiles, 7.62 mm—3,000 rounds; **Main armament elevation** 35°; **Main armament traverse** 53° left, 55° right.

FV102 Striker entered service during 1978 and at present at least one troop of each anti-tank battery allotted to each armoured division in 1 (Br) Corps is equipped with this vehicle. Using the same suspension and automotive components as fitted to the FV101 Scorpion, Striker uses a hull similar in shape and outline to that of the FV103 Spartan but at the hull top rear are five racks for Swingfire anti-tank missiles, with capacity for a further five ready for loading inside the hull. The resemblance to Spartan is no accident or manufacturing expedient. Striker is designed to be a tank killer capable of destroying enemy tanks out to a range of 4,000 metres, but like all similar tank killers, it is the prime target not only of enemy tanks but also of missile-armed helicopters and ground attack aircraft. Normally, Striker is deployed with the five missile bins lowered—only when the missiles are due to be launched are the racks raised 35° to the firing position. With the racks lowered Striker is then almost indistinguishable from Spartan, and enemy attention is thus far

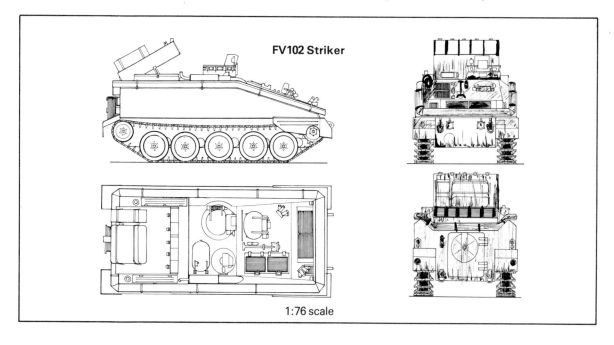

FV102 Striker

1:76 scale

less likely to be attracted towards it, while other contemporary tank killers betray their role by the prominent missiles strewn over their hulls and turrets.

Striker is not just a Spartan with missile racks. It can be regarded as a weapon system with several unusual features. Like all Swingfire launchers, the firing can be controlled from inside the vehicle or remotely from outside it. Troop trials have shown that controlling the Swingfire missile in flight is no easy task, especially in a cross-wind, so the vehicle sight has the unusual extra of a flight simulator built in. Operators can then gain valuable experience in using the sights and the missile controls, both in

training and, if necessary, on the battlefield. This simulator is considered to be a valuable aid to combat efficiency and to date, Swingfire is the only known missile system with this facility.

For close-in defence a 7.62 mm GPMG is fitted to the commander's No. 26 cupola, and the usual smoke dischargers are fitted to the hull front. As with all the Scorpion variants, night-driving and night-fighting vision devices can be fitted and the wading screens are optional.

FV103 Spartan

Armament 1 × 7.62 mm L37A1 Machine-Gun, 2 × 4-barrel smoke dischargers; **Crew** 3 + 4; **Weight in action** 8,172 kg; **Length overall** 4.93 m; **Height** 2.26 m; **Width** 2.242 m; **Track width** 0.432 m; **Ground clearance (approx)** 0.356 m; **Maximum road speed** 80.5 km/h; **Range (roads)** 483 km; **Engine type** Jaguar J60 No. 1 Mark 100B; **Engine power** 190 bhp; **Engine capacity** 4.235 litres; **Fuel capacity** 386 litres; **Ammunition capacity** 7.62 mm—3,000 rounds.

FV103 Spartan is the armoured personnel carrier (APC) component of the Scorpion range, and as such it consists of a box-type aluminium armour body built on to the basic Scorpion hull and suspension. Inside the box is accommodation for the driver, commander and machine-gunner, plus four men with all their equipment. As these 'four men' are rather les than the conventional infantry squad or team, Spartan is used as a special purposes vehicle rather than a normal APC. Possible roles that Spar-

Above *On the right, an FV103 Spartan—on the left the wider and longer FV4333.* **Left** *An FV103 Spartan.*

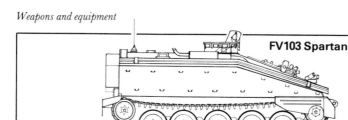

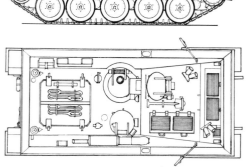

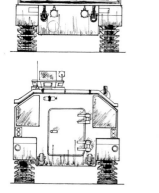

FV103 Spartan

1:76 scale

tan will fit are Blowpipe anti-aircraft missile team carrier, assault pioneer team carrier, anti-ambush patrols in rear areas, and as a carrier for the No. 14 (ZB298) battlefield surveillance radar. The first Spartans were issued for service in 1976.

The future role of Spartan might well be expanded into the anti-aircraft role even further for it has been repeatedly rumoured that it will be the carrier for some form of multiple Blowpipe launcher, with the launcher mounted on the roof over the escape hatch. This anti-aircraft role is probably the main reason for the development of a Spartan variant known as the FV4333 Stormer and shown for the first time during 1978. The FV4333 is some 18 cm wider than Spartan and has been extended to accommodate an extra road wheel. As an APC the FV4333 could accommodate ten men plus a crew of two but it is not thought that this is the reason that it was developed under the guidance of the MVEE. Although the project purpose has not been officially revealed it is widely believed that the FV4333 will emerge (if the project is continued) as an anti-aircraft vehicle mounting twin 35 mm cannon or a multiple Blowpipe launcher. But at the time of writing this is pure conjecture, even though an export version of the FV103 Spartan has been offered with a fitting of two 20 mm cannon.

FV104 Samaritan

Armament 2 × 4-barrel smoke dischargers; **Crew** 2 or 3; **Weight in action** 8,664 kg; **Length overall** 5.067 m; **Height (overall)** 2.416 m; **Height (top of hull)** 2.016 m; **Width overall** 2.242 m; **Track widwidth** 0.432 m; **Ground clearance (approx)** 0.356 m; **Maximum road speed** 72.5 km/h; **Range**

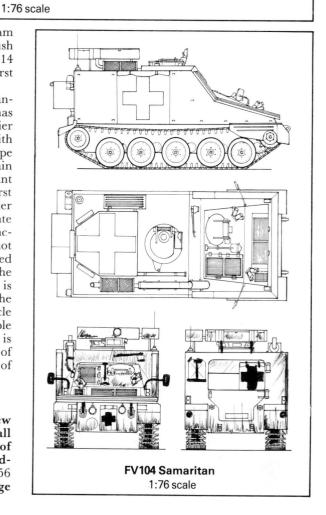

FV104 Samaritan
1:76 scale

Left *The FV104 Samaritan.* **Right** *An FV105 Sultan. The screens for the 'penthouse' can be seen stowed on the sloping front hull and extra stowage bins are fitted to the roof* (Alvis Ltd).

medical care and attentions. The carrying capacity of Samaritan is flexible according to the situation. In peacetime the commander doubles as a medical orderly which gives room for four stretcher cases, or five sitting wounded—a mix of two stretcher cases plus three sitting is possible. In combat conditions it is intended that the crew will be augmented by a medical orderly, leaving the commander to look after the vehicle, but this extra crew member reduces the casualty capacity to only four stretcher cases or four sitting wounded. For a mixed situation two stretcher cases and two sitting can be carried. Other facilities to suit the medical role are improved ventilation and some consideration has been given to reducing internal noise levels. An extra large door is also fitted. The hull shape and configuration is shared by FV105 Sultan.

The first Samaritans entered service in 1978. Being an ambulance, Samaritan carries no defensive armament other than the two multi-barrel smoke dischargers on the hull front. Like most other Scorpion variants wading screens are fitted.

(roads) 483 km; **Engine type** Jaguar J60 No. 1 Mark 100B; **Engine power** 190 bhp; **Engine capacity** 4.235 litres; **Fuel capacity** 395 litres.

FV104 Samaritan is the armoured ambulance component of the Scorpion range of vehicles, and as such uses the Scorpion automotive components allied to a new armoured box hull. The roof of the Samaritan has been appreciably raised to make more room for the stowage of casualties, together with space for a medical orderly to administer

FV105 Sultan

Armament 1 × 7.62 mm L7A2 Machine-Gun, 2 × 4-barrel smoke dischargers; **Crew** 5 or 6; **Weight in action** 8,664 kg; **Length overall** 4.8 m; **Height**

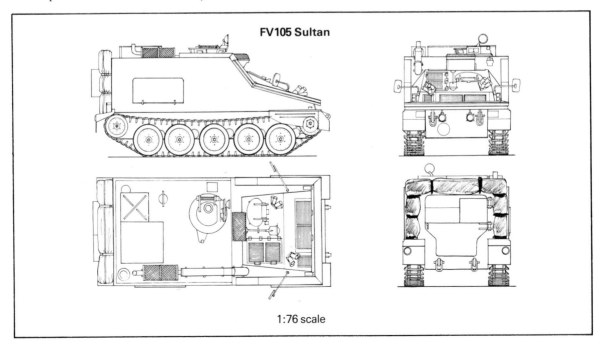

FV105 Sultan

1:76 scale

overall 2.559 m; **Height (top of hull)** 2.026 m; **Width (overall)** 2.242 m; **Width (over tracks)** 2.134 m; **Track width** 0.432 m; **Ground clearance (approx)** 0.356 m; **Penthouse length** 2.591 m; **Penthouse height** 2.235 m; **Penthouse width** 2.134 m; **Maximum road speed** 72.5 km/h; **Range (roads)** 483 km; **Engine type** Jaguar J60 No. 1 Mark 100B; **Engine power** 190 bhp; **Engine capacity** 4.235 litres; **Fuel capacity** 395 litres; **Ammunition capacity** 7.62 mm—2,000 rounds.

FV105 Sultan is the armoured command vehicle component of the Scorpion family, and as such uses a raised box hull to contain the radios, control equipment and mapboards, to say nothing of the extra men, that will be needed in this role. Command vehicles are subject to much coming and going and although the interior of the Sultan can accommodate its crew of five or six men, it cannot accommodate everyone who will require access to the information and communication equipment installed, so a collapsible 'penthouse' is fitted over the rear, ready for use as and when required. The exact 'fit' of the Sultan can be altered to suit the needs of any particular unit or type of unit, but mapboards, plastic screens and radios are standard, as is extra lighting. As with FV104 Samaritan, extra air conditioning is fitted in the roof (the hull shapes are the same), and the sloping front hull mounts a radio aerial which, like its supporting joists, is collapsible. The roof hatch is fitted with a pintle for an L7A2 GPMG which can be dismounted for local defence.

FV106 Samson

Armament 1 × 7.62 mm L7A2 Machine-Gun, 2 × 4-barrel smoke dischargers; **Crew** 3; **Weight in action** 8,738 kg; **Length overall** 5.004 m; **Length of vehicle** 4.788 m; **Height overall** 2.254 m; **Height (top of hull)** 1.718 m; **Width overall** 2.43 m; **Track width** 0.432 m; **Ground clearance (approx)** 0.356 m; **Maximum road speed** 72.5 km/h; **Range (roads)** 483 km; **Engine type** Jaguar J60

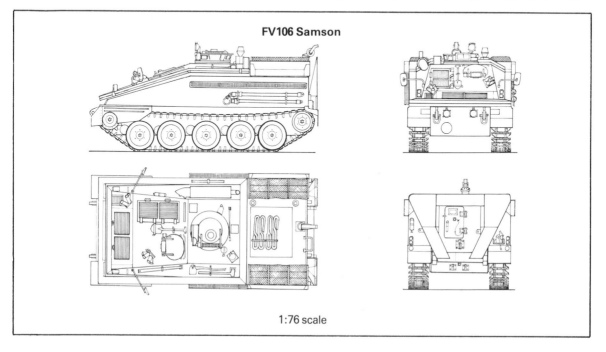

FV106 Samson

1:76 scale

No. 1 Mark 100B; **Engine power** 190 bhp; **Engine capacity** 4.235 litres; **Fuel capacity** 404.5 litres; **Ammunition capacity** 7.62 mm—2,000 rounds.

Entering production during 1979, FV106 Sultan was the last of the Scorpion family to be produced. It is an armoured recovery vehicle using the basic box structure of the FV103 Spartan carrier, but many interior design changes have been made. For its main recovery role, Samson is fitted with an internally-mounted winch driven from the main engine. The winch can be driven at variable speeds up to a maximum of 122 metres a minute and the drum is fitted with 229 metres of wire rope. Using a standard 4:1 snatch block the winch can pull a load of up to 12 tons and is thus capable of pulling a load greater than the weight of the Samson itself. To assist the pulling of such heavy loads, Samson is fitted with a large and heavy pair of spades hinged on the rear bulkhead—in use these are swung downwards and the vehicle is reversed so that the spades dig into the ground and lift the vehicle rear upwards. In this manner the winch can pull heavy loads without moving the Samson itself, and vehicles the size of the FV432 can be pulled without too much difficulty. Other fitments that can assist in the recovery role are a small jib crane, also driven from the main engine, and a bench vice, along with other specialised equipment. Racks on the sides hold baulks of timber for a hundred-and-one purposes, and extra hand tools. The rear door is rather small and the interior rather cramped as the winch takes up most of the available space. A GPMG is fitted to the commander's hatch pintle, but this can easily be dismounted for local defence.

FV107 Scimitar

Armament 1 × 30 mm Rarden L21 Gun, 1 × 7.62 mm L37A1 Machine-Gun and 2 × 4-barrel smoke dischargers; **Crew** 3; **Weight in action** 7,750 kg; **Length overall** 4.985 m; **Length of hull** 4.572 m; **Height** 2.096 m; **Width (overall)** 2.242 m; **Width (over tracks)** 2.134 m; **Track width** 0.432 m; **Ground clearance (approx)** 0.356 m; **Maximum road speed** 80.5 km/h; **Range (roads)** 644 km; **Engine type** Jaguar J60 No. 1 Mark 100B; **Engine power** 190 bhp; **Engine capacity** 4.235 litres; **Fuel capacity** 423 litres; **Ammunition capacity** 30 mm—165 rounds, 7.62 mm—3,000 rounds; **Main armament elevation** −10° to +35°; **Main armament traverse** 360°.

Despite having the highest FV number in the Scorpion family, Scimitar was actually the second variant to go into production and service (the last was delivered during late 1978). Scimitar is basically the same vehicle as the FV101 but the turret does differ in some ways from that of the Scorpion, and is armed with a 30 mm Rarden gun. Otherwise the two vehicles differ but little, but tactically their roles are not interchangeable, or at least, not in BAOR. In the armoured reconnaissance regiments of 1 (Br) Corps, each regiment has one squadron equipped with Scimitar for the close reconnaissance role. As such it is assigned in independent troops at task force level. In a UK-based armoured reconnaissance regiment the medium reconnaissance troops use both Scimitar and Scorpion. In the 1 (Br) Corps organisation Scimitar may be used in direct support of infantry combat teams or battle groups. Many of the mid-life changes

Far left *Rear view of an FV106 Samson, clearly showing the rear spade dug in, and the positioning of the winch and guy stays. Note also the handy vice on the rear bulkhead.*

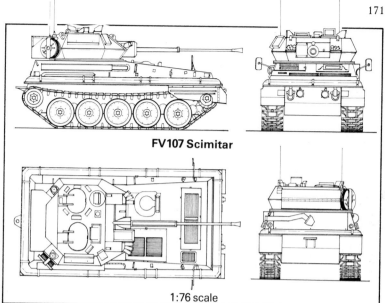

FV107 Scimitar

1:76 scale

Left *An FV107 Scimitar dug in overlooking San Carlos Bay, East Falkland, during the re-occupation of the islands in June 1982 (Popperfoto).*

planned for the FV101 Scorpion will also be applied to the Scimitar. Already many Scimitars used by the Royal Armoured Corps have had their wading screens removed.

FV721 Fox

Armament 1 × 30 mm Rarden L21 Gun, 1 × 7.62 mm L8A1 Machine-Gun and 2 × 4-barrel smoke dischargers; **Crew** 3; **Weight in action** 6,386 kg; **Length (gun forward)** 5.359 m; **Length of hull** 4.166 m; **Height** 2.2 m; **Width** 2.134 m; **Wheel track** 1.753 m; **Ground clearance** 0.3 m; **Maximum road speed** 104 km/h; **Range (roads)** 430 km; **Engine type** Jaguar J60 No. 1 Mark 100B; **Engine power** 195 bhp; **Engine capacity** 4.235 litres; **Fuel capacity** 145.47 litres; **Ammunition capacity** 30 mm—99 rounds, 7.62 mm—2,600 rounds; **Main armament elevation** −14° to +40°; **Main armament traverse** 360°.

During the early 1960s it was decided to produce a replacement for the Ferret reconnaissance vehicles and early studies and designs were evaluated at what is now the Military Vehicle Experimental Establishment at Chobham in Surrey. In 1965 the project, which was then known as the Combat Vehicle Reconnaissance (Wheeled), or CVR(W), emerged as a gradual development of the existing Ferret design incorporating such new technology as aluminium armour and a turret mounting the Rarden 30 mm gun. Prototype production was handled by Daimler at Radford, Coventry, who went on to complete a total of 15 prototypes, starting in 1966 with the first example being ready in late 1967. However, the main contract went to the Royal

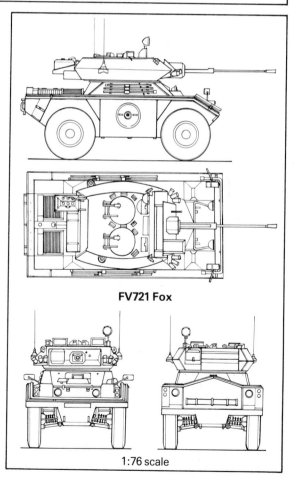

FV721 Fox

1:76 scale

Ordnance Factory at Leeds, which completed its first production version during 1973.

FV721 Fox is basically an updated version of the Ferret but every aspect of the former has been reworked and redesigned from scratch. The turret, produced by Alvis Limited, is the same as that used by the FV107 Scimitar but the internal stowage has been somewhat altered—for example the ammunition capacity is 66 rounds less. The Jaguar engine gives the Fox a lively performance, and its cross-country capabilities are such that it is likely to cross any type of terrain. Three Foxes can be carried in a single C-130 Hercules and two can be para-dropped together on a special platform. Early production models were fitted with wading screens for crossing deep water obstacles but these have now been removed and late production models have no provision for them.

During the early service career of the Fox some serious accidents occurred which caused some doubts to be expressed as to its stability, mainly in view of the seeming 'top-heaviness' of the design. Trials showed that the Fox was likely, in certain conditions to 'over-steer' and the driver's instinctive reactions only made the situation worse. A corrective course of training removed the likelihood of the 'over-steer' condition happening and the vehicle now no longer suffers its early accident rate.

The early plans to replace the Ferret as a general reconnaissance vehicle have now been virtually completed (despite the fact that the Ferret continues its distinguished service career). At the time of writing there are three armoured reconnaissance regiments equipped with the Fox, one regular and two TA. The UK-based armoured reconnaissance regiment close reconnaissance troops are equipped with the Fox, while in the TA regiments, all the recce squadrons are so equipped. (The TA regiments involved are the Royal Yeomanry and the Queens Own Yeomanry.) The Fox is also used in the medium reconnaissance role by the two Fox squadrons based at Omagh in Northern Ireland.

One off-shoot of the FV721 Fox was the FV722 Vixen, which was a simplified Fox fitted with a small turret mounting a GPMG. The intention was to provide a liaison vehicle suitable for Infantry and Engineer units, but it was a victim of one of the many Defence spending cuts and only prototypes were made. But the idea of a cheaper version of the Fox is not yet dead (although it is unlikely to enter British Army service), as Peak Engineering have produced a GPMG turret suitable for installation on a production Fox.

Top left *The FV721 Fox on an exercise—note the rear turret stowage.* **Above left** *At speed.* **Left** *The aluminium hull.*

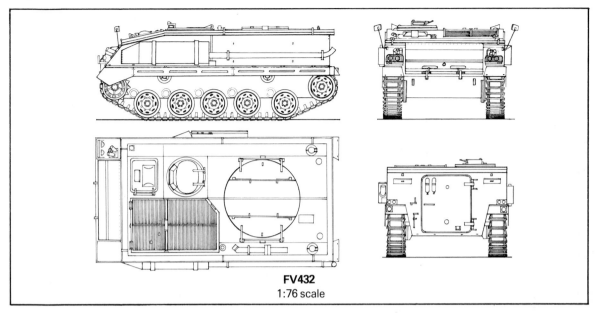

FV432
1:76 scale

FV432

Basic versions

Armament 1 × 7.62 mm L7A2 Machine-Gun, 2 × 3-barrel smoke dischargers; **Crew** 2 + 10; **Weight in action** 15,280 kg; **Length overall** 5.251 m; **Length of hull** 4.826 m; **Height overall** 2.286 m; **Height (to roof)** 1.879 m; **Width (overall)** 2.8 m; **Width (over tracks)** 2.527 m; **Track width** 0.343 m; **Ground clearance** 0.406 m; **Maximum road speed** 52 km/h; **Range (roads)** 580 km; **Engine type** Rolls-Royce K60 No. 4 Mark 4F; **Engine power** 240 bhp; **Engine capacity** 6.57 litres; **Fuel capacity** 454 litres; **Ammunition capacity** 1,600 rounds plus.

The FV432 is by far the most numerous of all the tracked vehicles used by the British Army, and exists in a wide variety of versions with an even greater variety of differing equipment installations. The FV432 is used by almost every branch of the British Army, and as every branch requires the vehicle to carry out a different role, this section of the book will deal with the FV432 as a basic vehicle, while I will deal separately with how it is used by the Infantry, the Royal Artillery and the Royal Engineers. Also included in this section will be those versions used by all branches of the Service.

The FV432 development cycle can be traced back to before 1939 when the Bren Gun and Universal Carriers were in widespread Army use. From these there gradually evolved a post-war family of carriers known as the FV400 series which were further developed into the FV420 series. There were six dif-

ferent vehicles in the FV420 series with each one intended for a different role and, from these, after trials with several prototypes, evolved the FV430 series. The first of the FV430s was the FV431 Load Carrier, but only a prototype was built. However, it did provide the basis for the rest of the FV432 series, production of which began in 1962. The concern that built the FV432 was GKN Sankey of Wellington, Shropshire, which kept the range in production until 1971. There have been four basic types of FV432 starting with the Mark 1 which had a prominent exhaust system on the left-hand side of the vehicle. Then came the Mark 1/1, the Mark 2 and the Mark 2/2. The later versions all had their exhausts re-routed to over the roof, and the last versions can be recognised by the almost-flush NBC filter box on the right-hand side plate.

Construction of the FV432 follows that of a steel-plate box mounted on tracks with the engine at the front. The main access door is at the rear while the commander and driver both have their own hatches. Over the main compartment is a four-piece circular hatch, while the engine compartment has access via a front plate and through a roof hatch next to the driver who sits on the right-hand side. This simple structure provides the basis for a wide number of variants, and some of them, the FV433 105 mm Self-Propelled Gun, the FV434 Maintenance Carrier, the FV438 Swingfire and the FV439 Signals Vehicle, warrant their own separate entries. With the exception of the last-mentioned vehicles, all the FV432 vehicles can be switched from one role or equipment fit to another.

Armoured Personnel Carrier: The APC role is the primary reason for the FV432's existence and as such it carries a crew of two and up to ten fully armed soldiers. The soldiers are carried in two rows of five along each side wall and face inwards. They have no external vision devices when the vehicle is closed down (only the driver and commander have these) and no way of using their own personal weapons unless a hatch is opened. The only weapon that is usually in use when closed down is the dismountable L7A2 GPMG by the commander's hatch, and to fire this the commander has to expose his head and shoulders to possible enemy fire. The inability of the soldiers to fire from the FV432, or even see anything from inside, is one of the FV432's most serious faults, as more modern APCs usually provide each soldier with a firing point and some form of vision device. From personal experience after a period of time spent travelling in a closed-down FV432, when the time comes to 'de-bus' and go into action, the most common reaction is one of serious disorientation while local conditions, directions and features are taken into account.

The FV432 is fitted with integral wading screens and has all the usual NBC air-cleaning equipment. Armour thicknesses vary from 6 to 12 mm over the vehicle. Any mark of FV432 is likely to be encountered in the basic APC role, but the very early Mark 1s with Rolls-Royce B-81 Mark 8F petrol engines are now used only at the Suffield Training Ground

Above left FV432 in its muddy element. **Left** *FV432s on the Suffield Ranges.* **Below left** *Four FV432s comprising a Regimental HQ—all are equipped for the Command role. Sennelager, 7.7.77.* **Below** *An RAMC section equipped with FV432s for the ambulance role.*

in Canada where they are gradually being worn out by repeated training exercises under all conditions of climate.

Command vehicle: The FV432 can be easily converted into a command vehicle by the fitting of a kit which includes sliding map boards, folding tables, fluorescent lamps and extra radios. However, many units have their own particular requirements and this 'fit' will vary accordingly. One feature on the command FV432s is a canvas 'penthouse' which extends from over the rear door. The dimensions of this are 3.66 × 2.74 × 1.98 metres. The usual weight in action of the command FV432 is about 15,500 kg, and the number of men carried is seven. A useful recognition feature of a command FV432 on the move is the stowage of the penthouse joists on the side.

Ambulance: Any FV432 can be easily converted to the ambulance role, and racks for four stretchers can be fitted, two to each side. If two stretchers are not fitted, up to five sitting casualties can be carried. When in the ambulance role, no armament other than the smoke dischargers is retained.

Cargo carrier: When the basic FV432 has its ten seats folded upwards, or removed altogether, the interior can accommodate a wide variety of different bulk cargos such as ammunition or fuel. Up to 3,670 kg can be carried.

Recovery vehicle: For the recovery role the FV432 can be fitted with an internal winch driven from the main engine, with a cable directed through the main rear door. The winch is a Plumett auto-capstan Type CA45 and uses a double capstan with a direct pull of 6,608 kg. If a three-part tackle is used, up to 18,300 kg can be moved. The winch alone weighs 470 kg and is fitted with 250 metres of heavy cable. An extra external spade is fitted to the rear bulkhead for the recovery role. Another special part for the role is a shortened rear door, the space being taken up by a pulley which directs the cable.

FV432 with Wavell: During the early 1980s a number of FV432s will be converted to take the Wavell equipment needed to accommodate the front-line task force Wavell terminals and other associated equipment. In this version, power generators and air conditioning equipment will be fitted on the roof with the interior housing the two-man Wavell operators and racks holding the various 'black boxes'.

Above right *Command FV432 with extra radio aerials erected.*
Right *FV432 with a rough outline of the equipment involved for Wavell (Plessey Defence Systems).*

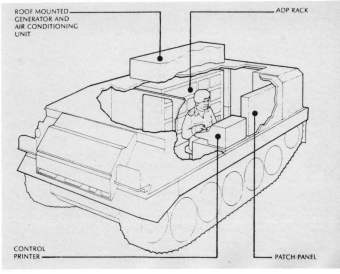

ROOF MOUNTED GENERATOR AND AIR CONDITIONING UNIT

ADP RACK

CONTROL PRINTER

PATCH PANEL

Top *A Wombat ready for use from the top hatch of an FV432.*
Top right *Cymbeline-equipped FV432 of the Royal Artillery.*
Above *FV432 with a twin-GPMG SCAT mounting for anti-aircraft defence.*

Infantry versions

81 mm Mortar: Each mechanised infantry battalion has on its support company strength a total of six FV432s fitted with the 81 mm Mortar L16A1 firing through the circular main roof hatch. The 81 mm Mortar can be fitted into any FV432 by the installation of a special turntable mounting which provides a full 360° traverse. Internal racks are fitted for the ammunition, and up to 160 bombs can be carried. When on the FV432 mounting only the barrel and the sighting unit are fitted—the baseplate and the bipod have been seen stowed both internally

and externally, ready for possible dismounted use. In the mortar role, the normal FV432 crew complement is increased to six, and the weight in action is about 16,400 kg.

120 mm Wombat: The 120 mm Wombat L6 is another weapon held at battalion level, and in a mechanised infantry battalion the number employed is four to six. Each Wombat is carried in a FV432 converted for its use by the addition of a small pivot mount, ramps, a small winch and racks for the ammunition. On the move the Wombat is carried inside the vehicle, but once in action it can either be dismounted for firing or it can be raised on to the internal pivot mounting. Once on the pivot the barrel protrudes through the large roof hatch and can be traversed through 270°. The normal crew is five and weight in action is about 15,870 kg. Only 14 rounds of the bulky 120 mm ammunition can be carried.

The introduction of Milan will mean the end of the FV432 Wombat vehicle and by the end of 1982 the changeover will be complete in BAOR.

84 mm Infantry Gun: In order to fire the 84 mm Carl Gustav from the FV432 a special bar rest can be fitted across the main roof hatch.

7.62 mm GPMG turret: In order to give the FV432 commander some degree of protection when firing the 7.62 mm GPMG from his hatch, some FV432s have been fitted with a small GPMG turret in a new location over a permanently closed circular main roof hatch. The new turret, made by Peak Engineering Limited of Stratford-on-Avon, mounts a L37A1 Machine-Gun and has an extra four smoke dischargers on each side. When closed down the machine-gun is aimed by a periscopic sight. As well as having a full 360° traverse, the gun can be elevated to about 50° giving it a limited anti-aircraft or anti-helicopter capability. All traverse and elevation controls are by hand, and the gunner sits on a small seat fitted to the turret ring.

7.62 mm GPMG 'SCAT' mounting: In an attempt to increase the firepower and anti-aircraft potential of the FV432, trials have been carried out with the mounting of twin L7A2 GPMGs on the commander's hatch. Various configurations have been made but the one selected for possible service is the SCAT mounting with a side-by-side arrangement. The usual 360° traverse is retained and elevation is possible up to 90°, at which elevation the gunner can obtain some degree of protection from within the hatch. The origin of the term 'SCAT' is uncertain but one likely source is that the mounting 'Should Cost A Tenner'! The exact status of this mounting is uncertain.

30 mm Rarden turret: Although this project has now been terminated, some conversions were made to allow the FV432 to accommodate an FV721 Fox turret complete with the 30 mm L21 gun. A small batch of 13 conversions was carried out and demonstrated, these being used for troop trials in Germany until the project was ended during mid-1976. The converted FV432s were then issued to the Berlin Field Force where they remain.

The turret was placed over the circular roof hatch but, although the Rarden would undoubtedly give the FV432 a useful offensive and fire-support potential, the vehicle is no doubt top-heavy and unwieldy. Space inside the main compartment is also rather cramped. As the FV107 Scimitar was also being produced for the same role, the Rarden FV432 was no doubt thought to be too much of an expensive luxury with no precise operational task.

Radar GS No. 14 Mark 1: Battlefield surveillance is an Infantry responsibility and to enable it to carry out this task at night or in poor visibility, some FV432s have been fitted with the Radar GS No. 14 Mark 1 (the ZB 298). As mentioned in the section on this radar, the No. 14 detects movement and has a range of 10,000 metres. When in use in an FV432, the No. 14 can be recognised by its distinctive 'suitcase' aerial, usually mounted on the roof towards the rear.

Milan: Each mechanised infantry platoon is shortly to be issued with a Milan anti-tank missile launcher and the corresponding missiles in their pre-packed tubes. The launcher and the missiles will be carried inside an FV432 stowed on special racks, but it is not intended that the missile be fired from the roof of the vehicle itself, although there is no reason why this should not be done if the tactical circumstances dictate such a method. Normally the Milan will be fired from a dismounted position.

Top *One of the few FV432s fitted with a 30 mm Rarden turret.*
Above *A FACE FV432—note the extra stowage bins on the roof.*

Beach version: For some years the Army used a 'one-off' beach version of the FV432 for general use in beach training operations at a location in Devon. The FV432 had special waterproofing and exhaust re-location and was often used to tow boat-launching trailers. Its present status is not known.

Royal Artillery versions

Royal Artillery FV432s use the L4A4 Bren Gun as their main armament.

FACE: Every Royal Artillery battery has at least one, and sometimes two, FV432s equipped with a FACE fire control computer. Looking from the

rear, the main computer is on the left-hand side—down the right-hand side are racks to take the books, tables and other paperwork associated with the computer. Also on the left is a teleprinter/typewriter used with the system. Extra racking is carried on the roof for the crew's bedding and belongings, and some are also fitted with the command 'penthouse'. The FACE FV432s cannot be easily converted to any other role.

Cymbeline: 105 mm field regiments of the Royal Artillery have a mortar-locating role and up to about 1976 the main radar used in this role was Green Archer. Some of these radars were fitted to a special FV432 variant, the FV436, but these have now passed from service as the current mortar-locating radar is Cymbeline. This equipment is carried in self-propelled mortar-locating batteries on converted FV432s where the folding radar aerial is mounted on the vehicle roof. On the move the aerial is folded and contained in a wire mesh cage

for protection; when in action it is erected and rotates on a mounting fitted to the main circular roof hatch. The radar controls and displays are housed in the main compartment.

Sonic detection: Some artillery FV432s have been equipped as sonic detection vehicles and as such have all the appropriate aerials and detectors necessary for the role. The crew of this version is eight and the interior is equipped not only with sound recorders but also with map boards and extra radios. The sonic equipment concerned is the Sound Ranging Radio Link No. 2 Mark 1 which uses a line of up to seven carefully sited microphones transmitting, via radio, to the main equipment in the FV432. A forward observer switches on the microphones when necessary—at the same time he alerts the receiving and recording equipment. The resultant paper trace can be used to calculate the enemy position.

Royal Engineer versions
Royal Engineer FV432s also use the L4A4 Bren Gun as their main armament.

Bar Mine Layer: The FV432 is used by the Royal Engineers as their usual towing vehicle for the Bar Mine Layer system. The Bar Mine Layer is towed behind the FV432 with the mine conveyor protruding into the main compartment. The Bar Mines can thus be loaded and sown with the FV432 crew being almost completely protected.

Ranger: The Ranger anti-personnel mine layer system can be fitted over the main roof hatch of the FV432. The Ranger launcher has a traverse to the rear of 180° and can be elevated from +5° to +35°. When fitted, the launcher weighs 630 kg fully loaded. One possible configuration for Engineer FV432s is to have the Bar Mine Layer towed from the rear with a Ranger launcher fitted to the roof. The combination is then able to render whole tracts of country impassable to men or machines without time-consuming clearance measures.

Giant Viper: The Giant Viper mine-clearing system (L3A1) can be carried in a trailer behind a FV432.

MCV-80

Armament see text; **Crew** 2 + 8; **Weight in action** 20,000 kg; **Weight in action (FV510)** 23,800 kg; **Length** 5.42 m; **Height (top of FV510 turret)** 2.82 m; **Width** 2.8 m; **Ground clearance** 0.5 m; **Maximum road speed** 75 km/h; **Range (road)** 500 km; **Engine type** Rolls-Royce 8V800 diesel; **Engine power** 800 hp.

During the early 1970s GKN Sankey were awarded a contract to develop a new armoured personnel carrier for the Army, a vehicle that eventually became known as the MCV-80 (Mechanised Combat Vehicle 80). As ever, defence budget restraints prompted the Ministry of Defence to consider alternatives for the Army's future APC and at one time considerable attention was given to the American M2 and M3 Infantry Fighting Vehicles as possible future equipments. As it turned out, the decision went in favour of the UK-built MCV-80 and development is now proceeding apace to provide the next generation of APCs for the British Army.

To date, only prototype development vehicles of the MCV-80 have been produced and one of them, the FV510, is fitted with a two-man turret housing a 30 mm Rarden L21 gun and a co-axially mounted Hughes 7.62 mm Chain Gun. This latter weapon is a new one for the British Army and its operation relies on an externally powered electrical motor which drives all the machine-gun operations via a metal link chain—hence the name Chain Gun. The FV510 is intended to be a general squad vehicle with a crew of two and carrying eight fully armed troops who leave via two doors at the rear of the vehicle. There is no provision for the troops to use their weapons from inside.

The MCV-80 uses a torsion bar suspension, but there does not appear to be any provision for wading or amphibious equipment. A full NBC pack is provided and there will be a full range of night driving and other vision equipment provided.

As with the FV432 series, it is expected that the MCV-80 will be developed into a range of specialised vehicles. The following are known to be under development for the British Army: **1** A platoon and command vehicle with a small turret mounting a GPMG; **2** A mechanised recovery vehicle with a dozer blade at the front, a winch and a cupola-mounted GPMG; **3** An 81 mm Mortar carrier firing through a roof hatch, and with a cupola-mounted GPMG; **4** An engineer combat vehicle mounting a Ranger mine launcher on the rear upper decking and with a cupola-mounted GPMG; **5** An artillery command vehicle; and **6** A combat repair vehicle with a roof-mounted hydraulic crane with an extending jib, and a cupola-mounted GPMG. Other developments, including forms of missile-launchers are anticipated.

In the short term, the MCV-80 will only supplement the FV432 and it may be a long time before it will replace it. As it stands the MCV-80 is a hefty and expensive-looking piece of equipment with seemingly few development or design advantages over the venerable box on tracks that it is intended to replace. But the FV510 will provide the infantry with much-needed fire support under their own control, and it is to be hoped that the MCV-80 will enter service as soon as possible.

Below *The FV510 armed with a Rarden and a Chain Gun.*
Bottom *The platoon and command vehicle with GPMG turret.*

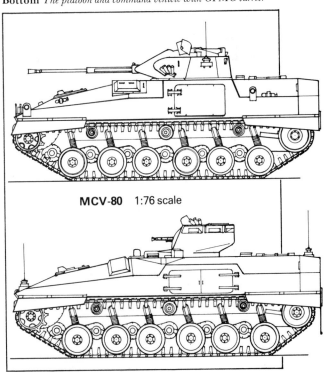

MCV-80 1:76 scale

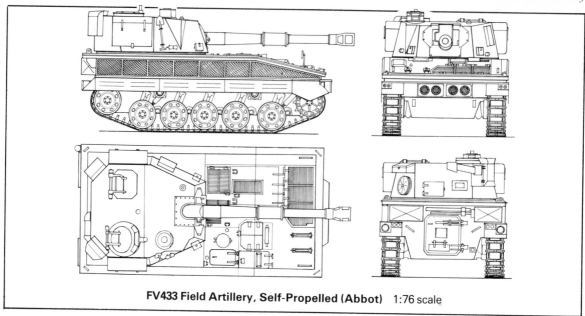

FV433 Field Artillery, Self-Propelled (Abbot)   1:76 scale

FV433 Field Artillery, Self-Propelled (Abbot)

Armament 1 × 105 mm L13A1 Gun, 1 × 7.62 mm L4A4 Machine-Gun and 2 × 3-barrel smoke dischargers; **Crew** 4; **Weight in action** 16,556 kg; **Length overall** 5.84 m; **Length of hull** 5.709 m; **Height (top of cupola)** 2.489 m; **Width** 2.641 m; **Track width** 0.343 m; **Ground clearance** 0.406 m; **Maximum road speed** 48 km/h; **Range (roads)** 390 km; **Engine type** Rolls-Royce K.60 Mark 4G; **Engine power** 240 bhp; **Engine capacity** 6.57 litres; **Fuel capacity** 386 litres; **Ammunition**

capacity 105 mm—40 rounds, 7.62 mm—1,200 rounds; **Main armament elevation** −5° to + 70°; **Main armament traverse** 360°.

The FV433 Abbot is the field artillery component of the FV432 family of vehicles and the first prototype was completed in 1961. The first battery was issued with production Abbots in 1965 and ever since then the vehicle has been the principal self-propelled weapon of Royal Artillery field regiments both in Germany and the United Kingdom. Each regiment has four batteries of Abbots and each battery has two troops of three guns each, although in some battle groups this might vary.

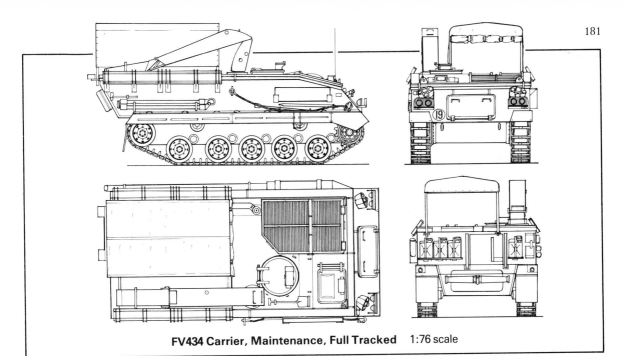

FV434 Carrier, Maintenance, Full Tracked   1:76 scale

The main production line for the Abbot was at the Vickers-Armstrong works at Elswick, Newcastle-upon-Tyne. Only the suspension components and the main engine are related at all closely to the FV432 for the Abbot differs in many ways from the rest of that family. The most obvious difference is the large and roomy turret at the rear which mounts the 105 mm L13A1 gun. The turret also provides the main stowage space for the 40 rounds of ammunition carried, six of which have HESH warheads for the possible engagement of enemy AFVs. (For convenience the number of rounds carried under normal circumstances is restricted to 38.) For ease of loading the gun is fitted with a power rammer, and power is also available for traversing the gun—elevation is by hand. The layer sits to the right of the gun.

As with all the rest of the FV432 family, wading screens are fitted as standard, and the full NBC air-cleaning gear is a normal fitment. In action the turret can be rotated for a full 360° and the hull need not be moved for any rapid change in traverse.

For export, Vickers-Armstrong developed a simplified version of the vehicle known as the Value-Engineered Abbot. In order to keep down costs of this version several features of the FV433 Abbot were left off, such as the wading gear, power ramming and traverse, the full NBC pack, and so on. The engine was de-rated to 213 bhp (and runs on

Far left Value-Engineered Abbots on the Suffield ranges. **Left** *A factory shot of an FV433 Abbot* (Vickers Ltd).

diesel fuel only) and anything that could be omitted, was omitted. The bulk of the Value-Engineered Abbots went to the Indian Army but the British Army obtained four for use at the Suffield Training Ground in Canada.

Operational experience in the various Middle East conflicts has shown that the smallest artillery calibre capable of breaking up massed armoured formations is now 155 mm. Thus the 105 mm Abbot is obsolescent in its main field artillery role and the Abbot batteries are now mainly used as close support systems for battle groups. However, the Abbot will still remain as one of the most important items in the Royal Artillery gun park for many years to come and there are at present no definite plans for its replacement unless it is to be by a substantially increased 'buy' of 155 mm equipment.

FV434 Carrier, Maintenance, Full Tracked

Armament 1 × 7.62 mm L4A4 Machine-Gun or 1 × 7.62 mm L7A2 Machine-Gun and 2 × 3-barrel smoke dischargers; **Crew** 4; **Weight in action** 17,750 kg; **Length overall** 5.72 m; **Height (top of crane)** 2.794 kg; **Height (roof)** 1.891 m; **Width (overall)** 2.844 m; **Width (over tracks)** 2.527 m; **Track width** 0.343 m; **Ground clearance** 0.419 m; **Maximum road speed** 47 km/h; **Range (roads)** 580 km; **Engine type** Rolls-Royce K60 No. 4 Mark 4F; **Engine power** 240 bhp; **Engine capacity** 6.57 litres; **Fuel capacity** 454 litres; **Ammunition**

Top *A REME FV434 at Larkhill—this example has the canvas tilt erected.* **Above** *FV438s at Sennelager, 7.7.77.*

capacity 7.62 mm—336 rounds (12 magazines) for L4A4, 1,000 rounds for L7A2.

The FV434 is a specialised version of the FV432 developed for use by the REME in the field. It is an open-backed vehicle fitted with a crane capable of lifting such items as AFV engine packs, gun barrels and similar parts in need of care and attention. Early FV434 prototypes were simply FV432s with a crane on the roof but in time the specialised FV434 emerged with several features unique to it apart from the crane. One such feature is the ability to lock the torsion bars on the front and rear axles to

give stability when using the crane. Other features are the tool bench, vice and tool kit for field repairs. The open rear can carry such large parts as a Chieftain engine pack, and the FV434 has a total carrying ability of 2,703 kg.

The most noticeable part of the FV434 is the hydraulic HIAB crane which has a two-piece jib. Mounted on the right-hand side and about half-way along, it is capable of lifting all manner of loads but its performance is affected by the radius at which the load is situated. For instance, at a radius of 2.25 metres it can lift 3,050 kg, but at about 4 metres the lift is limited to 1,250 kg.

The usual crew of the FV434 is four, the commander, driver/crane operator, and two fitters. While the FV434 rear is usually left open, it can be fitted with a canvas tilt for some measure of protection against the elements. The usual wading screens are fitted. If it is provided, the machine-gun is mounted on a pintle near the commander's hatch.

FV438 Swingfire launcher

Armament 14 × Swingfire missiles, 1 × 7.62 mm L4A4 Machine-Gun *or* 1 × 7.62 mm L7A2 Machine-Gun and 2 × 3-barrel smoke dischargers; **Crew** 3; **Weight in action** 16,200 kg; **Length overall** 5.105 m; **Height overall** 2.705 m; **Width (overall)** 2.972 m; **Width (over tracks)** 2.527 m; **Track width** 0.343 m; **Ground clearance** 0.406 m; **Maximum road speed** 52 km/h; **Range (roads)** 480 km; **Engine type** Rolls-Royce K60 No. 4 Mark 4F; **Engine power** 240 bhp; **Engine capacity** 6.57 litres; **Fuel capacity** 454 litres; **Ammunition capacity** 14 Swingfire missiles, 7.62 mm—1,200 rounds; **Main armament elevation** –20° to + 20°; **Main armament traverse** 90° (45° either side).

The FV438 now forms the main bulk of the Royal Artillery's anti-tank guided missile self-propelled equipment, and is issued at the scale of six to an armoured regiment and three to a mechanised infantry battalion. It is a straightforward conversion of the basic FV432 to accommodate the Swingfire ATGW system, and although the appearance of the FV438 is distinctive from that of the FV432, there are few major differences between them. The main recognition point of the FV438 is its large rear-mounted cupola, the missile bins just behind it (to the left), and the periscopic sight.

In action, the missile bins are raised and the commander/layer selects his target using the periscopic sight. If a purely defensive position has been selected, the sight can be taken up to 50 metres away from the vehicle—which enables it to be concealed behind cover and the missiles fired without the launcher being exposed. Once fired, the missile bins can be reloaded from within the vehicle.

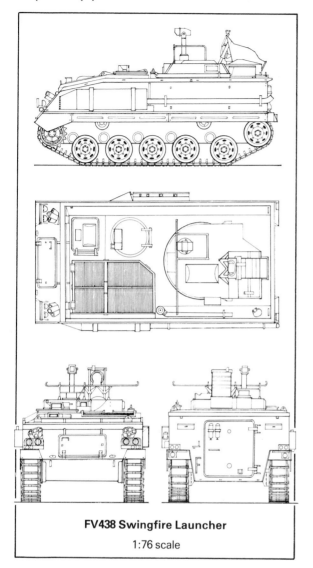

FV438 Swingfire Launcher
1:76 scale

Top *A Royal Signals FV439 on an exercise* (MoD). **Above** *A Pig during the early days on the Northern Ireland campaign—the extra armour and accessories have yet to be fitted* (Army PR HQ NI).

FV439 Signals vehicle

The Royal Signals use several versions of the FV432 series, the main one of which is a command type equipped with extra radios. A special version used only by the Royal Signals is the FV439 which acts as a mobile radio relay station. It is equipped internally with the necessary signals equipment, but externally the main differences from other FV432s is the large aerial mast which is carried partially dismantled ready for erection at the chosen station site. Extra stowage bins are provided on the roof and cable reels are also carried. For defensive purposes there is provision for an L4A4 machine-gun on the commander's hatch.

FV1611 Pig

Armament Nil—see text; **Crew** 2 + 6 to 8;. **Weight in action (approx)** 7,000 kg; **Length** 4.926 m; **Height** 2.12 m; **Width** 2.044 m; **Wheel track** 1.713 m; **Maximum road speed** 64 km/h; **Range (roads)** 402 km; **Engine type** Rolls-Royce B60 Mark 5A; **Engine power** 120 bhp; **Engine capacity** 4.25 litres; **Fuel capacity** 145 litres.

Exactly how the unlovely name of 'Pig' came to be bestowed upon this vehicle is unknown but it

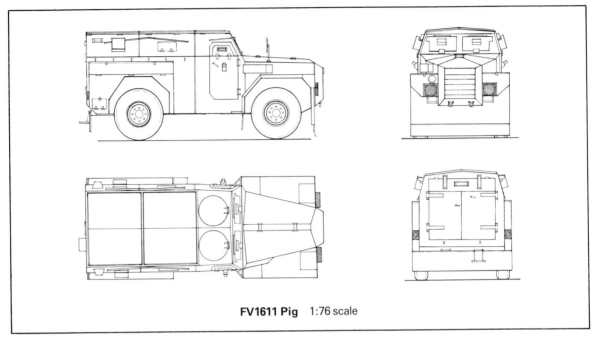

FV1611 Pig   1:76 scale

started life in the late 1940s. Originally it was a Humber 1-ton truck, the FV1601A, which was converted to the APC role by the addition of an armoured steel body as an expedient pending an adequate supply of the FV603 Saracen. The expedient turned into a production run of about 1,700 from both GKN Sankey at Wellington in Shropshire, and the Royal Ordnance Factory at Woolwich —the chassis came from the Humber Works at Maidstone. With the advent of the FV432 into

service the Pig was declared obsolete, but events in Northern Ireland enforced a return to active service, and numbers were brought out of storage and even re-purchased from civilian buyers.

In Northern Ireland the Pig has had a renewed service career. Being relatively small and innocuous it does not have the political 'tank' appearance that would arouse passions in civil unrest situations, yet it still provides a useful degree of protection and mobility to troops 'acting in support of a civilian power'. But in 1972 it was discovered that high-velocity armour-piercing bullets were in the hands of some of the dissenting groups operating in Ulster, and that these were capable of penetrating the armour of the Pig. In order to rectify this state of affairs, all the 500-odd Pigs in use in Northern Ireland were returned to various Royal Ordnance factories in the United Kingdom for additional armour plating to be applied (Operation Bracelet). At the same time the suspension was modified to accommodate the extra weight and the various vision blocks and ports were updated and an extra armoured shield added to the rear. On some vehicles smoke or CS canister dischargers were added to the roof.

The Pig most likely to be encountered is now the FV1611, but the FV1612, originally a radio vehicle, might still be seen, and a small number of FV1613s are still kept for use as ambulances. Despite its age, the Pig will be very much a part of the Army internal security scene for a long while yet.

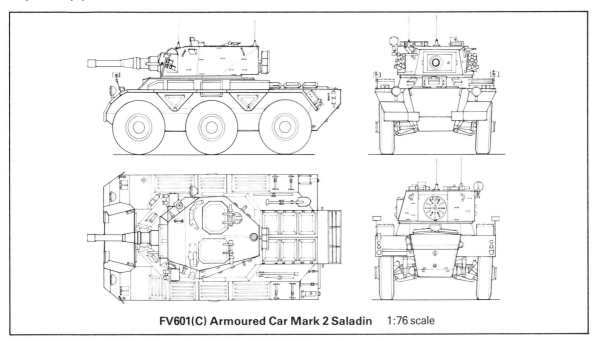

FV601(C) Armoured Car Mark 2 Saladin   1:76 scale

FV601(C) Armoured Car Mark 2 Saladin

Armament 1 × 76.2 mm L5A1 Gun, 1 × 7.62 mm L3A3 Machine-Gun, 1 × 7.62 mm L3A4 Machine Gun and 2 × 3-barrel smoke dischargers; **Crew** 3; **Weight in action** 11,583 kg; **Length (gun forward)** 5.27 m; **Length of hull** 4.93 m; **Height (top of cupola)** 2.39 m; **Width** 2.565 m; **Wheel track** 2.083 m; **Ground clearance** 0.426 m; **Maximum road speed** 72 km/h; **Range (roads)** 400 km; **Engine type** Rolls-Royce B80 No. 1 Mark 6D; **Engine power** 160 bhp; **Engine capacity** 5.67 litres; **Fuel capacity** 241 litres; **Ammunition capacity** 76.2 mm—42 rounds, 7.62 mm—3,500 rounds; **Main armament elevation** –10° to + 20°; **Main armament traverse** 360°.

Only a relative few FV601(C) Saladins remain operational—they are with the armoured reconnaissance squadron based in Cyprus—but the type is still used in the United Kingdom for a number of ancillary roles most of which involve training. Like so many post-war armoured vehicles, it had a long and protracted development history, but the Saladin's was rather longer than most as it had been under development for some 13 years before it went into production during late 1958. The first examples were issued during 1959 and thereafter served well in all sorts of climate and terrain. It has now

been replaced by the FV101 Scorpion in the reconnaissance regiments of the Cavalry. Some are still used (in small numbers) by TA units, and a few soldier on in Cyprus.

In service the Saladin was often used as a 'wheeled tank', a role made possible by its 76.2 mm L5A1 gun. This is the progenitor of the L23A1 fitted to the FV101 Scorpion but both fire the same ammunition—the L5A1 is heavier than its successor and is 2.164 m long.

Left *An updated Pig on patrol in the centre of Belfast (Army PR HQ NI).* **Right** *A Saladin, still retained for training purposes in 1979.*

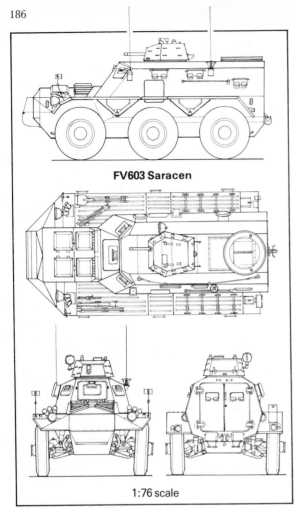

FV603 Saracen

1:76 scale

FV603 Saracen

Armament 1 × .30 L3A3 Machine-Gun, 2 × 3-barrel smoke dischargers; also see text; **Crew** 2 + 10; **Weight in action** 10,170 kg; **Length overall** 5.233 m; **Height (top of turret)** 2.463 m; **Height (top of hull)** 2.0 m; **Width** 2.539 m; **Wheel track** 2.083 m; **Maximum road speed** 72 km/h; **Range (roads)** 400 km; **Engine type** Rolls-Royce B80 Mark 6A; **Engine power** 160 bhp; **Engine capacity** 5.67 litres; **Fuel capacity** 200 litres; **Ammunition capacity (approx)** 1,600 rounds; **Main armament traverse (if fitted)** 360°; **Main armament elevation (if fitted)** −15° to + 45°.

The FV603 Saracen began life as a result of the Malayan emergency in about 1948 or 1949. It was then discovered that the need for an APC with some form of overhead cover for the passengers was very necessary and work began on the project with great haste to the extent that prototypes and production models were being constructed almost simultaneously. The basis for the new APC was the six-wheeled chassis of the FV601 Saladin armoured car, and the resultant APC, the FV603 Saracen, was in production by late 1952, well in advance of its progenitor.

The main assembly line for the Saracen was at Alvis Company Limited at Coventry. Progressive versions were the FV603(B) and the FV603(C), but the latter was the most numerous. As well as production for the British Army, the Saracen became a great export success and many still remain in service all over the world with several armies. As well as the APC version the Saracen family expanded into the FV611 ambulance and the FV610(A) artillery command vehicle for the Royal Artillery as well as the FV604 armoured command vehicle, some of which are still in service pending the delivery of the FV105 Sultan.

With the coming into service of the FV432 and its variants the Saracen gradually faded from the scene. Many were issued to TA units, driving schools and to various trials units. Some were even used as hard targets on firing ranges. But the coming of the disturbances in Northern Ireland changed all that. Saracens were taken out of their various stores and special-duty hiding places and sent to Ulster where they formed the APC backbone of the units on duty there. Their numbers were swelled by a batch of export Saracen Mark 3s, originally intended for sale to Libya but not delivered. They arrived in Northern Ireland with their desert camouflage still applied. Once in the province they were gradually uparmoured and fit-

Left *An FV604 Command Vehicle converted for use in Northern Ireland.*

ted with various anti-riot equipment such as CS canister or smoke dischargers, anti-wire posts to protect the commander, loudspeakers, and the like (Operation Kremlin 1 and 2). Some Saracens have had their turrets removed, while variants such as the FV610 and FV604 have been pressed into use after their special equipment was removed.

Most Saracens are used purely as APCs carrying ten soldiers, a driver and a commander. Very few have retained their main Browning machine-gun armament (but they are held in reserve) although those with turrets often carry riot guns or grenade dischargers in their place. The ability of the Saracen suspension to continue on its way after any two of the six wheels have been blown off by mine explosions has been invaluable on many occasions, but to reduce the risk of injury after an explosion which could tip the vehicle on its side, the occupants wear protective headgear and seat belts—each seat position is also fitted with head restrainers. Some ordinary Saracens have been converted into ambulances.

So, as with the Humber 'Pig', the disturbances in Northern Ireland have kept in service a vehicle that might otherwise have passed from use. It seems likely to be around for a long while yet.

One possible use for the Saracen that has not been adopted up to the time of writing is that as the carrier of a special anti-riot weapon known as the Special Water Dispenser, or SWD. The use of water cannon in riot control is nothing new and many a riotous assembly has been dispersed by a soaking from water jets. While the SWD can be used as a water hose for large scale drenchings, its special property is that it can fire water 'slugs'. Capable of being quite accurately aimed at specific individuals up to 40 metres away, these 'slugs' are short, sharp bursts of water which can impart disabling but not fatal blows. The effect of being struck by such a water missile has been likened to a blow from a fist. Although the SWD has been ready for use for some years, and has been fitted to some Saracens, it has not yet been used 'in action'.

Top A Saracen after the full Operation Kremlin treatment. The extra wire mesh acts as a rocket grenade screen and extra armour has been added (Army PR HQ NI). **Above** *Waiting for the 'off'—a Saracen, fully equipped and ready for a training demonstration at Bovington.* **Below** *A Shorland armoured car in service with the Ulster Defence Regiment (Army PR HQ NI).*

FV18061 Shorland Mark 3

Armament See text; **Crew** 3; **Weight in action** 3,360 kg; **Length** 4.597 m; **Height (top of turret)** 2.286 m; **Width** 1.778 m; **Wheel track** 1.359 m; **Ground clearance (approx)** 0.21 m; **Maximum road speed** 88.4 km/h; **Range (roads normal tank)** 257 km; **Range (roads/long-range tank)** 514 km; **Engine type** Rover 6-cylinder; **Engine power** 91 bhp; **Engine capacity** 2.625 litres; **Fuel capacity (normal tank)** 64 litres; **Fuel capacity (long-range tank)** 128 litres.

Although they had already been carrying out a

considerable amount of development before then, the Northern Ireland troubles prompted one local firm, Short Brothers and Harland Limited of Belfast, to produce an armoured patrol vehicle that would suit the requirements of the Royal Ulster Constabulary in their thankless task of patrolling large stretches of country roads always under danger of ambush or other attack. The same vehicle also had to be capable of use in riot situations where the more conventional Army vehicle would be either a liability or political hazard. In 1965 Short Bros produced their first Shorland armoured patrol car. Since then they have developed the basic design up to the present Mark 3, and not only has it been exported to over 20 countries but it is in service with the Royal Ulster Constabulary and the Ulster Defence Regiment.

The Shorland is based on the well-tried chassis of the Land Rover and shares some 80 per cent of its spares with that vehicle. The outline of the original Land Rover is still apparent but the body is ar-moured, as is the floor, and a small turret is mounted on the roof. All the vision ports and the front windscreen can be covered by armour screens, while at the rear an armoured boot encloses the fuel tank and the spare wheel.

The main turret armament is variable and can be either a .30 Browning L3A3 or a 7.62 mm L7A2 machine-gun. However, in some internal security situations a machine-gun would be an 'overkill' weapon, so it is often not fitted or a L1A1 rifle used in its place. Other likely turret weapons are riot guns or grenade dischargers, and some Shorlands have smoke dischargers fitted to the turret sides, along with a searchlight.

Short SB.301

Armament See text; **Crew** 2 + 6; **Weight in action** 3,543 kg; **Length** 4.292 m; **Height** 2.159 m; **Width** 1.764 m; **Wheel track** 1.358 m; **Ground clearance (approx)** 0.21 m; **Maximum road speed** 96 km/h; **Range (roads)** 368 km; **Engine type**

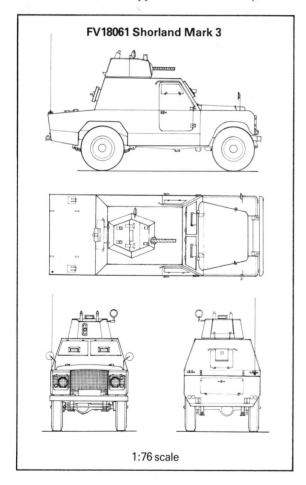

FV18061 Shorland Mark 3

1:76 scale

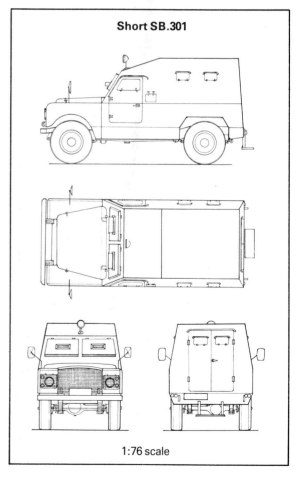

Short SB.301

1:76 scale

Rover 6-cylinder; **Engine power** 91 bhp; **Engine capacity** 2.625 litres; **Fuel capacity** 100 litres.

When the FV18061 Shorland Mark 3 armoured car was under development it was decided to produce an armoured personnel carrier as a companion vehicle. Using the same Land Rover-based chassis as the Shorland, the result was the SB.301 with the first prototype being rolled out in 1973 and production getting under way during 1974. The Royal Ulster Constabulary was an early customer as the SB.301 was virtually designed with their rural patrolling and internal security needs in mind. With the close co-operation that has grown up between the Army and the RUC, it is not surprising that the Army have taken over some SB.301s for their own use, but they are used only in Northern Ireland.

The SB.301 is protected by 8.25 mm thick armour and is liberally provided with visors and firing ports. Normally no weapons are fitted but smoke or CS dischargers can be attached to the roof. Six fully armed men can be carried in the rear with access being provided by two large doors. As with the Shorland, the Land Rover ancestry is still discernable, despite all the many changes from the original. A recent development is the SB.303 anti-hijack vehicle for use at airports, which can be fitted with a sniper's rifle.

Above *The Short SB.301 armoured personnel carrier.*

The Ferrets

One of the few armoured fighting vehicles to remain in production throughout the Second World War was the Daimler Scout Car, a remarkable little vehicle that was pressed into a variety of roles throughout the war years. After 1945 it was felt that the basic design was capable of further development, and Daimler Company Limited were given a development contract. They completed their first prototype in June 1950, and a production contract followed almost immediately. In 1952 the first production versions came off the Coventry lines and the new vehicle, soon known as the Ferret, remained in production until 1971 by which time a total of 4,409 had been completed, many for export to other nations.

The Ferret has been produced in several versions, not all of which remain in Army service. Over the years the Ferret has been gradually developed and updated and at the present time there is an ongoing programme to modernise all the Ferrets in service to enable them to remain in active use until the late 1980s. This longevity is necessary for the Ferret is one of those vehicles that the British Army deems it cannot do without. It fills a variety of roles. The Infantry use it for liaison, the Royal Artillery for general reconnaissance with their field batteries, the

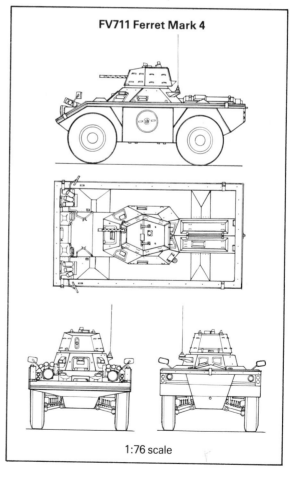

FV711 Ferret Mark 4

1:76 scale

armoured regiments use it as a general run-about and again for reconnaissance, and just about every branch of the service seems to have a few somewhere around. It is in active service in Germany and Northern Ireland, and is one of the standard items pressed into use whenever the Army is involved in a local conflict or United Nations peace-keeping force.

The basic version of the Ferret is the Mark 1/1 or FV701(J). In this form it is an open-topped 4 × 4 vehicle with armour varying from 6 mm at the rear to 16 mm on the superstructure and hull front and sides. The open hull can house a crew of two or three men, and a machine-gun, usually a .30 Browning or 7.62 mm Bren, is mounted on a pintle. The suspension is the same as that of the older Daimler Scout Car but has been strengthened, while the engine is more powerful giving an increased cross-country performance. A canvas cover provides some protection against the elements.

The Ferret designations do not follow a particularly tidy pattern so the next version to be considered is the Mark 1/2 or FV704. This is almost the same as the Mark 1/1 but it has a small flat-topped turret with an external machine-gun pintle.

Perhaps the most commonly encountered version of the Ferret is the Mark 2/3 or FV701(H). Structurally and mechanically it is the same as the Mark 1/1 but has a small turret mounted on the superstructure. For armament the turrret mounts either a .30 Browning or a 7.62 mm Bren but no doubt the GPMG will be mounted in one form or another.

The Ferret Mark 3 is an updated Mark 1/1 with bigger wheels, a flotation screen stowed all around the body and the suspension modified to support the extra weight involved. Relatively few of these vehicles were made from new but it is the basis for the present updating programme of Mark 1s. It was originally the FV701(J).

	Ferret Mark 1/1 FV701(J)	Ferret Mark 1/2 FV704	Ferret Mark 2/3 FV701(H)	Ferret Mark 4 FV711
Armament	1 × .30 L3A4 MG or 1 × 7.62 mm L4A4 MG	1 × 7.62 mm L4A4 MG	1 × .30 L3A4 MG	1 × .30 L3A4 MG
Crew	2 or 3	3	2	2 or 3
Weight in action	4,210 kg	4,370 kg	4,395 kg	5,400 kg
Length	3.835 m	3.835 m	3.835 m	3.962 m
Height	1.448 m	1.651 m	1.879 m	2.336 m
Width	1.905 m	1.905 m	1.905 m	2.133 m
Wheel track	1.549 m	1.549 m	1.549 m	1.75 m
Ground clearance	0.33 m	0.33 m	0.33 m	0.41 m
Maximum road speed	93 km/h	93 km/h	93 km/h	80 km/h
Range (roads)	300 km	300 km	300 km	300 km
Engine type	All: Rolls-Royce B60 Mark 6A			
Engine power	129 bhp	129 bhp	129 bhp	129 bhp
Engine capacity	4.26 litres	4.26 litres	4.26 litres	4.26 litres
Fuel capacity	96 litres	96 litres	96 litres	96 litres
Ammunition capacity	450 rounds	450 rounds	2,500 rounds	2,500 rounds

Left *Troops of the Royal Welch Fusiliers set out on a patrol from Ebrington Barracks, Londonderry* (Army PR HQ NI).

Right *A Ferret still serving with the Yeomanry during a TA exercise on Salisbury Plain.*

The most modern of the Ferrets in service is the Mark 4 or FV711. It is a turreted Ferret with large wheels, an integral wading screen and strengthened suspension.

The heaviest of all the Ferrets to date was the Mark 5 or FV712 which had a drastically modified turret with bins for four Swingfire missiles and a machine-gun mounting. Once again the suspension had to be strengthened to take the weight involved, but the Mark 5 was intended only as an interim and training vehicle until the FV438 and FV102 Striker could get into service in sufficient numbers. By the end of 1978 they were no longer in use and will no doubt be re-worked into Mark 4 or similar status.

The Ferret has been used for many trials and experiments, some of which reached a form of service status. One of these was the Mark 2/6 or FV703 which had two Vigilant anti-tank guided missiles mounted, one to each side of the turret. With the missile equipment removed this version became the Mark 2/7. The FV701(H), the Mark 2/3 was at one time used for trials with the No. 14 radar (ZB298). There were various trials conducted in the search for swimming gear which involved at one time the use of external flotation bags. Another approach was the use of a 'bolt-on' polyurethane hull, but the final answer proved to be that now adopted for nearly all similar British vehicles, and that is the collapsible wading screen. Plastic stowage boxes add to the buoyancy.

155 mm Self-Propelled Howitzer M109A1 and M109A2

Armament 1 × 155 mm M185 Howitzer, 1 × 7.62 mm L4A4 Machine-Gun; **Crew** 6 + 2; **Weight in action** 24,070 kg; **Length (gun forward)** 9.042 m; **Length of hull** 6.256 m; **Height (less machine-gun)** 3.06 m; **Width (with fenders)** 3.295 m; **Width (less fenders)** 3.149 m; **Track width** 0.381 m; **Ground clearance** 0.467 m; **Maximum road speed** 56 km/h; **Range** 360-390 km; **Engine type** GMC Model 8V71T Detroit Diesel; **Engine power** 405 bhp; **Engine capacity** 9.3 litres; **Fuel capacity** 511 litres; **Ammunition capacity** 155 mm—28 rounds; 7.62 mm—1,200 rounds; **Main armament elevation** –3° to + 75°; **Main armament traverse** 360°.

The M109A1 is an American self-propelled howitzer with a rather involved development history that at one point touched on that of the M113 APC. The development test vehicle was the T196 Howitzer Motor Carriage that went into production as the M109 in November 1962 but that vehicle was fitted with the 155 mm Howitzer M126. It entered British Army service in 1965 and during 1978 these vehicles were fitted with longer barrels known as the M185 to give their self-propelled carriages a new designation of M109A1.

The M109A1 is the standard equipment of the Royal Artillery's medium self-propelled batteries based in Germany. The first two vehicles were obtained for trials in 1975, and the barrel retrofit programme was scheduled to be completed by the end of 1978.

The M109A1 is a rather bulky vehicle but the turret is roomy and the vehicle has a limited swimming ability. As with many other self-propelled artillery pieces, the engine and transmission are at the front of the vehicle and the turret at the rear, where a large hatch is used for ammunition replenishment. On the move, the driver and five of the gun crew remain with the vehicle but for a full detachment another two ammunition numbers travel in an ammunition limber vehicle. Hatches in the roof provide not only vision but also access to the 7.62 mm L4A4 Bren Gun mounting which is fitted for limited local and anti-aircraft defence. One rather

Above *An M109A1. Just visible on the rear hull side is the name 'Armageddon'.*

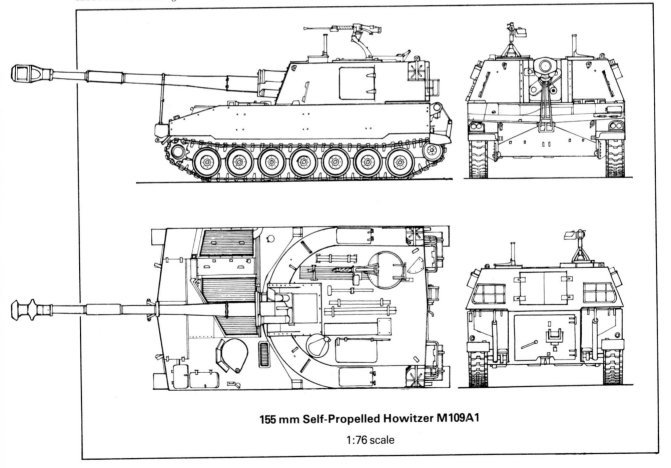

155 mm Self-Propelled Howitzer M109A1

1:76 scale

unusual feature on such a large vehicle is that the hull and turret are of all-welded aluminium construction—which enables it to be more amphibious than similar vehicles of its bulk. To provide stability when firing two small recoil spades are fitted to the hull rear. Full night-driving and NBC equipment can be fitted.

The M109A1 will remain in service for some while yet as the SP70 self-propelled howitzer which is intended to replace it is still in the prototype stage as this is written. It seems almost certain that the M109A1 will continue in service until at least the mid-1980s, and after that it will no doubt be issued to TA batteries.

In mid-1979 it was announced that a further 18 M109A2s were to be procured for the Royal Artillery. The M109A2 is the production version of the M109A1 with various changes incorporated on the production line. Effectively they are the same vehicle as the M109A1. Further M109A2 purchases followed and by early 1982 it had been issued to 26 Field Regiment RA, and at least one battery of 45 Field Regiment RA.

SP70

It is not yet possible to give any data on the SP70 as it is still in an early stage of development. It was intended to be the self-propelled counterpart of the 155 mm FH70 howitzer but delays with the programme have become so pronounced that the project now seems likely to be redesignated SP80.

The ordnance used on SP70 is based on that used for the FH70 and it fires the same range of ammunition. Like FH70, SP70 is an international project shared between West Germany, the United Kingdom and Italy. One of the main reasons for the delay has been the determination of the final chassis to be used, as it was at one stage intended that this would be shared with that of the West German Kampfpanzer 3 which has itself undergone a number of design changes and alterations in philosophy. It now seems likely that the final form of SP70 has been determined with the engine, suspension, tracks and transmission being chosen to correspond with the new German MBT, but the hull is constructed from aluminium armour and based on that

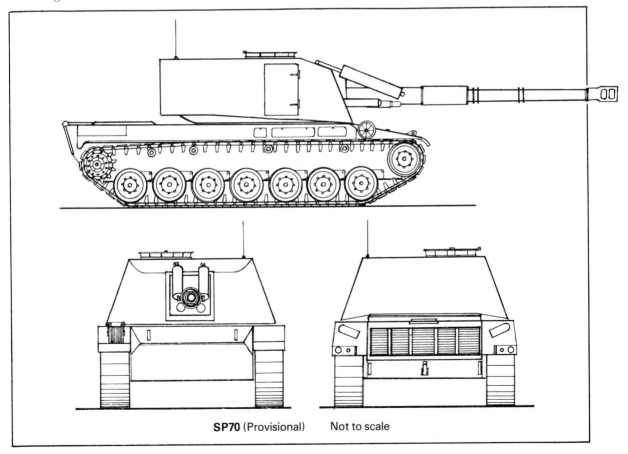

SP70 (Provisional)   Not to scale

Above SP70 prototype. **Below** *The 175 mm M107.* **Above right** *The long 175 mm barrel can be well appreciated from this photograph, taken at Bovington.*

of the Leopard MBT. (The exact type of aluminium armour was still undecided at the time of writing, with the United Kingdom favouring one alloy and the West Germans another.) The 360° turret is a British responsibility and will be manufactured at various Royal Ordnance factories. The German share is under the aegis of Rheinmetall but MaK at Kiel are constructing the chassis. In Italy, Oto-

Melara of La Spezia have already carried out a considerable amount of development work, part of which involved mounting a prototype 155 mm howitzer in a much-modified M109. They will be responsible for much of the howitzer cradle and mounting.

The delays to the SP70 programme have caused many adverse criticisms and the first public demonstration of the first prototype in January 1978 has resulted in more. Much of this has been directed at the complexity and nature of the howitzer's automatic loader which holds 25 rounds ready for loading—a selection of the type of round can be made. The main problem is that in action the 25 rounds would soon be fired and the vehicle would then have to retire to cover to reload, an operation which takes a considerable time. Doubtless this aspect will be investigated as the 12 pre-production prototypes are built and tested before full production gets under way. In time, the SP70 will replace the existing 105 mm Abbots and 155 mm M109A1s, but that time seems a long way off yet, if it ever comes.

175 mm Self-Propelled Gun M107

Armament 1 × 175 mm M113 Gun; **Crew** 5 + 3; **Weight in action** 28,168 kg; **Length (gun forward)** 11.246 m; **Length (hull only)** 5.72 m; **Height (top of mounting (0°)** 2.809 m; **Height (top of barrel, travelling)** 3.679 m; **Width** 3.149 m; **Track width** 0.457 m; **Ground clearance** 0.441 m; **Maximum road speed** 56 km/h; **Range (roads)** 725 km; **Engine type** GMC Model 8V71T Detroit Diesel; **Engine power** 405 bhp; **Engine capacity** 9.3 litres; **Fuel capacity** 1,137 litres; **Ammunition capacity** 175 mm—2 rounds; **Main armament elevation** −2° to +65°; **Main armament traverse** 60°.

The M107 is one of a family of American self-propelled artillery vehicles that were the result of a design requirement put forward in 1956. The first prototypes appeared in 1958 and were built by the Pacific Car and Foundry Company at Renton, Washington. The version mounting the 175 mm gun was the T235 powered by a petrol engine, but when a diesel engine was substituted it became the M107. The first M107s entered British Army service in 1965-1966.

The M107s with 1 (Br) Corps come directly under HQ control as a Corps general support regiment. As they use the same self-propelled carriage as the 8-in M110s and the same engine as the 155 mm M109A1s, a great deal of spares commonality is possible. Indeed, the 175 mm gun and the 8-in howitzer are interchangeable. The changeover involves only about two hours' work,

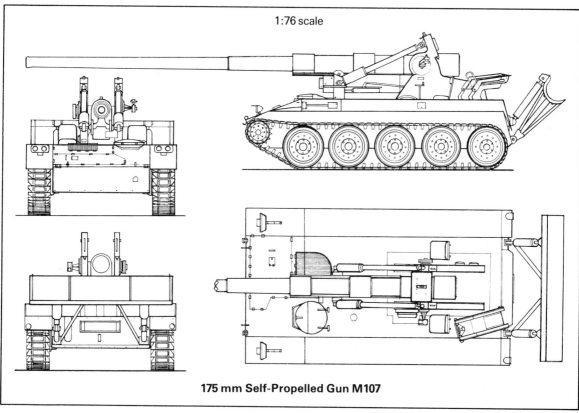

1:76 scale

175 mm Self-Propelled Gun M107

and if necessary, can be accomplished in the field. As the M107 is intended for use well behind the front lines, no armour or other protection is provided for the crew, but consideration is now being given to some form of canvas or nylon housing over the breech area. Even such a flimsy structure can provide some protection against the elements and nuclear fall-out.

On the move, up to five of the gun detachment can travel on the gun carriage, with a further three gun numbers on one of the ammunition limber vehicles. Ammunition space on the carriage is limited and only two rounds are normally carried. To assist the loading procedure a hydraulically operated ammunition lift and ramming mechanism is fitted to the vehicle rear. Hydraulic operation is also used to power the large recoil spade which stabilises the gun when fired, and further stabilisation is provided by locking out the suspension cylinders.

8-in Self-Propelled Howitzer M110A1

Armament 1 × 8-in M201 Howitzer; **Crew** 5 + 8; **Weight in action** 28,350 kg; **Length (gun forward)** 10.7 m; **Length (hull only)** 5.72 m; **Height (top of mounting (0°)** 2.809 m; **Height (top of barrel, travelling)** 2.93 m; **Width** 3.149 m; **Track width** 0.457 m; **Ground clearance** 0.441 m; **Maximum road speed** 56 kkm/h; **Range (roads)** 725 km; **Engine type** GMC Model 8V71T Detroit Diesel; **Engine power** 405 bhp; **Engine capacity** 9.3 litres; **Fuel capacity** 1,137 litres; **Ammunition capacity** 8-in—2 rounds; **Main armament elevation** − 2° to + 65°; **Main armament traverse** 60°.

As the M110 had the same origins as the M107 it only remains to mention that its trial designation for the US Army was T236E1. Apart from the barrel and mounting it is almost identical to the M107, but the heavier projectiles involved dictates the use of eight ammunition numbers travelling in the ammunition limber vehicles.

Operationally the M110A1s are used singly and from carefully pre-selected and prepared positions. They operate in a 'shoot-and-scoot' mode as it is well known that their nuclear capability marks them

US Army M110A1s on trials. These prototype vehicles have provision for some form of weather covering which may not be fitted to British Army examples (US Army).

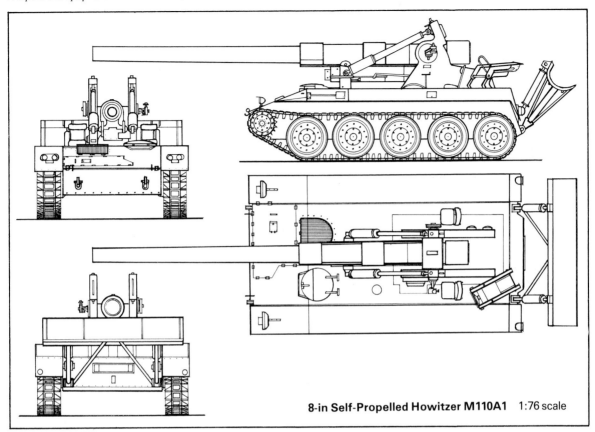

8-in Self-Propelled Howitzer M110A1   1:76 scale

out for special attention by enemy counter-battery forces.

Tracked Rapier

Armament 8 Rapier ground-to-air missiles, 1 × 7.62 mm machine-gun and smoke dischargers; **Crew** 3; **Weight in action** 13,381 kg; **Length** 6.143 m; **Height (tracker raised)** 2.78 m; **Width** 2.65 m; **Track width** 0.381 m; **Ground clearance** 0.41 m; **Maximum road speed** 61.2 km/h; **Range (cruising)** 483 km; **Engine type** GMC model 6V53 diesel; **Engine power** 210 hp at 2,800 rpm; **Fuel capacity** 398 litres.

The Tracked Rapier started life as a British Aerospace private venture to attract export orders for the Rapier missile, and was initiated in 1974. The chassis chosen for the system was the American M548 tracked carrier, a development of the well-known and widely used M113 APC, but by the time the Rapier system had been added the M548 was greatly modified. A major export order was placed by the then Shah of Iran, and construction work began soon after that order was placed in late 1974.

The Food Machinery Corporation of America produced and delivered the necessary chassis, but then the Shah was deposed in the Iranian Revolution, and in 1979 the Iranian order was cancelled.

Thus British Aerospace found itself saddled with a quantity of Rapier systems and tracked chassis for which it no longer had any customer. Fortunately, the British Army had long been giving consideration to some form of mobile mounting for the Rapier missile system, and the ex-Iranian Tracked Rapiers seemed to be an ideal solution. But, as ever, the funds for procurement were not so easy to obtain and it was not until June 1981 that it was announced that the Army would receive 50 Tracked Rapiers to be issued to three RHA batteries.

Tracked Rapier carries eight Rapier missiles in a launcher on the rear of the modified M548 chassis. The missiles are arranged four to each side of a central drum mounting that also houses the search radar and the tracking aerial dish mounted on elevating arms. Overall, the system operates much the same as the conventional Rapier system but target acquisition is much improved by the provision

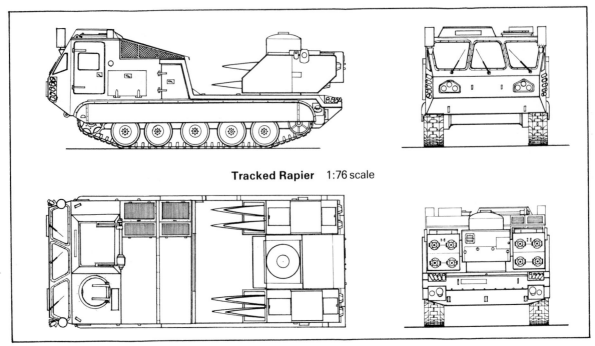

Tracked Rapier   1:76 scale

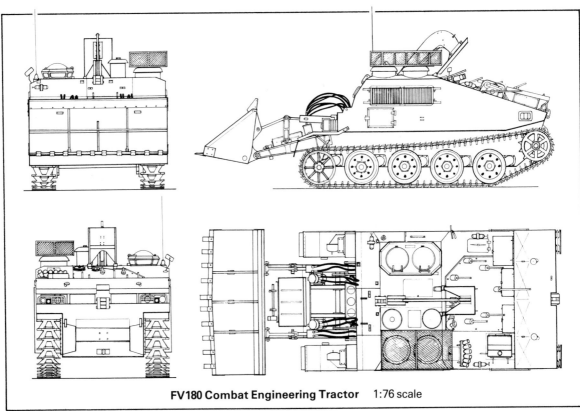

FV180 Combat Engineering Tractor   1:76 scale

Above Tracked Rapier from the rear, showing the missile launcher arrangement. The tracking dish is lowered and is housed in front of the central radar drum. Right The M548 Support Vehicle.

of a helmet sight worn by the commander as he looks through his roof hatch. All he has to be is align the helmet sight with a target and the system radar can then align itself automatically and rapidly. There is also an optical tracker. The launcher bins are protected by 25 mm armour, and the vehicle armour is generally provided with splinter and small-arms fire protection.

Once fired, the Tracked Rapier launcher is reloaded from a support vehicle. Although it is not certain, it would appear that this support vehicle will be an unaltered American M548 cargo carrier capable of carrying 20 missiles. The M548 will have a crew of two and there is provision for a roof-mounted GPMG.

FV180 Combat Engineering Tractor
Armament 1 × 7.62 mm L4A4 Machine-Gun, 2 × 4-barrel smoke dischargers; **Crew** 2; **Weight in action** 17,010 kg; **Length overall** 7.544 m; **Length of hull** 5.334 m; **Height overall** 2.667 m; **Height (top of hull)** 2.286 m; **Width of bucket** 2.896 m; **Width of hull** 2.793 m; **Width over tracks** 2.769 m; **Track width** 0.508 m; **Ground clearance** 0.457 m; **Maximum road speed** 56 km/h; **Range (roads)**

480 km; **Engine type** Rolls-Royce C6TFR; **Engine power** 320 bhp; **Engine capacity** 12.2 litres; **Fuel capacity** 430 litres; **Ammunition capacity** 336 rounds (12 magazines).

The FV180 Combat Engineering Tractor, or CET, is a unique vehicle which has been developed from the outset for the combat engineering role, a duty that is usually fulfilled by converted AFVs. Starting as an international project with the West German Army and the French involved, early design studies were carried out at the Military Engineering Experimental Establishment (MEXE) at Christchurch, now part of the MVEE. In time, both France and West Germany withdrew to foster their own comparable projects, but the Christ-

Above left *This CET, having fired its rocket-propelled anchor, is winching itself up an incline.* **Above** *A CET ready for wading.* **Left** *A CET enters the Chatham water course.*

church work continued, and in 1968 two test rigs were completed to test the basic concepts. As a result seven prototypes were built in 1973 and 1974, and these underwent extensive trials before production got under way at the Royal Ordnance Factory, Leeds during 1977.

As its name implies, the CET is used by the combat engineer regiments of the Royal Engineers. In action it fulfils a variety of roles from preparing or clearing obstacles, digging vehicle or gun pits, path-finding river crossings, preparing river banks for crossings, recovering disabled vehicles from water or other obstacles, and so on. Having been developed specially for these tasks, the CET can carry out the bulk of them with surprising facility and efficiency. As it is intended to spend a fair amount of its working life in or near water, the CET

has been built as lightly as possible and the hull is largely constructed from aluminium alloy, as are many other parts and sub-assemblies. The CET can be rendered amphibious after about ten minutes' work, and once in the water it is driven by two Dowty water jets. Normally, the CET is driven with its large earth-moving bucket to the rear and the crew of two sit on the left of the hull. Both crew positions have driving controls and the CET can be driven in either direction by either crew member—both their driving seats are reversible. To assist the CET out of water obstacles with steep banks, the CET can be equipped with a Laird rocket anchor which can be fired over them. Once dug-in, the anchor is used to tow the CET upwards as the vehicle is fitted with a two-speed winch with a towing capacity of up to 8,000 kg. This can also be used to tow other vehicles out of difficulties, and then the earth bucket doubles as a winch anchor—the winch has 107 metres of cable.

On dry ground the CET still has a multitude of uses. The 1.72 cubic metres capacity earth-moving bucket can be used for either earth-moving or digging, and is powered from hydraulic pumps driven from the main engine. When a small jib crane is fitted into the bucket it can also be used for loading and unloading stores. Other extras which can be fitted are a pusher bar for launching bridging spans or pontoons, track-laying equipment, and other Engineer stores such as the Giant Viper mine-clearer can be towed.

All in all, the CET is a very versatile vehicle. It can even be carried in a C-130 Hercules but for this it has to be partially stripped down to a weight of 15,400 kg.

FV4003 Centurion Mark 5 AVRE

Armament 1 × 165 mm Demolition Gun, 1 × .30 L3A3 Machine-Gun, 1 × .30 L3A4 Machine-Gun and 2 × 6-barrel smoke dischargers; **Crew** 5; **Weight in action** 51,810 kg; **Length** 8.686 m; **Height** 3.009 m; **Width (over blade)** 3.962 m; **Width (over hull)** 3.39 m; **Track width** 0.61 m; **Ground clearance** 0.46 m; **Maximum road speed** 34.6 km/h; **Range (roads)** 176 km; **Range (cross-country)** 113 km; **Engine type** Rolls-Royce Meteor Mark IVB; **Engine power** 650 bhp; **Engine capacity** 27 litres; **Fuel capacity** 1,037 litres; **Ammunition capacity (approx)** 165 mm—20 rounds, .30—3,000 rounds; **Main armament**

elevation −10° to + 20°; **Main armament traverse** 360°.

The FV4003 is a specialised version of the Centurion Mark 5 MBT for use by the Royal Engineers, hence the designation Assault Vehicle Royal Engineers, or AVRE. The first prototype was built in 1957 and the bulk of the production run was undertaken by the Royal Ordnance Factory, Leeds, during the early 1960s. Ever since then the AVRE has been part of the equipment of the armoured engineer squadrons serving in Germany.

The main armament of the AVRE is a 165 mm demolition gun intended for the destruction of field fortifications and obstacles. Details regarding this gun are still classified (the American M135 gun used on the M728 Combat Engineering Vehicle appears to be a very similar weapon) but it is known that it has an effective range of about 1,200 metres

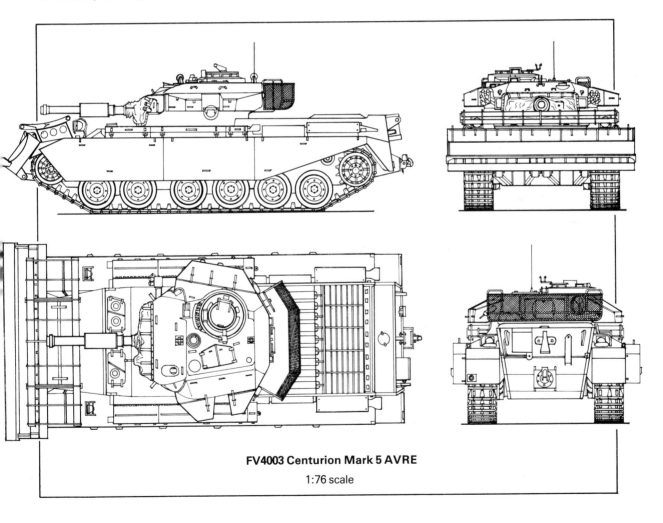

FV4003 Centurion Mark 5 AVRE

1:76 scale

Above *A Centurion AVRE loaded with fascines for crossing anti-tank obstacles—the fascines themselves are plastic piping.* **Below left** *The FV4003 Centurion Mark 5 AVRE* (MoD). **Below right** *The FV4006 Centurion ARV Mark 2.*

and fires a HESH projectile weighing 29 kg: The other obvious engineer accessory is the large dozer blade fitted to the front hull. Above the blade is a fascine carrier which can double as a trackway carrier. The use of fascines for crossing ditches (or anti-tank obstacles) is an ancient engineering ploy, but it still has its uses, and if required the fascine can be unrolled to provide a rough form of trackway over soft ground. The front hull also has fitting for a jib crane if required. Normally the AVRE tows some form of trailer, one of the more usual being the two-wheeled trailer carrying the Giant Viper mine-clearing equipment.

Another possible towed load is a 7.5-ton four-wheeled trailer which is used to carry all manner of stores from fuel to extra ammunition. In an emergency the towed load can be jettisoned electrically. The trailer was specially developed for use with the AVRE, and its full designation is FV2721 Trailer 7½ ton Centurion AVRE. Full details are as follows: **Weight laden** 14,936 kg; **Weight empty** 7,316 kg; **Length overall** 6.59 m; **Length** 4.216 m; **Height** 2.083 m; **Width** 2.972 m; **Floor height** 1.168 m.

In time many of the duties of the FV4003 will be taken over by the FV180 CET, but the AVRE seems destined to remain in service for some while yet.

FV4006 Centurion ARV Mark 2

Armament 1 × .30 L3A4 Machine-Gun, 2 × 5-barrel smoke dischargers; **Crew** 4; **Weight in action** 50,295 kg; **Length** 8.966 m; **Height** 2.895 m; **Width** 3.39 m; **Track width** 0.61 m; **Ground clearance** 0.45 m; **Maximum road speed** 34.6 km/h; **Range (roads)** 102 km; **Engine type** Rolls-Royce Meteor Mark IVB; **Engine power** 650 bhp; **Engine capacity** 27 litres; **Fuel capacity** 1,045 litres; **Ammunition capacity** .30—2,000 rounds.

Developed from the Centurion ARV Mark 1 (which was little other than a specialised tractor), the Centurion ARV Mark 2 is now nearing the end of its service life as it is gradually replaced by the FV4204 Chieftain ARV. The first Centurion ARV Mark 2s entered service circa 1956 and were produced at the Royal Ordnance Factory, Leeds. The main improvement over the Mark 1 was that the Mark 2 had a large-capacity winch capable of towing a load of up to 31,000 kg. To take advantage of this facility the Centurion hull was modified to take a large earth anchor at the rear. The internal winch was electrically driven with the power generated from an auxiliary engine, also internally mounted. The engine used in this operation is a Rolls-Royce B80 petrol engine with an output at 3,750 rpm of 160 bhp. Using various blocks and tackle the ARV Mark 2 winch can pull up to 90,000 kg, and is supplied with a cable length of 137 metres. For lifting purposes a crane jib with a lifting capacity of 10,000 kg can be erected. Like most ARVs, the FV4006 carries a wide variety of extra equipment, stowage bins and tools, including a hand vice mounted directly on to the front hull glacis.

FV4018 Centurion BARV

Armament 1 × 7.62 mm L4A4 Machine-Gun; **Crew** 4; **Weight in action** 40,643 kg; **Length** 8.076 m; **Height** 3.453 m; **Width** 3.402 m; **Track width** 0.61 m; **Ground clearance** 0.5 m; **Maximum road speed** 34.6 km/h; **Range (roads)** 63 km; **Engine type** Rolls-Royce Meteor Mark IVB; **Engine power** 650 bhp; **Engine capacity** 27 litres; **Fuel capacity** 550 litres; **Ammunition capacity** 7.62 mm—400 rounds.

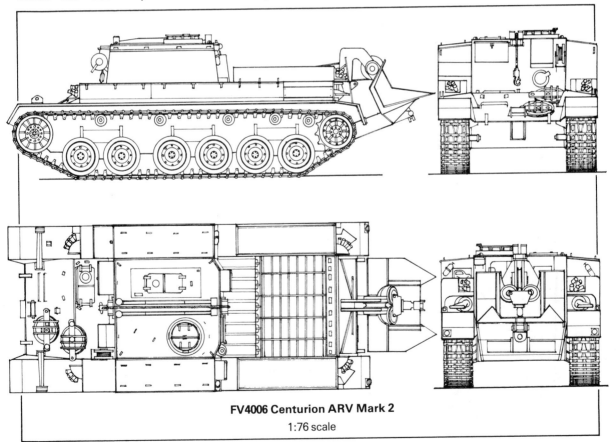

FV4006 Centurion ARV Mark 2

1:76 scale

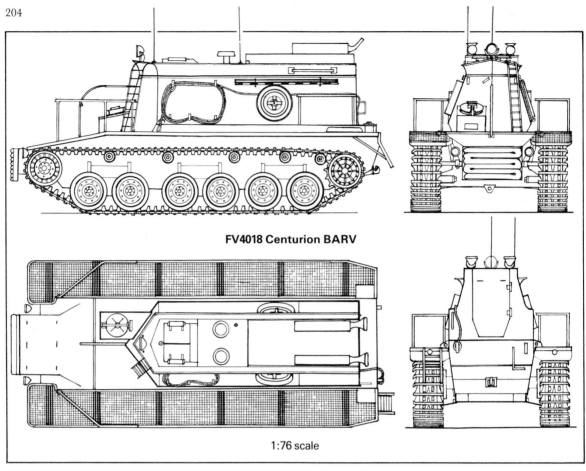

FV4018 Centurion BARV

1:76 scale

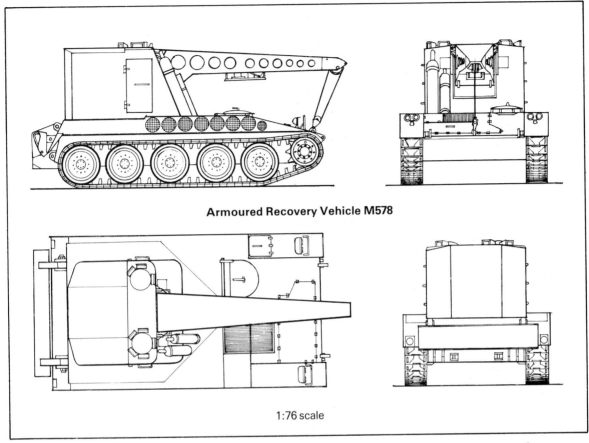

Armoured Recovery Vehicle M578

1:76 scale

The Centurion Beach Armoured Recovery Vehicle, or BARV, is a very specialised recovery vehicle originally intended for use in beach operations attendant on an amphibious landing. Experience in many landings showed that landing vehicles were very likely to founder in surf or become bogged down in soft sand. The BARV was seen as a solution to beaches being littered with stranded vehicles. The first production model was produced in 1959 and the resultant short production run began in 1961 at the Royal Ordnance Factory, Leeds.

The BARV can operate at up to a depth of 2.895 metres. This has been achieved by the erection of a new superstructure built up over the turret location and extending right to the rear of the vehicle over the engine bay. The driver's position has been moved from the hull to the left-hand side of the superstructure with a vision panel set into the plating. The crew hatch is at the top of the super-

structure, and the engine exhausts over the rear.

In its watery environment the BARV has two main tasks. One is to push stranded vehicles out of trouble, and for this purpose a fender is fitted over the front hull. To rescue bogged-down vehicles the BARV is fitted with towing cables and as one of the crew is a trained diver, there should be no problem in attaching the cables to a stranded vehicle.

The production run of the Centurion BARV was short and only four now remain. As their original role in amphibious large-scale landings has now passed from probability, these are now stationed in West Germany ready to be situated at selected river crossings where their particular abilities might be called upon.

Armoured Recovery Vehicle M578
Armament 1 × 7.62 mm L4A4 Machine-Gun; **Crew** 3; **Weight in action** 24,470 kg; **Length overall** 6.42 m; **Length of hull** 5.937 m; **Height (top of cupola)** 2.921 m; **Width of hull** 3.14 m; **Track width** 0.457 m; **Ground clearance** 0.47 m; **Maximum road speed** 60 km/h; **Range (roads)**

Left *A Centurion BARV pulling a Logistic LCM ashore during an exercise in Norway* (RN photo).

725 km; **Engine type** General Motors Model 8V71T; **Engine power** 405 bhp; **Engine capacity** 9.3 litres; **Fuel capacity** 1,137 litres; **Ammunition capacity** 7.62 mm—1,200 rounds.

When the British Army adopted the American M109 self-propelled howitzer it was placed in something of a quandary in that existing recovery and repair vehicles would be unable to lift the large and heavy engine pack from these vehicles. The answer was to purchase a relatively small number of the American M578 armoured recovery and repair vehicles direct from the USA (three more were purchased during 1979). The M578 is the recovery vehicle counterpart to the M107 and M110 self-propelled artillery carriages but in place of the gun there is an armoured turret mounting a crane. The turret houses the hoisting gear and winch, while a towing winch is fitted at the rear—this can also be used in conjunction with the rear-mounted spade. In use the turret can rotate through a full 360°. While the M578 has a good cross-country performance it has only a very limited wading capability.

Operationally the M578's role is not limited to the M109A1 batteries as it is also used with the M107 and M110 regiments where it is employed when field changes of barrels are carried out, as well as engine pack changing.

Carrier, Full Tracked, Articulated, LHD, Bv202E

Armament 1 × 7.62 mm L7A2 Machine-Gun (if fitted); **Crew** 2 + 8-10; **Weight in action** 4,200 kg;

Above *M578 of P Battery, 5 Heavy Regiment, RA* (PR HQ 2 Div). **Above right** *Bv202 over-snow vehicle, seen here towing a Bar Mine Layer during an exercise in Norway* (PR HQ UKLF).

Length 6.172 m; **Height** 2.21 m; **Width** 1.759 m; **Ground clearance** 0.3 m; **Maximum road speed** 39 km/h; **Range (roads)** 400 km; **Engine type** Volvo type B18 petrol; **Engine power** 91 bhp; **Engine capacity** 1.78 litres; **Fuel capacity** 156 litres.

The Bv202 is a Swedish over-snow vehicle designed under the aegis of the Swedish Army, the first prototypes being constructed in 1958. Volvo of Eskilstuna became the overall project leader and the production line was set up by Bolinder-Munktell, also at Eskilstuna, with the first examples coming off the production line during 1962 and 1963. When the British Army took over its NATO role of flank defence in Norway, the Bv202 was selected for British Army service and ever since it has been a maid-of-all-work with a number of important Army roles.

The Bv202 was designed from the start with an over-snow performance in mind, and the final design used an articulated configuration. The engine and driving compartment are in the front half while the main load carrier is at the rear with a driving shaft imparting drive to the rear section track. The two tracks, front and rear, are one-piece rubber with steel reinforcing inserts. They are wide enough to spread the loads involved and consequently the Bv202 has a very lively cross-snow performance which is far better than its performance

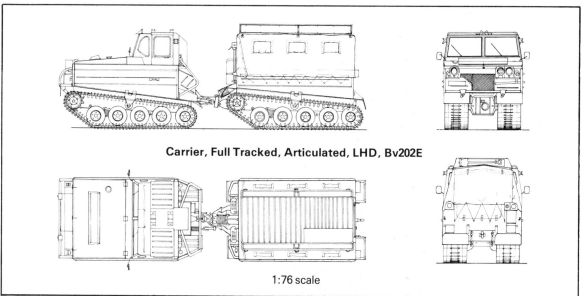

Carrier, Full Tracked, Articulated, LHD, Bv202E

1:76 scale

across snowless terrain. The rear compartment has a number of configurations. It can have either a hard or soft cover, or it can be left open to provide an area of 2.3 × 1.56 metres. As a personnel carrier it can accommodate eight men but ten can be carried at a squeeze. It has been used as an artillery tractor towing the 105 mm Pack Howitzer L5, and in the artillery role, some were altered to carry the battery FACE computer. In the Infantry support role, the Bv202 is used as a carrier for the 81 mm Mortar and the 120 mm Wombat. There is a

REME fitters' version, and a command version. Some have also been converted to the ambulance role. A fairly common fitment is that of a GPMG to a ring over the driver's compartment, but this is not universal.

As well as being a versatile over-snow vehicle, the Bv202 is also amphibious, and uses its tracks for propulsion to reach a water speed of 3.3 km/h. The bulk of the Bv202s in British service were obtained between 1968 and 1970. About 150 were bought at that time although more have been purchased since.

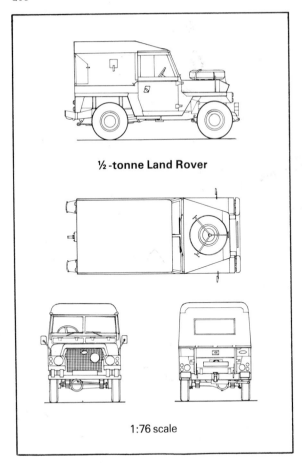

½-tonne Land Rover

1:76 scale

Below A ½-tonne Land Rover converted for use as a light ambulance. **Below right** *A Royal Artillery ½-tonne Land Rover used as a battery command vehicle for a 105 mm Light Gun battery.*

'B' vehicles
The ½-tonne Land Rover

Crew 1 + 2; **Weight loaded** 2,018 kg; **Length** 3.632 m; **Height** 1.95 m; **Width** 1.524 m; **Wheel track** 1.308 m; **Ground clearance** 0.21 m; **Maximum road speed** 105 km/h; **Range on roads** 560-600 km; **Engine type** Rover 4-cylinder OHV; **Engine power** 77 bhp; **Engine capacity** 2.286 litres; **Fuel capacity** 91 litres.

The ½-tonne Land Rover was designed to a general military requirement for a version of the Land Rover that could be carried slung under a helicopter—originally the specified helicopter was the RAF Wessex but this was later changed to include the Puma. Using the 88 in/2.235 metre wheelbase chassis as a basis, the first prototypes were ready in 1965 but it was not until 1968 that the new model was introduced into service.

Despite some rather drastic modifications to the Land Rover design it was not possible for the new version to be airlifted by the Wessex without further stripping of items such as the windscreen, all the doors, the tarpaulin and its support, and many of the internal fittings. But as the Puma has now taken over many of the lifting roles of the Wessex such stripping, although desirable, is now no longer strictly necessary. For more general use, the ½-tonne Land Rover has now almost entirely replaced the earlier ¼-tonne version (although some are still in limited use).

There are at present only two basic versions in use. One has a normal 12 volt electrical system, while the other has a 24 volt system for use with radios. Although some of these small Land Rovers have been altered to suit local requirements the

changes involved have not been so drastic or varied as they have been with the larger ¾-tonne version, and the only major fitting likely to be seen is that of racks for two stretchers to convert the ½-tonne Land Rover into an emergency ambulance. One possible variant that might be adopted is one initiated by the Royal Marines. They have converted small numbers of the ½-tonne Land Rover to carry the 120 mm Wombat recoilless gun.

The ¾-tonne Land Rovers

Crew 1 + 2-8; **Weight loaded** 2,620 kg; **Length** 4.648 m; **Height** 2.057 m; **Width** 1.689 m; **Wheel track** 1.308 m; **Ground clearance** 0.228 m; **Maximum road speed** 90 km/h; **Range (roads)** 450/500 km; **Engine type** Rover 4-cylinder OHV; **Engine power** 77 bhp; **Engine capacity** 2.286 litres; **Fuel capacity** 91 litres.

Without a doubt the Land Rover has been one of the outstanding production feats of the British automotive industry since 1945. It has been produced in hundreds of thousands and it is used all over the globe. It is still in production in 1980 and it will probably remain so for years yet—there seems to be no replacement for it, and many competitors have come and gone during the years the Land Rover has reigned supreme.

The Land Rover was first mooted in the lean years following 1945. Rover, long a leading light in the British automobile ranks, were unable to continue their high-cost saloon car range and searched for a new product. They chose the all-purpose cross-country vehicle and the Land Rover was the result. It soon became an immediate commercial success and the production line at Solihull got under way in 1948.

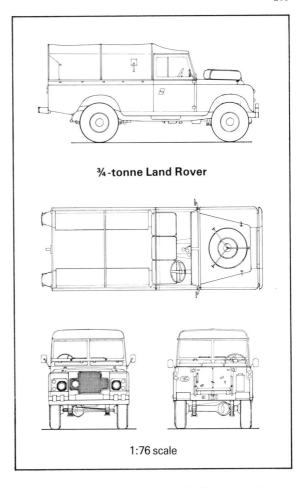

¾-tonne Land Rover

1:76 scale

Below A Land Rover fitted with a SLAP mounting for anti-aircraft defence.

Left *Typical of the 'hard-topped' Land Rovers is this Royal Engineers EOD example.*

Right *A 1-tonne Land Rover towing a 105 mm Light Gun.*

Left *One of the most recent additions to the Land Rover stable is the Tactical Command Post variant produced by Carawagon Coachbuilders of Sunbury-on--Thames. 35 have been ordered by the Army and the Command Post interior has all the usual map tables, extra lighting and impedimenta needed for the role. Extra stowage is supplied over the cab and a 'penthouse' can be fitted to provide more space. There is even provision for folding bunks inside.*

The first models had an 80 in/2.032 metre wheelbase, and some of these were ordered for the British Defence Forces as early as 1949. Gradual production changes and increases in engine power led to two models being in production, one with a wheelbase of 88 in/2.235 metres, and the other with a wheelbase of 109 in/2.768 metres. Both were officially adopted for British Army service in 1956 but by them there were many already in widespread use. In time the smaller wheelbase version became the ¼-tonne Land Rover. There are few in service today as they have been replaced by the ½-tonne version.

The long wheelbase version became the ¾-tonne

Land Rover. Over the years there have been many variations in engine power and such details as the headlamp positioning but the general appearance has remained the same, as has the layout. The main problem for a book of this nature is that no two service Land Rovers appear to be the same. They are issued to every branch of the Army and every unit seems to have its own particular 'fit'. Some have radios, some do not. Some are used only as troop carriers and thus have seating for two in the front, apart from the driver, and bench seats for up to eight at the rear. Some carry battery charging equipment. Some are used as mobile command posts. Some are equipped as miniature workshops.

Some are used as signals or telephone switching vehicles. Others have very specialised installations such as FACE computers. Many units convert the Land Rover to their own particular requirements by· using Dexion or similar racking.

The basic Land Rover is usually fitted with a canvas tilt but some units use them fully open and others have 'hard' tops, especially if they have signals or similar equipment installed. Land Rovers intended for use in really cold climates have extra heating fitted as well.

Land Rovers are also used to carry weapons. The 120 mm Wombat recoilless gun is one load, while the 81 mm mortar is another. Some Special Air Service vehicles have been seen liberally festooned in GPMGs but these are now uncommon.

As well as being used to carry things, Land Rovers are also used to tow various loads such as Cymbeline Mark 1 radars and components of the Rapier missile system. Numerous other types of trailer are used, from ordinary general service types to special ones containing water filtration equipment, and some small water or fuel tanks. The listing of all the possible trailer types would be a very long one. The following list gives details of but three trailer types in widespread use. All are manufactured by GKN Sankey, and are general purpose models. The FV2361 and FV2381 are both box-type trailers for general use and are equipped with canvas covers. The FV2380 is a flat-bed trailer for carrying such items as generators and water tanks.

Weight empty 404 kg (FV2361)/390 kg (approx) (FV2380)/408 kg (FV2381); **Length** 2.92 m/2.92 m/2.851 m; **Height** 0.94 m/0.8 m/1.113 m; **Width** 1.425 m/1.6 m/1.676 m; **Wheel track** 1.2 m/1.416 m/1.416 m.

The Land Rover has been the subject of some rather drastic modifications, to the extent that they have virtually become new vehicles. Two of these are mentioned elsewhere in this book—the FV18067 Ambulance and the FV18061 Shorland patrol car.

There is no replacement for the Land Rover in sight and it seems set to see out the century. Ever since the first examples were painted in military shades they have become associated with the British Army, to such an extent that wherever the British soldier has been stationed, the Land Rover has been not far away. The future seems to indicate that this state of affairs will not change.

The 1-tonne Land Rover

Crew 1 + 1-8; **Weight loaded** 3,120 kg; **Length** 4.127 m; **Height** 2.138 m; **Width** 1.842 m; **Wheel track (front)** 1.524 m; **Wheel track (rear)** 1.549 m; **Ground clearance** 0.254 m; **Maximum road speed** 120 km/h; **Range (roads)** 560 km; **Engine type** Rover V8; **Engine power** 128 bhp; **Engine capacity** 3.5 litres; **Fuel capacity** 109 litres.

The 1-tonne Land Rover was a joint venture, being designed not only by Rover but also by the MVEE at Chobham. The original requirement called for a 1-tonne vehicle capable of towing a power trailer but in the event the latter was not adopted by the Army. Other demands on the design which had to be met were that there should be seating for eight soldiers in lieu of the 1-tonne payload, and that it should be light enough to be airlifted by helicopter or aircraft. After the usual

Left *The 1-tonne Land Rover ambulance conversion produced by Marshall of Cambridge* (Marshall).

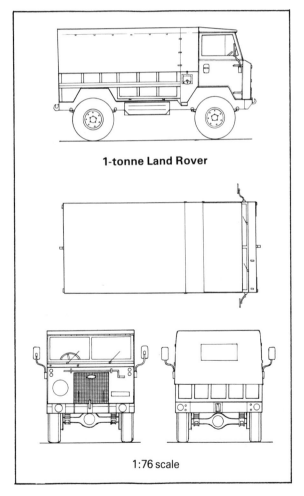

1-tonne Land Rover

1:76 scale

prototypes were made in 1968 a pre-production run for further trials was completed at Solihull in 1972 with the full production run starting in 1974.

One of the first tasks assigned to the 1-tonne Land Rover once it was in service was to tow the 105 mm Light Gun. In this role the towing vehicle carries the gun crew and other following vehicles carry the ammunition. Another role is that of carrying the 81 mm Mortar and in this form the 1-tonne Land Rover has been issued to the TA. It is also used to carry and pull part of the Rapier guided missile system. Other 1-tonne Land Rover conversions are being made to provide hard-tops as cover for electronics equipment to be used for specialised purposes in BAOR.

One more involved conversion of the 1-tonne Land Rover's 101 in/2.565 metre wheelbase chassis was ordered during 1976, the Marshalls of Cambridge-built lightweight ambulance.

FV18067 Ambulance 2/4 Stretcher (Rover 0.75-tonne 4 × 4)

Crew 1-2; **Weight in action** 2,670 kg; **Length** 4.826 m; **Height** 2.146 m; **Width** 1.905 m; **Wheel track** 1.308 m; **Maximum road speed** 96 km/h; **Range (roads)** 450 km; **Engine type** Rover 2.5; **Engine power** 77 bhp; **Engine capacity** 2.286 litres; **Fuel capacity** 90.86 litres.

The FV18067 is a conversion of the long wheelbase Land Rover to take a new aluminium ambulance body constructed by Marshall of Cambridge. The first developments to meet an Army requirement for a light vehicle capable of evacuating casualties from forward battle areas began in 1963 and production started in 1968. Ever since then the Land Rover ambulance has been a

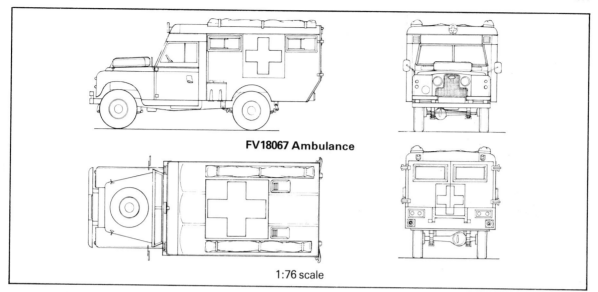

FV18067 Ambulance

1:76 scale

common sight wherever the Army has been posted or in action—it has even become a fairly common sight on public roads, especially during the ambulance drivers' strikes of early 1979.

The FV18067 has a large hard-topped body equipped with extra heating and ventilation. Casualty accommodation is variable and can vary from two or four stretchers, to two stretchers and three seated casualties. As another alternative the stretchers can be folded away and six seated casualties carried. There is also a small seat for a medical orderly, and if necessary extra casualties can be seated next to the driver.

Below An FV18067 Ambulance. **Below right** *Mercedes-Benz Unimog.*

Mercedes-Benz Unimog

Crew 1 + 1; **Weight loaded** 4,400 kg; **Length** 4.925 m; **Height** 2.54 m; **Width** 2.14 m; **Wheel track** 1.63 m; **Maximum road speed** 85 km/h; **Range (roads)** 500 km; **Engine type** Daimler-Benz M180 6-cylinder; **Engine power** 80 bhp; **Engine capacity** 2.195 litres; **Fuel capacity** 90 litres.

The first Mercedes-Benz Unimogs (Universal Motor Gerät) were produced during 1949 and ever since then they have been manufactured in a variety of models with different engines to suit the numerous military and civilian customers who have acquired them. The British Army acquired a number some years ago for service with the Berlin Brigade but their use has since spread to the depots

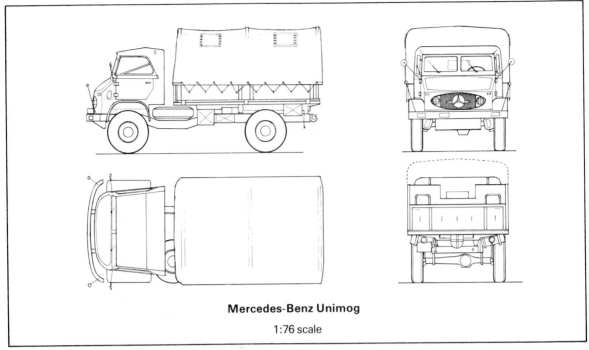

Mercedes-Benz Unimog

1:76 scale

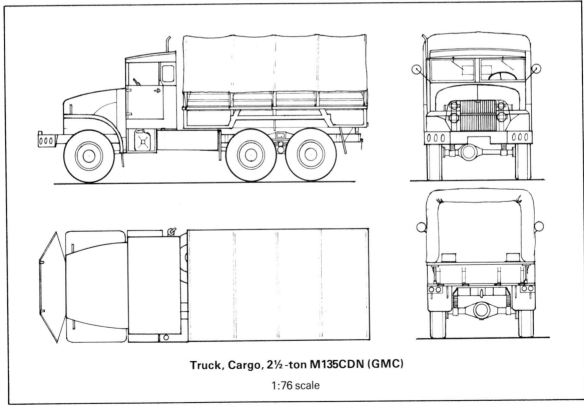

Truck, Cargo, 2½-ton M135CDN (GMC)

1:76 scale

A 'deuce-and-a-half' on the Suffield Ranges.

and rear areas of BAOR. The type mainly encountered in the British Army is the Model S-404 and the data above relates to this version.

Truck, Cargo, 2½-ton M135CDN (GMC)

Crew 1 + 1 or 2; **Weight loaded (approx)** 8,200 kg; **Length** 6.477 m; **Height (top of cab)** 2.032 m; **Height (tarpaulin)** 2.667 m; **Width** 2.235 m; **Wheel track** 1.755 m; **Maximum road speed** 93 km/h; **Range (roads)** 480 km; **Engine type** General Motors 302 M; **Engine power** 130 bhp; **Engine capacity** 4.942 litres; **Fuel capacity** 212 litres.

The General Motors (GMC) trucks in British Army service are all used on the Suffield Training Area in Canada, and nowhere else. They were obtained locally from Canadian Army stocks in an attempt to keep down the costs involved in establishing the area, as to bring 4-tonne and other trucks over from Europe would have been a very expensive operation (even so, a few MKs have made the journey). To the British soldier, as to

many others, this truck is known as the 'deuce-and-a-half' from its weight rating. As far as can be determined, all the vehicles involved in the Suffield operation were built in Canada by the General Motors plant at Oshawa, Ontario. They are used as general service cargo trucks, and are fitted to tow water tankers and other trailers. A few have been fitted with ammunition-handling cranes behind the cab, while others have winches. Nearly all the trucks involved show the signs of extensive and hard use.

Bedford RL (4 × 4) 4-tonne Truck

Crew 1 + 1; **Weight loaded** 8,800 kg; **Length** 6.36 m; **Height (top of cab)** 2.602 m; **Height (tarpaulin)** 3.11 m; **Width** 2.39 m; **Wheel track** 1.854 m; **Maximum road speed** 75 km/h; **Range (roads)** 400 km; **Engine type** Bedford 6-cylinder OHV; **Engine power** 130 bhp; **Engine capacity** 4.93 litres; **Fuel capacity** 118 litres; **Load area** 4.267 × 2.178 m.

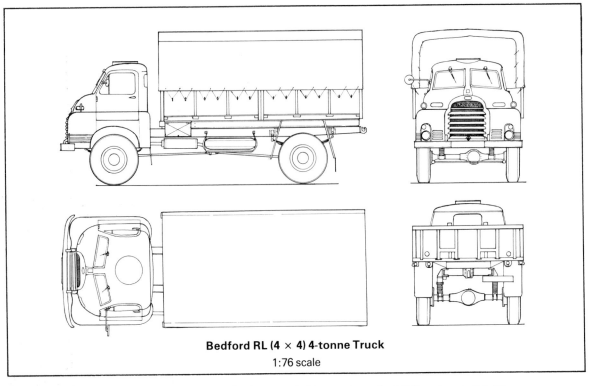

Bedford RL (4 × 4) 4-tonne Truck
1:76 scale

Below *Typical of the many special uses the RL series has been put to is this example carrying MGB components* (MoD).

The Bedford RL series of 4-tonne trucks can be said to be among the Army's veterans as the first examples were delivered for service back in 1952. Ever since then they have been the workhorses of the Army and have been produced in a wide range of variants for an almost equally wide range of purposes. When they were first issued they were designated 3-tonne vehicles but this was uprated to 4-tonne in 1968.

The RL series was based on a commercial chassis and, although gradually numerous changes were made to suit the exacting military role, the range was so successful that they remained in production until 1969 by which time 73,135 had been made for military and civilian use, many for export. By the early 1970s the RLs began to be replaced by the Bedford MK series, although large numbers remain in service in many roles, and the last of them is not likely to be seen for a long while yet. They soldier on in many guises and the table below can give only a rough outline of the many variants that have been used by the Army. Not all remain in use, and several of the following types have long since passed from service and been disposed of, but it is likely that just as many more have been stockpiled against some likely future employment.

FV13101 GS Cargo Truck; **FV13102** Container Stores, Binned; **FV13103** Charging Vehicle—Signals; **FV13104** Charging Vehicle—MT Batteries; **FV13105** Cargo—with winch (Dropside); **FV13106** Tanker—3,636 litres; **FV13109** GS Cargo Truck; **FV13110** Signals Truck; **FV13111** Tipper—short wheelbase; **FV13112** Truck, Cargo, Dropside; **FV13113** MT Repair Shop Truck; **FV13115** Recovery Vehicle, Wheeled; **FV13120** Tanker—1,728 litres; **FV13136** Container, Flatbed; **FV13142** Cargo, Dropside (Airportable); **FV13143** Cargo (LH Drive); **FV13149** Tanker, Fuel Dispensing, 2,730 litre; **FV13152** Container Truck; **FV13165** Dental Truck; **FV13197** Water Tanker (4 × 2).

5,000 kg winches were fitted to many of the above variants. Apart from these specialist roles, many RLs were used as artillery tractors, and some were converted as Midge drone launchers. Some may still be found in use as Laird Class 30 Trackway carriers and layers. One role that has now been passed to the newer Bedford MK is that of carrier for Medium Girder Bridge components, although some are still used for training in this capacity.

Several types of trailer have been developed for use with the Bedford RL, some of which are now being used by the MK. A small selection of these are included below along with the relevant data: **FV2501(A)** Trailer, Cargo, 2-tonne Mark 2; **FV2505(D)** Trailer, Flat Platform (2-tonne); and

Top *This RL load is a mobile office-workshop used at the AAC Centre, Middle Wallop.* **Above** *Looking rather battered is this FV13111.*

FV2508 Trailer, Low Platform, Earth Moving Ancillaries (2-tonne). **Weight laden** 3,734 kg (FV2501(A))/5,270 kg (FV2505(D))/4,650 kg (FV2508); **Length** 4.902 m/7.671 m/7.645 m; **Height** 1.55 m/0.775 m/1.473 m; **Width** 2.159 m/2.362 m/2.134 m; **Wheel track** 1.702 m/2.057 m/1.702 m.

The CB 101 container bodies were produced for the Bedford RL by Laird (Anglesey) Limited, and many are still used for a wide range of purposes which can vary from mobile offices to small workshops. They are carried on flatbed versions of the RL and have the following dimensions: **Weight empty** 590 kg; **Length** 2.756 m; **Height** 1.854 m; **Width** 2.235 m.

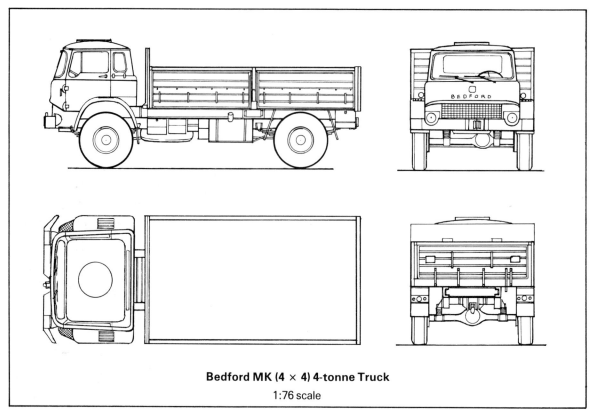

Bedford MK (4 × 4) 4-tonne Truck
1:76 scale

Below *MK laying a Class 30 Trackway. Once laid the trackway is 45.95 metres long and 3.35 metres wide.*

Bedford MK (4 × 4) 4-tonne Truck

Crew 1 + 2; **Weight loaded** 9,650 kg; **Length** 6.579 m; **Height (top of cab)** 2.501 m; **Height (tarpaulin)** 3.404 m; **Width** 2.489 m; **Wheel track (front)** 2.05 m; **Wheel track (rear)** 2.03 m; **Maximum road speed** 73 km/h; **Range (roads)** 560 km; **Engine type** Bedford 6-cylinder; **Engine power** 106 bhp; **Engine capacity** 5.42 litres; **Fuel capacity** 150 litres; **Load area** 4.28 × 2.01 m.

The Bedford MK was the successful entry in a three-sided contest to meet the Army's requirement for a new 4-tonne 4 × 4 truck to replace the Bedford RL. The requirement was issued during the early 1960s, and the unsuccessful entries were made by Austin and Commer. The Bedford entry was a 4 × 4 version of the commerical 4 × 2 TK model, and was so successful that by the end of 1977 a total of over 11,700 MKs had been produced, although not all of these went to the British Army for the truck has proved to be a very successful export to many overseas military forces.

Right *A flatbed MK of the Royal Engineers.*

Below *An MK equipped for the bulk re-fuelling role.*

Above *A Bedford MK Tipper truck in use as an engineer support vehicle in Gibraltar.* **Below** *A 4-ton Bedford MK fitted with a snow plough during Exercise 'Hard Fall' in northern Norway* (UKLF). **Below right** *An MK with a crane for handling ammunition.*

Like the Bedford RL that preceded it, the MK has been produced in many versions. There are two basic variants, one of which is the FV13801/13802 cargo truck and the other the FV13803/13804; this is essentially the same vehicle but with the addition of a winch having a pull of 3,500 kg and 76 metres of cable. Both vehicles can be converted into flatbed versions and another variation is the changing of the single-tyred rear wheels to two-tyred wheels to give extra traction for cross-country work.

Although the earlier RL is still in service in appreciable numbers, the MK has by now assumed the role of general workhorse for the Army. Apart from its general purpose stores-carrying role, the removal of the dropside and rear panels easily converts the MK into a flatbed truck for the carrying of containers and container bodies. The usual container bodies carried are manufactured by Marshall's of Cambridge as their CB.300 series. In this series are all manner of bodies ranging from simple rest-rooms to computer terminals (as with Wavell). The CB.300 containers are produced or converted into numerous configurations such as command centres, workshops, offices, simulator housings, repair and testing shops, signal stations, post offices and for many other similar functions. Any MK can be thus converted into any number of specialist roles.

More complex conversions have been made to turn the MK into the carrier/launcher for the Midge drone system or the carrier/layer for the Laird Class 30 Trackway. The MK is also used to carry Medium Girder Bridge components and bulk refuelling dispensers. A tipper version is also in use. The list of different roles the MK is called upon to perform is beyond the scope of this book but most of them are based on the two main truck versions.

The 4 × 2 Bedford TK which is almost identical to the MK is also used in large numbers for general stores carrying and driver training.

Basic details of the CB.300 series of container bodies are as follows: **Weight empty** 952 kg; **Length** 4.674 m; **Height** 1.905 m; **Width** 2.515 m.

FV622, Truck, Cargo, High Mobility Load Carrier, Stalwart Mark 2

Crew 1 + 2; **Weight loaded** 14,480 kg; **Length** 6.356 m; **Height (with tilt)** 2.64 m; **Height (top of cab)** 2.312 m; **Height (rear floor)** 1.5 m; **Width** 2.616 m; **Wheel track** 2.03 m; **Maximum road speed** 63 km/h; **Range (roads)** 515 km; **Engine type** Rolls-Royce B81 Mark 8B; **Engine power** 220 bhp; **Engine capacity** 6.522 litres; **Fuel capacity** 455 litres; **Load area** 3.6 × 2.4 × 925 m.

The very first member of the Stalwart family was built by Alvis Limited of Coventry in 1959 and was based on the chassis of the FV652 Salamander used

by the Royal Air Force as a fire tender. Continued development resulted in the amphibious Stalwart Mark 1, or FV620, from which the present FV622 Stalwart Mark 2 evolved. Production started in 1966 and continued until 1971.

The Stalwart is a very mobile load-carrying vehicle which can cross almost any type of country and is amphibious as well. All six of its wheels impart drive; while in water, driving jets can propel a loaded vehicle at speeds up to 9.6 km/h. The large load area can carry a wide range of stores and a special pack has been produced which can convert the Stalwart into a bulk fuel carrier. Alternatively, the Stalwart can carry up to 38 fully equipped soldiers. The load-carrying capacity is 5,000 kg and if trailers are attached up to 10,000 kg can be towed. For use in self-recovery, or the recovery of other vehicles, a 4,990 kg-capacity winch is fitted to the front.

Apart from the amphibious load carrier there are two variants in service. The first of these is the FV623, fitted with a hydraulic crane behind the

cab. This is used as an ammunition limber vehicle with the Artillery regiments based in Germany, where its crane is used to handle ammunition packed on to pallets. The all-up weight of the FV623 is 15,600 kg and the height is increased to 3.124 metres. Second of the Stalwart variants is the FV624 which is a repair vehicle used by the REME.

For all the success of the Stalwart as a cross-country vehicle, it has shown itself to be rather prone to mechanical breakdowns, and as the engine and main fuel tank are under the load area, something of a fire hazard. If the Stalwart is carrying fuel and an engine fire results, the end product is likely to be a very expensive blaze. Its fuel consumption of a steady 71 litres for every 100 road kilometers is considered by many to be rather high.

Bedford TM 4-4 (4 × 4) 8,000 kg Truck
Crew 1 + 2; **Weight loaded** 16,300 kg; **Length** 6.604 m; **Height (top of cab)** 2.997 m; **Width** 2.476 m; **Wheel track** 2.078 m; **Ground clearance** 0.352 m; **Maximum road speed** 88 km/h; **Range** unknown; **Engine type** Bedford 500 OHV; **Engine**

A Stalwart delivering stores on Salisbury Plain.

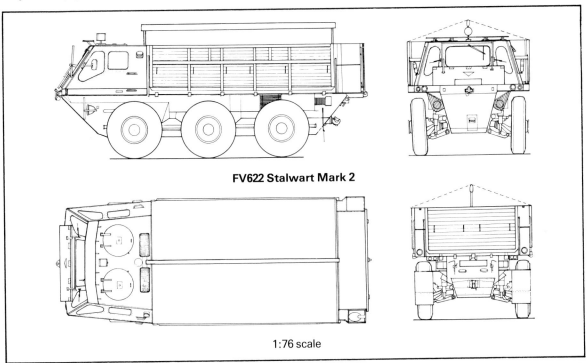

FV622 Stalwart Mark 2

1:76 scale

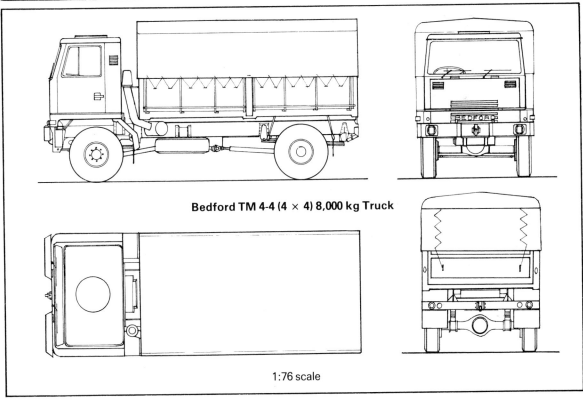

Bedford TM 4-4 (4 × 4) 8,000 kg Truck

1:76 scale

*Above A Bedford TM carrying ammunition and equipped with a hydraulic hoist. **Above right** FV11013 Militant Mark 1 delivering ammunition at Libenau, West Germany (Army PR HQ 1 Div).*

power 202 bhp; **Engine capacity** 8.198 litres; **Fuel capacity** 150 litres; **Body plus cargo payload** 10,000 kg.

During 1970 an Army requirement for a new 8-tonne truck was issued with an expected into-service date of 1980. Three concerns entered designs for the requirements and the result was a series of trials that began as soon as the first prototypes emerged during 1976. The three firms involved were Foden, Vauxhall Motors and Leyland, and the successful contestant emerged in 1977 as Vauxhall Motors of Luton. Their entrant was the Bedford TM 4 × 4, based on a commercial model but suitably modified to suit the needs of its exacting military role, namely that of being the main component of the Army's Medium Mobility 8-tonne range. A production contract worth £40 million was duly signed for around 2,000 vehicles. The first examples came off the Luton production lines during 1978 and these were subsequently subjected to a rigorous programme of tests and trials ready for the main production run starting in late 1979.

Four main versions have been ordered by the Army. The first will be a straightforward cargo truck, with its loading bed height compatible with that of existing 4-tonne trucks. Then will come two slight variants of the basic cargo truck, one with an 8,000 kg winch and the other with an Atlas AK 3500 crane mounted behind the cab. The fourth version will be a tipper truck with a shorter wheelbase of 3.883 metres as opposed to the normal 4.325 metres. Other versions that have been mentioned are a tanker and a recovery vehicle. An airportable version has also been suggested.

Once in service the Bedford TM will be an important part of the Army's front-line logistic support. Starting in 1982 it will begin to replace some of the existing 4- and 10-tonne trucks at second and third-line level, but at whatever level it is used the Bedford TM will no doubt prove to be as capable as its 4-tonne RL and MK forebears.

AEC Militant Mark 1 (6 × 6) 10,000 kg trucks

Crew 2; **Weight loaded** 21,200 kg; **Length** 9.14 m; **Height** 3.6 m; **Width** 2.49 m; **Wheel track (front)** 1.99 m; **Wheel track (rear)** 1.91 m; **Maximum road speed** 40 km/h; **Range (roads)** 480 km; **Engine type** AEC 6-cylinder diesel; **Engine power** 150 bhp; **Engine capacity** 11.3 litres; **Fuel capacity** 218 litres.

The AEC 10-tonne range has been in British Army service for many years now and, although they are scheduled for replacement by 1983, they are still an important part of the Army's heavy-lift logistic range. The first of them were developed from existing commerical models by AEC during the early 1950s and ever since the first cargo versions were produced the basic design has been used for a variety of purposes. Some of these have been 6 × 4 vehicles and different wheelbase versions are still in service. The wheelbases built were either 3.92, 4.49 or 4.887 metres. Some vehicles have been fitted with HIAB cranes, and most examples in service are fitted with a 7,000 kg winch. A listing of the main variants is given below but not all are still in service and many have been converted to flat-bed trucks for carrying stores and ammunition pallets. All are due to be replaced by the new Bedford TM 8-tonne range but the old AECs will not be finally replaced until at least 1983.

FV11001 Artillery Tractor, 6 × 4, w/b 3.92 m; **FV11002** Artillery Tractor for Bofors, 6 × 6, w/b 3.92 m; **FV11003** Crane Bridging, 6 × 6, w/b 4.493 m; **FV11005** Tipper, 6 × 4, w/b 3.92 m; **FV11008*** Cargo Truck, 6 × 6, w/b 4.877 m; **FV11009** Fuel Tanker, 6 × 4, w/b 4.877 m; **FV11010** GS Semi-trailer, 6 × 6, w/b 3.92 m; **FV11013** Crane GP, 6 × 4, w/b 3.92 m; **FV11014** Excavator Carrier, 6 × 6, w/b 3.92 m; **FV11041** AEC Mark 2—trials only.

*The data refers to this version.

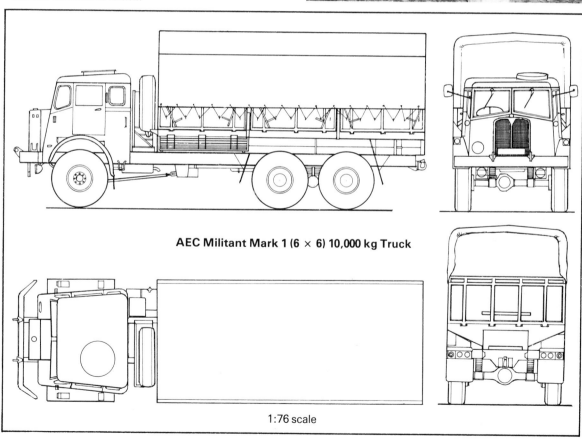

AEC Militant Mark 1 (6 × 6) 10,000 kg Truck

1:76 scale

AEC Militant Mark 3 (6 × 6) 10,000 kg cargo truck

Crew 2; **Weight loaded** 22,000 kg; **Length** 9.07 m; **Height (to tarpaulin)** 3.5 m; **Width** 2.44 m; **Wheel track (front)** 2 m; **Wheel track (rear)** 2.06 m; **Maximum road speed** 53 km/h; **Range (roads)** 483 km; **Engine type** AEC AV760 diesel; **Engine power** 226 bhp; **Engine capacity** 12.473 litres; **Fuel capacity** 218 litres; **Load area** 6.248 × 2.337 m.

The AEC Mark 3 10-tonne truck was developed during the mid-1960s in answer to an Army requirement for a new 10-tonne general cargo truck. Production took place at the AEC factory at Southall in Middlesex and most of the output (the FV11046/11047) are now used in Germany. The cargo body has drop sides for fork-lift loading, and most vehicles are fitted with a 7,000 kg winch. They are scheduled to be at first supplemented, and finally replaced, by the Bedford TM 8-tonne trucks during the early 1980s, but it will be at least 1983 before the last of them passes from use. A variant is the FV11044 Medium Recovery vehicle.

Foden 6 × 6 Medium Mobility FH70 vehicles

Crew 1 + 8 (tractor)/1 + 2 (limber); **Weight loaded** 26,570 kg/28,488 kg; **Length** 9.15 m/9.046 m; **Height** 3.75 m/3.607 m; **Width** 2.489 m (tractor and limber); **Maximum speed (roads)** 109 km/h (tractor and limber); **Maximum speed (cross-country)** 54.5 km/h (tractor and limber); **Range** Unknown; **Engine type** Rolls-Royce Eagle 305 Mark III (tractor and limber); **Engine power** 305 bhp (tractor and limber); **Engine capacity** 12.17 litres (tractor and limber); **Fuel capacity** 409 litres (tractor and limber); **Ammunition capacity (155 mm)** 68/136 rounds.

The Foden 6 × 6 Medium Mobility vehicles share many of their components with the 8 × 4 Low Mobility range (perhaps the most obvious being the tilting S90 cab). The Medium Mobility range was developed primarily to provide towing and limber vehicles to service the 155 mm FH70 howitzer. Foden produced the 23 prototype vehicles used during the early howitzer trials and as a result were awarded the production contract for 111 vehicles during 1977. All the vehicles will be produced at the Foden Works at Sandbach, Cheshire.

The FH70 tractor and the limber vehicle both use

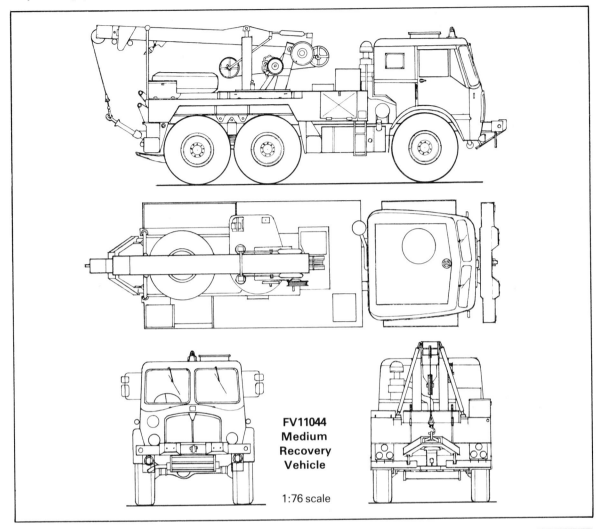

**FV11044
Medium
Recovery
Vehicle**

1:76 scale

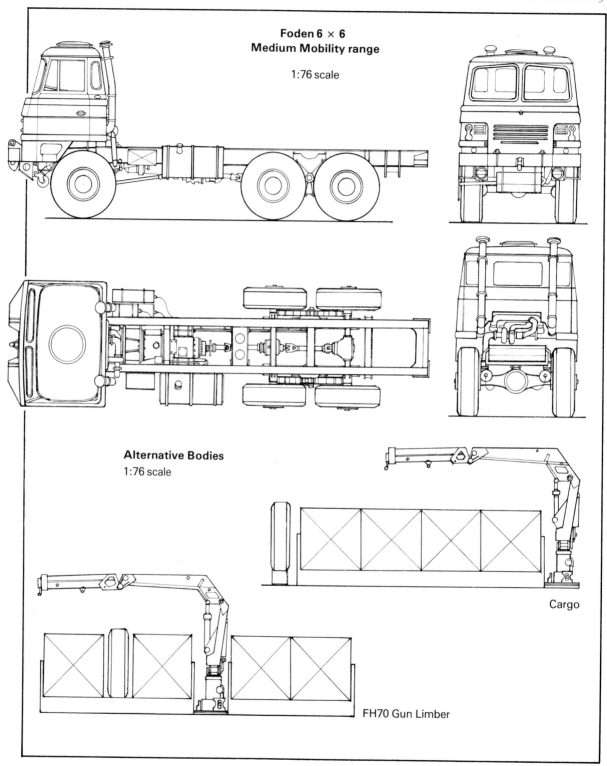

**Foden 6 × 6
Medium Mobility range**

1:76 scale

Alternative Bodies

1:76 scale

Cargo

FH70 Gun Limber

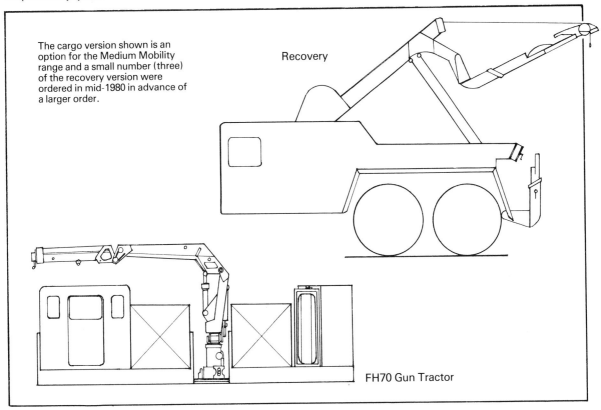

The cargo version shown is an option for the Medium Mobility range and a small number (three) of the recovery version were ordered in mid-1980 in advance of a larger order.

Recovery

FH70 Gun Tractor

Below *Foden FH70 Limber.*

the same basic chassis and body, each of which has an auxiliary gearbox for use when crossing rough ground—this can be switched in or out as required. Both use the same articulated suspension and are equipped with an Atlas hydraulic crane for lifting the ammunition pallets. The tractor version carries a heated cabin pallet which can accommodate the eight-man howitzer crew, which is situated just behind the driver's cab. Also on the tractor are two standard NATO ammunition pallets each containing 34 rounds. At the rear is space for some of the howitzer spares and stores. The limber vehicle carries four ammunition pallets. Controls for the lifting crane are on the side of the vehicle.

Exactly how successful the FH70 vehicles will be in their role remains to be seen. The turbo-supercharged Eagle engines will certainly have enough power for prolonged cross-country travelling but the view of some serving gunners is that they will prove to be too bulky and too high. Even at the ranges at which FH70 will be employed, the bulk of the tractor or limber will prove difficult to hide.

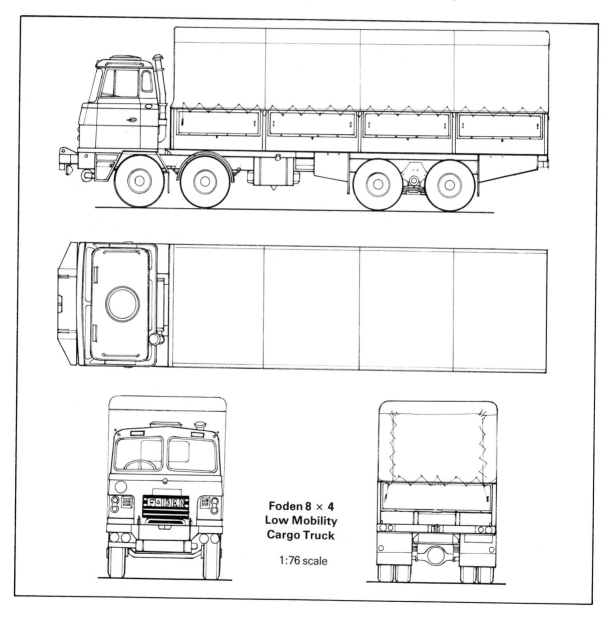

Foden 8 × 4 Low Mobility Cargo Truck

1:76 scale

Top *Foden 8 × 4 loaded with ammunition* (MoD). **Above** *Foden 8 × 4 Low Mobility Tanker.*

FV11701/11702 cargo truck

Crew 1 + 2; **Weight loaded** 29,553 kg; **Length** 10.278 m; **Height** 3.137 m; **Width** 2.497 m; **Maximum road speed** 76 km/h; **Range** Unknown; **Engine type** Rolls-Royce Eagle 220 Mark III; **Engine power** 220 bhp; **Engine capacity** 12.17 litres; **Fuel capacity** 227 litres; **Payload** 20,000 kg; **Body area** 8.23 × 2.5 m.

The Foden Low Mobility range has been produced to meet a British Army requirement for a new family of vehicles that could supply the various needs of service units, not only when travelling on roads but also on rough tracks. The Army vehicles are all based on commerical models which not only lowers the overall procurement costs but also makes provision for spare parts that much easier. Production of the Foden Low Mobility range began in 1976 and was substantially complete by 1978, and an indication of the importance of the range is that 70 per cent of the total run of 1,007 units were built with left-hand drive for use on the continent.

The most numerous of the range is the 8 × 4 cargo truck of which 703 were produced. Each vehicle has a payload of 20,000 kg and has drop sides and a dropping tailgate. A tilt can also be fitted when required. The engine, transmission, cab, suspension and many other features are shared with the other vehicles in the Low Mobility range. Ease of accessibility is a feature carried over from the commercial models—for instance the cab can be tilted forward to expose the engine for removal without the cab being removed entirely. One item of note regarding the cab is that 20 were enlarged for driver training.

Foden 8 × 4 Low Mobility tanker

Crew 1 + 2; **Weight loaded** 28,888 kg; **Length** 10.27 m; **Height** 3.25 m; **Width** 2.502 m; **Maximum road speed** 76 km/h; **Range** Unknown; **Engine type** Rolls-Royce Eagle 220 Mark III; **Engine power** 220 bhp; **Engine capacity** 12.17 litres; **Fuel capacity** 227 litres; **Tank capacity** 22,500 litres.

The Foden Low Mobility 8 × 4 tanker is the second most numerous of the Low Mobility range as 134 were produced. The large tank body is sectioned off internally into five compartments, each holding 4,500 litres. The tank itself is produced by Clarke Chapman of Bilston, Cheshire. It is expected that fuel will be the normal load for this tanker.

Below Foden 8 × 4 Low Mobility Tipper (Fodens Ltd).
Bottom Foden 6 × 4 Low Mobility Tanker (Fodens Ltd).

FV 11703 Truck Tipper 11m³

Crew 1 + 2; **Weight loaded** 29,705 kg; **Length** 8.09 m; **Height** 3.139 m; **Width** 2.497 m; **Maximum road speed** 76 km/h; **Range** Unknown; **Engine type** Rolls-Royce Eagle 220 Mark III; **Engine power** 220 bhp; **Engine capacity** 12.17 litres; **Fuel capacity** 227 litres; **Body capacity** 11 m³.

The Low Mobility tipper was produced in smaller numbers than the rest of the range as only 70 were delivered. This version differs from the other 8 × 4 vehicles as it has a shorter wheelbase.

Foden 6 × 4 Low Mobility tanker

Crew 1 + 2; **Weight loaded** 22,786 kg; **Length** 8.75 m; **Height** 3.124 m; **Width** 2.497 m; **Maximum road speed** 87 km/h; **Range** Unknown; **Engine type** Rolls-Royce Eagle 220 Mark III; **Engine power** 220 bhp; **Engine capacity** 12.17 litres; **Fuel capacity** 227 litres; **Tank capacity** 12,000 litres.

One hundred of the 6 × 4 Low Mobility tankers were delivered to the British Army. Like their larger 8 × 4 counterparts, they will be used mainly for the carriage of fuel. (NB: Foden is now part of Sandbach Engineering Ltd.)

FV 12004 Tractor Wheeled Semi-Trailer (Thornycroft Antar Mark 3, 30 tonne 6 × 4)

Crew 3; **Weight (with ballast)** 23,040 kg; **Weight (less ballast)** 21,900 kg; **Length** 8.7 m; **Height** 3.15 m; **Width** 3.2 m; **Wheel track (front)** 2.25 m; **Wheel track (rear)** 2.286 m; **Maximum road speed** 32.18 km/h; **Range (roads—laden)** 702 km; **Engine type** Rolls-Royce C8SFL-843 diesel; **Engine power** 333 bhp; **Engine capacity** 16.2 litres; **Fuel capacity** 910 litres.

The Thornycroft Antar was originally a commercial design that originated during the late 1940s, and was subsequently adopted by the Army for towing tank transporter trailers. The first service Antar was the FV12001 which was used for pulling trailers only. The FV12002 could be converted to pull semi-trailers as well, as could the next version, the FV12003. With the FV12004 Antar Mark 3 considerable improvements were made over the earlier marks. The ability to tow either trailers or semi-trailers was retained but a new and more powerful engine was fitted along with a new transmission, and some alterations were made to the cab. In this form the Antar Mark 3 is the current tank-towing tractor in service today. Originally the Antars towed Centurions but now they tow Chieftains, and many are being driven by their second generation of drivers. To assist with the loading of

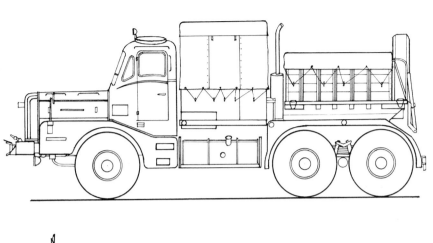

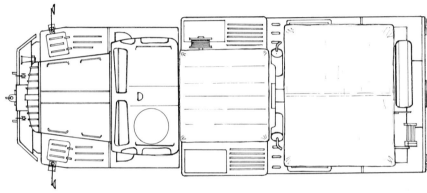

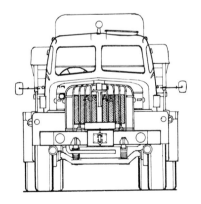

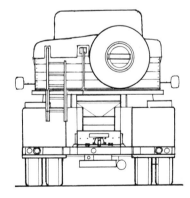

FV12004 Tractor Wheeled Semi-Trailer
(Thornycroft Antar Mark 3, 30 tonne 6 × 4)

1:76 scale

Above *A fully-loaded Antar crossing a MGB* (MoD). **Below** *A Scammell Commander prototype* (Scammell Motors).

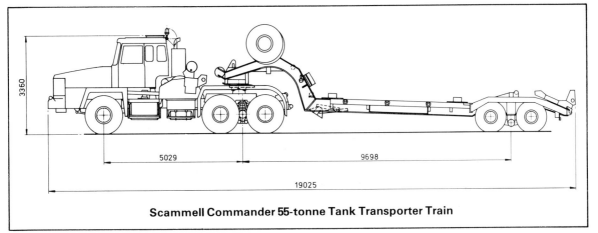

Scammell Commander 55-tonne Tank Transporter Train

disabled vehicles on to their trailers, the Antars are fitted with a 20,000 kg winch.

The Antar Mark 3 is usually employed to tow a semi-trailer when Chieftains are the main load, but a trailer, the origins of which can be traced back to the Second World War, is still an alternative. The types involved and their relevant data are as follows: FV30011 Semi-trailer Tanker-transporter (50 tonne) and FV3601 Trailer, Tank Transporter No. 1 Mark 3 (50 tonne). **Weight laden** 66,360 kg (FV30011/68,640 kg (FV3601); **Weight unladen** 16,360 kg/18,640 kg; **Length** 11.925 m/10.211 m; **Height** 3.086 m/2.21 m; **Width** 3.353 m/3.2 m; **Wheel track (outer)** 2.692 m/2.4 m.

During 1979 it was anounced that a new tank transporter, the Scammell Commander, was under development as the eventual replacement for the Antar. As it is not anticipated that their replacement will take place before the mid-1980s, during 1979 a re-building and refurbishing programme began to ensure that the Antars will remain fully serviceable for at least another five years.

Scammell Commander tank transporter

Crew 2 to 4; **Weight (unladen)** 19,920 kg; **Length** 19.025 m; **Height** 3.36 m; **Width** 3.15 m; **Wheelbase** 5.029 m; **Maximum road speed** 61 km/h; **Range** Unknown; **Engine type** Rolls-Royce Condor 12V625; **Engine power** 675 bhp; **Engine capacity** 26.11 litres; **Fuel capacity** 817 litres; **Weight with loaded trailer (approx)** 10,400 kg.

The above data should be regarded as provisional.

The 1979 Defence White Paper announced that the evaluation of a new tank transporter tractor to replace the ageing Antars was in progress. The new tractor is the Leyland Scammell Commander. Development of this model had been well under way for some time before the White Paper disclosure, for

the Commander is a military derivative of the commercial Scammell Contractor series. At one time there was some uncertainty as to which engine would be fitted as it was hoped to provide some form of logistic compatability with the engine chosen to power the MBT-80 tank. As the Rolls-Royce Condor 12V1500 was finally selected for the MBT-80, the early choice of the Rolls-Royce CV12 TCE diesel was seen to be correct, and this engine is now part of the Rolls-Royce Condor range as the 12V625 and the expected compatability has been achieved.

A new Crane Fruehauf trailer has been produced for use with the Commander. The Commander itself is fitted with a winch which has a possible pull of 20.3 tonnes, and the winch drum is equipped with 110 metres of 26 mm diameter rope.

The initial 1979 procurement was for only two trials vehicles which differ in some details from the eventual production versions. The exact status of this programme is uncertain at present.

FV12006/FV12007 Scammell Crusader

Crew 1 (20,000 kg version)/4 (35,000 kg version); **Weight empty** 9,200 kg/10,567 kg; **Length** 6.661 m (both versions); **Height** 3.3 m (both versions); **Width** 2.502 m (both versions); **Wheel track (front)** 2.05 m (both versions); **Wheel track (rear)** 1.845 m (both versions); **Maximum road speed** 85 km/h/66 km/h; **Range (roads—approx)** 500 km (both versions); **Engine type** Rolls-Royce Eagle Mark III (both versions); **Engine power** 305 bhp (both versions); **Engine capacity** 12.17 litres (both versions); **Fuel capacity** 318 litres/455 litres; **Load capacity** 20,000 kg/35,000 kg.

The Scammell Crusader is a commercial vehicle used by the Army mainly as a tractor for trailers carrying heavy plant and equipment. Most of the

Crusaders in service are used for towing Royal Engineer low-loader trailers carrying such items as dozers, graders and the FV180 CET. There are two versions in service, the smallest of which is the 20,000 kg type with a two-man cab, and the other the 35,000 kg version with a four-man cab. Both vehicles can double as tank transporter tractors if so required but the 20,000 kg version will not be able to tow MBTs. There are various trailers in use but one has been specially developed for use with the 20,000 kg version by Crane Fruehauf. It is a 10-tonne tilt trailer with the following dimensions: **Length overall** 8.535 m; **Height of platform (unladen)** 1.118 m; **Width** 2.438 m; **Wheel track** 1.82 m.

Tractor, Wheeled, Fork Lift 4,000 lb—Eager Beaver Mark 2

Crew 1; **Weight complete** 2,961 kg; **Weight airportable** 2,560 kg; **Length** 5.461 m; **Height (fork raised to maximum)** 3.708 m; **Height (top of mast)** 2.388; **Height (airportable)** 1.829 m; **Width** 1.854 m; **Wheel track** 1.55 m; **Maximum road speed** 64 km/h; **Range (roads)** 644 km; **Range (cross-country)** 322 km; **Engine type** Perkins 4-236 diesel; **Engine power** 78 bhp; **Engine capacity** 3.8 litres; **Fuel capacity** Unknown; **Maximum lift** 1,814 kg.

The Eager Beaver is a rough terrain fork lift tractor specially designed for the needs of the modern Army. It is very much a 'go-anywhere' vehicle capable of carrying a wide range of loads from ammunition and fuel pallets to engine packs and spares. A product of the Royal Ordnance Factory, Nottingham, the Eager Beaver is used by many branches of the Army for rapid loading of trucks and vehicles under a range of conditions. It can be either a 4 × 2 or a 4 × 4 vehicle, and can ford up to 0.76 metres of water.

The fork lift itself is mounted on an adjustable mast which can be tilted 13° forward and 20° backwards—for air transport it can be laid back at an angle of 60°. The lift can be raised to a maximum of 2.737 metres. Extras are a small crane and an enclosed cab to protect the driver from really inclement weather.

Above A 35,000 kg Crusader carrying a CET (British Leyland). *Left Eager Beaver. Above right An Eager Beaver bringing fuel ashore from a RPL. On the right a Mexeflote jetty can just be seen* (MoD).

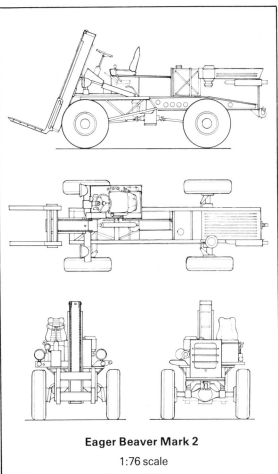

Eager Beaver Mark 2

1:76 scale

Experiments have been made with some Eager Beavers to allow them to be operated by radio remote control. These experiments went on through 1978 in an attempt to counter the use of car bombs in Northern Ireland and elsewhere. The idea is to lift a suspect car bomb and remove it to a position where its possible destructive effect will be minimised or where bomb clearance crews can use their specialised equipment to better effect.

Giraffe 342

Crew 1; **Weight unladen** 5,488 kg; **Length overall** 5.667 m; **Height (overall)** 2.438 m; **Height (top of cab)** 2.4 m; **Width** 2.255 m; **Wheel track** 1.892 m; **Ground clearance** 0.325 m; **Maximum road speed** 30.4 km/h; **Engine type** Perkins D3-152; **Engine power** 49 bhp; **Engine capacity** Unknown; **Fuel capacity** Unknown; **Maximum lift** 2,359 kg.

The Giraffe 342 is a product of Liner Limited of Gateshead, Tyne and Wear, and is a militarised development of their Giraffe 321. It is a rugged materials handling vehicle fitted with a telescopic boom which acts as the main handling device, but where the Giraffe 342 really comes into its own is the versatility of the boom itself. Depending on the weight of the load to be carried (the standard NATO 1,814 kg pallet is typical) the telescopic boom can be extended out to 3.7 metres and raised to 5.64 metres. There is a small 0.152 m sideways traverse for accurate load placing. The usual handling component is a fork carriage with two forks 1.066 metres long and adjustable in width from 0.38 metres to 1.22 metres. Optional extras are extension forks, a crane hook, a scoop bucket, a working platform and an extension jib, all of which add to the versatility of the Giraffe 342.

For working in confined areas all four of the Giraffe 342's wheels can be steered to give a turning circle of 3.8 metres, although for road work the front wheels only are steered. The transmission gearbox provides six forward gears and two reverse.

The Giraffe 342 will be used mainly in ordnance depots handling ammunition and fuel, but its rugged design and performance will mean that it can also be used in forward areas in direct support of troop formations. The initial order for 32 machines at a cost of some £600,000 was announced during 1979, but this is to be shared between the Army and the Royal Air Force—doubtless more orders will follow.

FV13115 Recovery Vehicle Wheeled— Light (Bedford 4-tonne 4 × 4)

Crew 2; **Weight loaded** 8,128 kg; **Length** 7.976 m; **Height** 2.705 m; **Width** 2.324 m; **Wheel track (front)** 1.854 m; **Wheel track (rear)** 1.708 m; **Maximum road speed** 80 km/h; **Range (roads)** 400 km; **Engine type** Bedford 6-cylinder OHV; **Engine power** 130 bhp; **Engine capacity** 4.93 litres; **Fuel capacity** 118 litres.

The FV13115 is the recovery vehicle variant of the Bedford RL family, and mounts a jib crane at the rear. The crane, like the vehicle winch, is powered by a power take-off from the main engine, and can lift up to 3,000 kg. The winch can be used to either the front or rear, but in the latter case an earth anchor is provided which can increase the maximum pull from 7,000 kg to 13,000 kg. Despite the gradual introduction of the Bedford MK and its variants, there is no equivalent vehicle to the FV13115 and it will remain in service for some time to come.

FV11044 Recovery Vehicle Wheeled— Medium (AEC Mark 3 6 × 6)

Crew 3/4; **Weight loaded** 21,019 kg; **Length** 8.23 m; **Height** 3.1 m; **Width** 2.502 m; **Wheel track** 2 m; **Maximum road speed** 78 km/h; **Range (roads)** 483 km; **Engine type** AEC AV 760 diesel; **Engine power** 226 bhp; **Engine capacity** 12.47 litres; **Fuel capacity** 218 litres. (See plans on page 227.)

The AEC Mark 3 recovery vehicle was developed during the 1960s as a replacement for the old FV11301 Scammell 6 × 6. Only the chassis and engine are actually AEC-produced, and emanate from their Southall factory. The recovery equipment came from the Thornycroft works at

Above left *The Giraffe 342* (MoD) and Giraffe). **Left** *FV13115 Recovery Vehicle Wheeled* **Right** *FV11044 in action towing an FV101 Scorpion.*

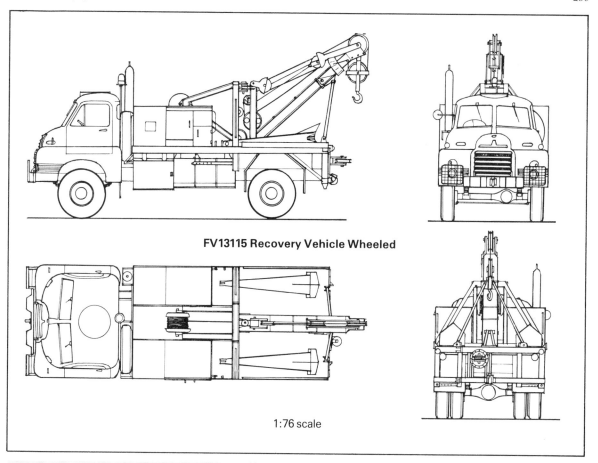

FV13115 Recovery Vehicle Wheeled

1:76 scale

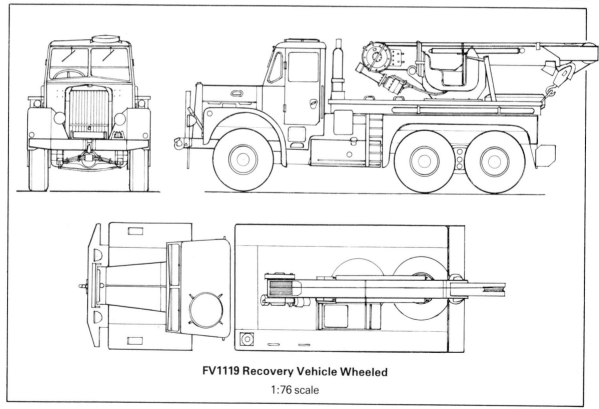

FV1119 Recovery Vehicle Wheeled

1:76 scale

Basingstoke, and the crane from Sunderland.

The AEC Mark 3 can be used to recover vehicles up to the 10-tonne class, its main lifting component being the Coles hydraulic crane fitted to the rear chassis. The crane has a jib which can extend from 3.124 to 5.563 metres. The jib can also be slewed through 240°. Outrigger jacks can be used to stabilise the vehicle and crane when it is used to lift up to 2,600 kg at maximum jib extension. A winch fitted to the rear can pull up to 15,000 kg but when a hydraulically-operated earth spade is lowered, this can increase the pull up to 30,000 kg. There are towing hooks at the front and rear, and the vehicle is well provided with all the special tools required for the recovery role. (See drawing on page 227.)

FV1119 Recovery Vehicle Wheeled—Heavy (Leyland 10-tonne 6 × 6)

Crew 3; **Weight loaded** 21,604 kg; **Length** 8.89 m; **Height** 3.1 m; **Width** 2.591 m; **Wheel track (front)** 2.089 m; **Wheel track (rear)** 2.096 m; **Maximum road speed** 56.2 km/h; **Range (roads)** 562 km; **Engine type** Rolls-Royce B81 Mark 5K;

Above left FV1119 Recovery Vehicle Wheeled.

Engine power 195 bhp; **Engine capacity** 6.62 litres; **Fuel capacity** 446 litres.

The Leyland 10-tonne recovery vehicle is based on the chassis of the FV1103 cargo truck, but the main difference is the provision of a swivelling hydraulic crane with a lifting capacity of up to 15,000 kg. The crane can swivel through 240° and has a jib which extends from 3.048 to 5.486 metres. A two-speed hydraulic winch is fitted which, in conjunction with the hydraulically operated rear earth spade, can pull up to 39,000 kg. As with all other similar vehicles, rear and front towing eyes are fitted. A special low-loader trailer was developed for this vehicle and is designated FV3221 Trailer Recovery (10-tonne). The FV1119 uses its winch to load the trailer. Dimensions for the trailer are as follows: **Weight loaded** 20,067 kg; **Weight empty** 7,130 kg; **Length** 7.28 kg; **Height** 1.9 m; **Width** 2.74 m; **Wheel track** 2.057 m.

Crusader/EKA 6 × 4 Recovery Vehicle

Crew 1 + 3; **Weight loaded (approx)** 46,700 kg; **Length** Unknown; **Height** 3.25 m; **Width** 2.502 m; **Wheel track (front)** 2.166 m; **Wheel track (rear)** 1.845 m; **Maximum road speed** 78 km/h;

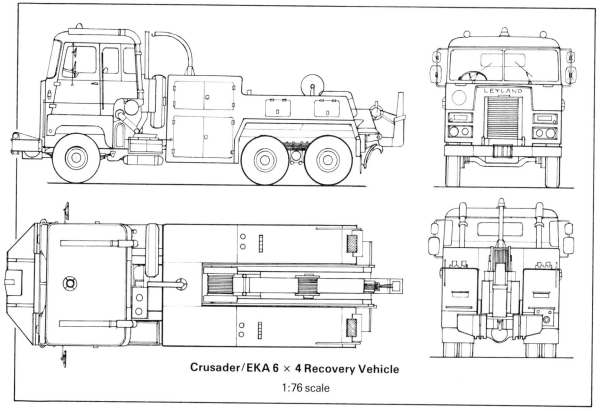

Crusader/EKA 6 × 4 Recovery Vehicle

1:76 scale

Above *Crusader/EKA lifting a Stalwart.*

Left *1-5 tonne Dummy Axle* (MoD).

Below *10-30 tonne Dummy Axle.*

Below right *M2 on parade at Sennelager, 7.7.77.*

Range (roads—approx) 500 km; **Engine type** Rolls-Royce Eagle 305 Mark III; **Engine power** 305 bhp; **Engine capacity** 12.17 litres; **Fuel capacity** 454.5 litres.

Based on the Crusader 35,000 kg tractor, the Crusader 6 × 4 Recovery Vehicle was ordered by the British Army in late 1977. At that time it was announced that 130 were to be delivered. It uses the Swedish EKA hydraulic recovery equipment mounted on the rear of the vehicle and, as well as being used as a recovery hoist, the jib can also be used as a crane. As with all other recovery vehicles the Crusader version is well equipped with winches. The main one is at the rear and, in conjunction with a hydraulically operated spade, has a pulling power of up to 22 tonnes—50 metres of cable is supplied for it. The front winch is mainly used for self-recovery and has a maximum pull of 7.7 tonnes with 40 metres of cable. Carried over from the Crusader tractor are the four-man cab and the 15 forward-speed gearbox.

The main feature of the Crusader Recovery Vehicle is its main lifting gear. This is a most adaptable piece of equipment that can be fitted with a variety of attachments to make it an extremely versatile hoist capable of tackling many recovery tasks. It has a maximum lifting capacity of 22 tonnes, power for the hydraulic mechanism coming from the vehicle's main engine.

FV2692 Trailer, Dummy Axle, Recovery, 1-5 tonnes

Weight unladen 1,183 kg; **Length** 3.47 m; **Height** 2.31 m; **Width** 2.362 m; **Wheel track** 1.816 m.

Developed from the earlier FV2691, the 1-5-tonne Dummy Axle is used in the recovery role for the rapid transport of disabled vehicles up to a weight of 6.25 tonnes. In use, the vehicle is lifted by the Dummy Axle's crane, and after being secured, the axle can then be towed carrying its load. The lifting crane, or winch, does not carry the load once it has been secured to the Axle by spreader bars. The FV2692 is produced by Rubery Owen (Warrington) Limited, of Darlaston.

FV3561 Trailer, Dummy Axle, Recovery, 10-30 tonnes

Weight unladen 2,900 kg; **Length** 3.658 m; **Height** 3.226 m; **Width** 2.388 m; **Wheel track** 1.778 m; **Engine type** Hatz air-cooled diesel; **Engine power** 7.5 bhp; **Engine capacity** 0.433 litres.

The FV3561 Trailer follows the same general lines as the lighter FV2692 but, due to the extra weight it will have to raise, it is fitted with a small diesel engine to drive the hydraulic pump for the winch. This has a lifting capacity of 10,400 kg, and a small hand winch is used to position the A frame and towing bar which actually carries the load. Almost any wheeled vehicle up to the size of an Antar can be carried on the 10-30 tonne Dummy Axle. Production is carried out by the Royal Ordnance Factories.

Bridges

M-2 Alligator

Crew 4; **Weight in action (approx)** 22,000 kg; **Length** 11.35 m; **Height (travelling)** 3.58 m; **Width (travelling)** 2.995 m; **Width (in use)** 14.16 m; **Wheel track (front)** 2.13 m; **Wheel track (rear)** 2.16 m; **Maximum road speed** 60 km/h; **Maximum water speed** 15 km/h; **Range (roads)** 1,000 km; **Engine type** 2 × Deutz Model F8L 714A; **Engine power** 2 × 178 bhp.

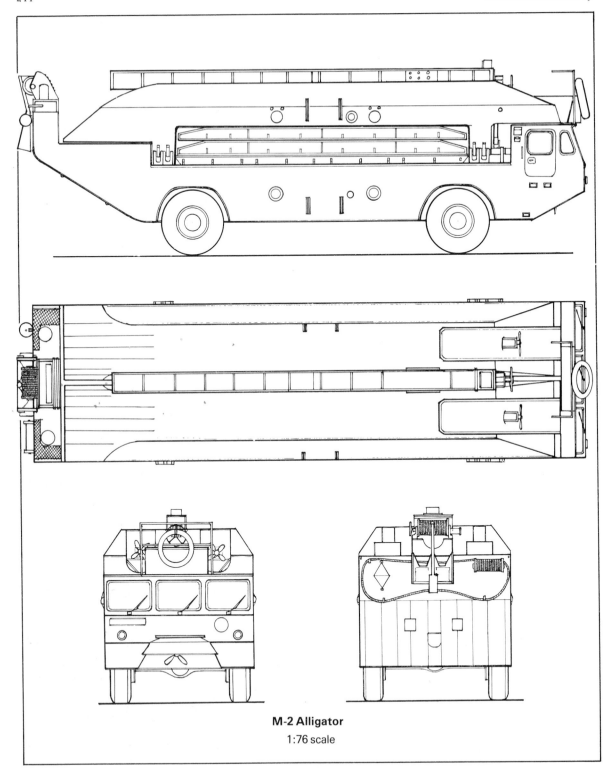

M-2 Alligator

1:76 scale

The M-2 Aligator is a West German amphibious ferry and bridging system which was first produced in prototype form in 1963. It was 1968 before the first production versions were available and these went to the West German Bundeswehr. During the early 1970s a batch was acquired for the British Army in Germany, where most of them have remained, only a few being used in the UK for training purposes. In Germany, the M-2s are used by the Royal Engineer Amphibious Engineer Regiment directly under HQ 1 (Br) Corps control.

The Amphibious Engineer Regiment is organised into two squadrons, each with 30 M2 units. Each squadron has two troops, with each troop using 15 M2s, but each troop has an extra four M2s that are normally held 'under wraps' in peacetime conditions. Thus the Amphibious Engineer Regiment has a total of 76 M2 units.

The M-2 on the road is a bulky four-wheeled vehicle, but when required for its amphibious role two hinged buoyancy tanks (which are carried on top of the vehicle) are hydraulically hinged outwards. Once in position a crane is used to lift and lock the trackway into position. When lowered, the trackway measures 7.62 metres long and 5.486 metres wide. If the M-2 is to be used as a ferry the vehicle is driven on and propelled through the water on the trackway by the M-2s's main engines. One engine drives two sideways propellers and the other a single steering propeller under the cab—thus the cab is to the rear when 'swimming'. For bridging, M-2s are joined together in pairs and keep their stations against the flow of a river by using their steering propellers—in this mode one of the side-mounted propellers can be swivelled to assist. Three M-2s can by themselves form a bridge suitable for a Chieftain to cross and, theoretically, there is no limit as to how many can be joined together; the more there are side-by-side, however, the more difficult the 'bridge' becomes to control. Once in the water, the main road wheels are raised to reduce water drag. The M-2 was developed by a West German consortium formed by Eisenwerke Kaiserlautern and Klöckner-Humboldt-Deutz (EKW/KHD). Production was actually carried out by Kaiserlautern Göppner, at Kaiserlautern.

The Medium Girder Bridge

The Medium Girder Bridge is an important component of the British Army's planned mobility in Europe and for this reason is here considered in some detail. Rapid bridging of defiles, river or

water obstacles and other terrain gaps is an important factor in the consideration of fluid modern warfare, and to keep large armoured formations moving the military bridge is thus an essential item.

With a wealth of experience gained in combat by the exploits of the Royal Engineers, consideration of a new bridge led to an extensive design and development programme at the MVEE at Christchurch during the 1960s. The result was what is now known as the Medium Girder Bridge, the first examples of which were introduced into service during 1971. Production was, and still is, by Fairey Engineering Limited at Stockport, for the Medium Girder Bridge (MGB) has proved to be a tremendous export success and has been sold to over 25 countries, including the USA.

There are several factors involved in the success of the MGB, one of which is the material employed for most of the components. It is a novel alloy of aluminium, zinc and magnesium which is not only weldable and tough but also very light. As a result the bridge is constructed from components that can

Top right *MGB pontoons stacked on their special trailer. These pontoons are still in the development stage.* **Right** *A single span MGB (Fairey Engineering).*

Scorpions crossing a Double-Storey MGB (MoD).

be manhandled, and no mechanical aids are necessary in the assembly of the bridge itself—everything can be accomplished by manpower alone. Another important factor is that any type of bridge can be constructed using only seven types of component, rather in the manner of an oversize Meccano set. The largest of these components is capable of being handled by six men—others only require four. These parts and their weights are as follows: **Top panel** 175 kg; **Bottom panel** 197 kg; **Junction panel** 182 kg; **End taper panel** 272 kg; **Ramp unit** 120 kg; **Bankseat beam** 258 kg; **Deck unit** 74 kg. They are stored and carried on standard pallets, and can be used to assemble several types of bridge, as outlined below.

Single span: This is the most basic of all the MGB structures and can be up to 31 metres long if a Chieftain tank is to be the heaviest vehicle to cross—lighter vehicles can cross longer spans. The construction can be either single- or double-storey with the double-storey method being capable of carrying the heavy loads. A building party of 25 men is needed to construct a double-storey single-span bridge 30 metres long, but they can complete the task in about 45 minutes. One of the most useful features of the MGB is that it can be constructed by relatively untrained personnel.

Assembly of all the various bridge types follows the same basic pattern. Working from one bank only, a building frame is constructed on which the various components are fixed. As construction progresses, the frame supports the completed portions and holds them as they are progressively

pushed out over the gap—rollers on the frame enable this to be done. As the lengthy completed portions hang over the gap, counterweights made from unused bridge components counteract the completed weight, and at the front of the completed portion a launching nose unit is fitted. Small bridges can be pushed by manpower alone but bridges over about 30 metres require the use of some form of pusher vehicle.

Link reinforcement set: The addition of a link reinforcement set to a single-span bridge enables much longer spans to be made capable of carrying up to Class 60 vehicles such as Chieftain. The longest single span capable of carrying such a vehicle is 31 metres—by the addition of the reinforcement set this can be substantially increased. For instance, single spans up to 49.4 metres capable of carrying a Chieftain can be built. An extra eight men are needed in addition to the normal 24/25 needed for single span construction. The reinforcing links are fitted beneath the bridge girders.

Multi-span: For really wide gaps or water crossings it may not be possible to construct a single span long enough so multi-spans have to be used. These are made up of single spans utilising one or more intermediate piers. Piers may be formed from the remains of demolished bridges or specially constructed parts made up from whatever can be gleaned locally—spare MGB components are one possibility. The separate single spans are joined by a span junction set, which consists of a linking component which can be set to any suitable angle, and other parts such as capsills. If required, a portable pier set can be used to provide custom-made piers.

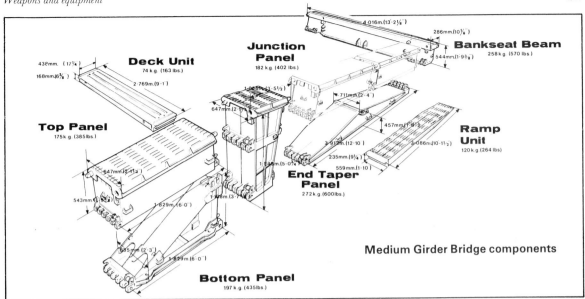

Medium Girder Bridge components

Deck Unit — 74 k.g. (163 lbs.) — 2·769m.(9·1) — 438mm. (17¼) — 168mm.(6⅝)

Junction Panel — 182 k.g. (402 lbs.) — 4·016m.(13·2⅛) — 286mm.(10¾) — 544mm.(1·9⅜) — 647mm.(2·1½) — 711mm.(2·4) — 457mm.(1·8) — 1·861m.(3·5½)

Bankseat Beam — 258 k.g. (570 lbs.)

Ramp Unit — 120 k.g. (264 lbs.) — 3·086m.(10·1½)

Top Panel — 175 k.g. (385 lbs.) — 647mm.(2·1½) — 543mm.(1·9½) — 1·829m.(6·0)

End Taper Panel — 272 k.g. (600lbs.) — 3·912m.(12·10) — 1·546m.(5·0¾) — 235mm.(9¼) — 559mm.(1·10)

Bottom Panel — 197 k.g. (435 lbs.) — 585mm.(2·3) — 1·078m.(3·7) — 1·829m.(6·0)

When multi-span bridges are used the length of each single span is limited to 26.5 metres, so a two-span bridge will be up to 51 metres long and a three-span bridge up to 76 metres long.

Floating bridge: In the absence of fixed piers, pontoons can be used to construct floating bridges. Again, a custom-made pontoon can be used with the MGB, but almost any suitable military engineering pontoon can be pressed into service. The length of the bridge can be virtually infinite but again, for heavy loads, double-storey construction is necessary. In some circumstances the MGB components can be used to assemble floating ferries using the pontoons.

The special MGB pontoons are joined end-to-end to form floating piers. Each pontoon is 7.96 metres long × 2.6 metres wide × 1.17 metres deep and weighs about 1,000 kg. They are carried on trailers stacked inside one another so that four pontoons form one load. They can then be launched direct from the trailer. Each pontoon has an available buoyancy of about 12 tonnes.

Although MGB components are stored and carried on pallets, the make-up of each pallet varies. There are eight different pallet 'kits', each type of bridge being assembled from differing kits. Whatever the bridge type, the components are usually carried on 4-tonne trucks, each of which tows more components on a special trailer known as the FV2842; this has the following dimensions: **Weight unladen** 1,461 kg; **Length** 5.867 m; **Height overall (loaded)** 2.616 m; **Width** 2.565 m; **Wheel track** 2.261 m.

One small detail worth mentioning regarding the MGB is that a special training model has been produced that exactly duplicates the construction and handling methods used on the real thing in 1:12 scale. It is made by Miltra Training Aids of Harrow.

The range of different types of military bridge that can be formed from MGB and special MGB components is enormous, and its versatility and ease of adaptation to almost any military bridging need makes the MGB an important part of the Army's equipment. It will remain in service for a very long time. Considering that the old World War 2 Bailey Bridge is still a fairly common engineering tool, the MGB may continue in service in the year 2000 and long beyond.

Class 16 Air-portable bridge

The Class 16 Air-portable bridge is yet another design product of the Military Engineering Establishment at Christchurch, and is constructed from the same aluminium-zinc-magnesium alloy as that used on the Medium Girder bridge. Like the larger bridge, the air-portable version is made up of a number of standard components.

For a straightforward clearspan bridge capable of spanning a gap of up to 15.2 metres only two standard parts are necessary: deck boxes and ramps, the dimensions of which are as follows: **Weight** 305 kg (deck box)/346 kg (ramp); **Length** 3.6 m/3.6 m; **Height** 0.38 m/0.38 m; **Width** 1.2 m/1.8 m.

For a 15.2-metre clearspan bridge seven deck boxes and four ramps are required. Such a bridge can be constructed by 16 men in about 20 minutes. The complete bridge can be carried on three ¾-

Top A US Army Chinook carrying a Class 16 Bridge into a Royal Engineer demonstration. **Above** *A Lynx in its battlefield environment* (Westland Helicopters Ltd).

tonne Land Rovers pulling special trailers. The trailer used is the FV2420 with the following details: **Weight unladen** 340 kg; **Length** 3.81 m; **Height** 0.711 m; **Width** 2.006 m; **Wheel track** 1.752 m.

A more general application of the Air-portable bridge is as a floating structure but for this role extra components are needed. These are articulator boxes and float and support units. The deck boxes are laid across the float and support frames and the articulator boxes are fitted at each end. The floating

bridge can be up to 58 metres long. The floats themselves are collapsible and are inflated by the exhausts of the Land Rovers used to carry the bridge. Five Land Rovers and trailers can carry a floating bridge and the assembly takes 24 men about 45 minutes.

One extra application of the Air-portable bridge is as a powered raft. Such a raft uses all the components of a floating bridge with the addition of sponsons, each of which carries an outboard motor. A standard powered raft measures 22 metres overall (with a 12.2 metre long deck) and has four sponsons, and thus four motors. Longer rafts up to 28 metres long overall can be constructed but need six outboard motors and sponsons. Production of the Class 16 Bridge is carried out by Laird (Anglesey) Limited.

Aircraft
Lynx AH Mark 1

Crew 1 + 1 or 10; **Armament** 6 × TOW missiles, 2/4 × 7.62 mm L20A1 Machine-Guns, and reconnaissance flares; **Length (rotors turning)** 15.164 m; **Length (fuselage)** 11.665 m; **Height (to rotor hub)** 3.43 m; **Width (fuselage)** 1.78 m; **Rotor diameter** 12.8 m; **Maximum speed** 333 km/h; **Cruising speed** 296 km/h; **Range** 885 km; **Engine type** 2 × Rolls-Royce BS 360/07/26 turboshafts; **Engine power** 2 × 850 bhp; **Fuel capacity** 909 litres; **All-up weight** 3,620 kg.

The Lynx is a product of Westland Aircraft Limited of Yeovil, Somerset, and was originally designed as a general purpose and transport helicopter. When the prototype first flew in March 1971, it was known as the WG.13 and was developed at first in two marks. The first became the Lynx AH Mark 1 for the Army while the second became the Lynx HAS Mark 2 for the Royal Navy. More were scheduled to be delivered to the French Navy as the Lynx was one of the three helicopters involved in the Anglo-French helicopter deal of the mid-1960s.

The Lynx is now in the process of gradually replacing the Scout AH Mark 1 as the Army's standard general utility helicopter. As such it has to be able to undertake a wide variety of roles which vary from troop transport (carrying ten soldiers), to anti-tank guided missile launcher (using TOW missiles), fire support (using L20A1 podded machine-guns), casualty evacuation (up to three stretcher cases in the cabin), general liaison, cargo-carrying, tactical airborne command post, air-to-ground photography, and a hundred-and-one other tasks. To add to all the above the Lynx is also used for pilot training.

As it is a very advanced design, the Lynx has a

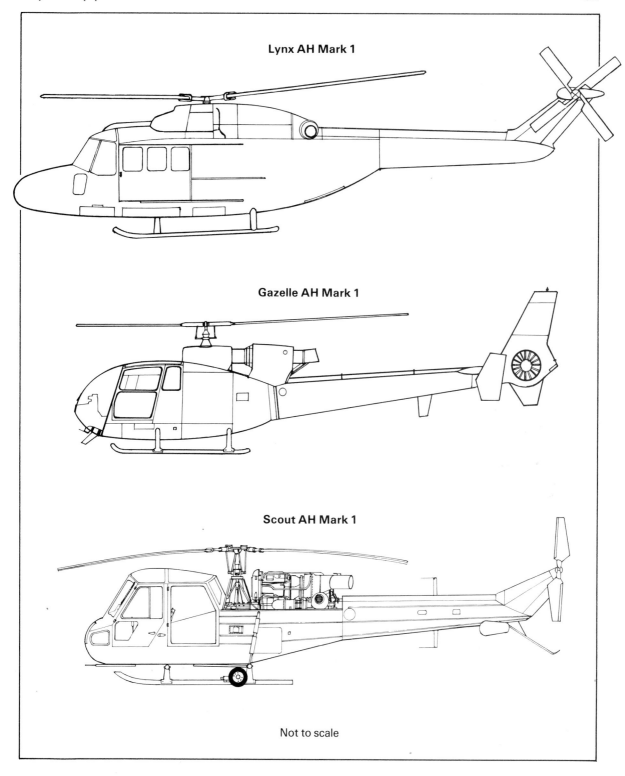

Lynx AH Mark 1

Gazelle AH Mark 1

Scout AH Mark 1

Not to scale

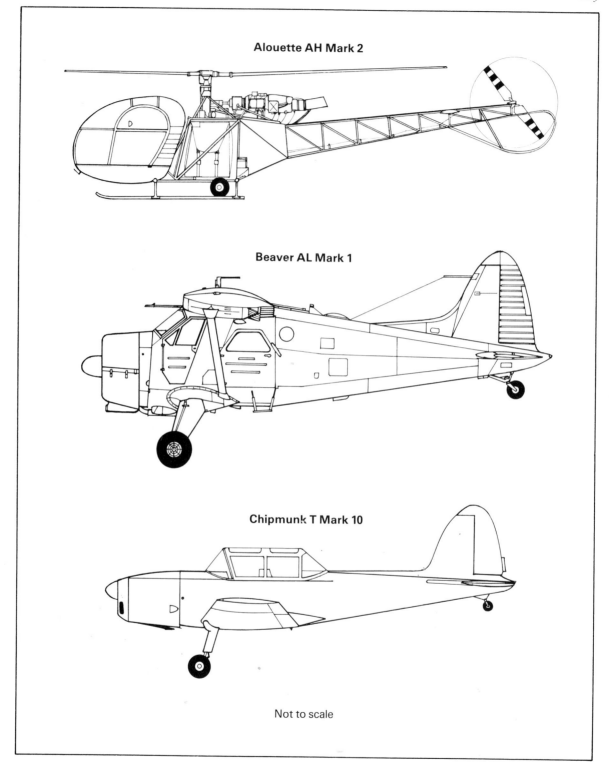

Alouette AH Mark 2

Beaver AL Mark 1

Chipmunk T Mark 10

Not to scale

lively battlefield performance, and despite its relative bulk should prove an effective weapons platform. The choice of anti-tank missiles for the Lynx was an involved contest with three missile systems involved—the Franco-German HOT, the British Hawkswing and the American TOW. The TOW system was finally selected and will be carried on the Lynx, three to each side in 2.2-metre-long launching tubes over the landing skids. As a gunship, the Lynx should prove a formidable opponent as it can carry up to two machine-guns firing either out of the side hatches or mounted firing directly forward.

The first Lynx AH Mark 1 flew during 1973 and 100 were ordered for the Army. But, as with so many other weapon programmes, the machine ran into troubles as the main contractors, Westland, encountered financial problems, and made a loss on each item built. Thus the Lynx became a political problem for a while, but the first production examples were issued for full service during 1978.

Gazelle AH Mark 1

Crew 1 + 4; **Armament** 2 × 7.62 mm L20A1 Machine-Guns and reconnaissance flares; **Length (rotors turning)** 12.09 m; **Length (fuselage)** 9.519 m; **Height (to rotor hub)** 3.02 m; **Rotor diameter** 10.5 m; **Maximum speed** 265 km/h; **Cruising speed** 240 km/h; **Range** 650 km; **Engine type** Turbomeca/Rolls-Royce Astazou 111N; **Engine power** 592 shp; **Fuel capacity** 445 litres; **All-up weight** 1,800 kg.

The Gazelle was originally a French design produced by Aerospatiale but the British Army version was produced by Westland at Yeovil in Somerset. The original French design was produced in a number of versions but the designation for the Army model was SA 341B, and it has now replaced the earlier well-known Sioux AH Mark 1 as the light general purpose helicopter of the Army Air Corps. Within the AAC it fulfils a number of roles from general battlefield observation to ambulance, and can also be employed as a light mobile command helicopter and runabout. In most roles armament is not carried, although a machine-gun can be mounted in the area behind the pilot, firing out to the side. Machine-gun pods can alternatively be fitted over the landing skids. Pilot training is also carried out on the Gazelle.

One optional function for the Gazelle is as the carrier for the 'Skyshout' airborne loudspeaker equipment. This is used for crowd and disaster control or for the airborne command role.

Scout AH Mark 1

Crew 1 + 4; **Armament** 4 × SS11 missiles; 2 × 7.62 mm L20A1 Machine-Guns and/or 2 × 7.62

Above *Skyshout fitted to a Gazelle.* **Below** *Gazelle AH Mark 1* (Westland Helicopters Ltd).

Left *Scout fitted with SS11s—note the sight in the cabin roof.*

Above right *Beavers para-dropping supplies.*

mm L7A2 Machine-Guns and reconnaissance flares; **Length (rotors turning)** 12.29 m; **Length (fuselage)** 9.335 m; **Height (to rotor hub)** 2.718 m; **Width (fuselage)** 1.65 m; **Rotor diameter** 9.83 m; **Maximum speed** 210 km/h; **Cruising speed** 196 km/h; **Range** 507 km; **Engine type** Rolls-Royce Bristol Nimbus 102 or 105; **Engine power** 710 shp; **Fuel capacity** 709 litres; **All-up weight** 2,404 kg.

The Scout has had a fairly protracted existence as the very first prototype first flew in mid-1958. At that stage is was known as the P.531, but it was not until 1962 that the first deliveries were made of the final service version. Even then, service trials further delayed the full in-service date and it was not until the mid-1960s that the Scout became fully in-

tegrated into the Army. Originally the P.531 was a Saunders-Roe design but it was produced eventually by Westland Aircraft at Yeovil in Somerset.

The Scout is now due for replacement by the Lynx AH Mark 1 but no doubt it will soldier on for some years yet. Throughout its service career it has proved rugged and versatile. It has been used in a wide variety of roles. Originally it was designed as a general purpose helicopter runabout but it has also been used as an ambulance, a trainer, a gunship, and eventually as an anti-tank missile carrier. In the latter role, which was taken over in 1970, the Scout carries four SS11 anti-tank missiles aimed and guided by a roof-mounted AF 120 sight over the front left-hand seat. As a gunship the Scout is not in the same class as the specialised American armed helicopters, but it has been used to try out many of the installations that will be used on the Lynx. A Minigun has been mounted experimentally to fire out of the side hatches and swivelling GPMGs have been mounted on similar pivots.

Alouette AH Mark 2

Crew 1 + 4; **Armament** None; **Length (rotors turning)** 12.06 m; **Length (fuselage)** 9.677 m; **Height (to rotor hub)** 2.769 m; **Width (fuselage)** 1.803 m; **Rotor diameter** 10.82 m; **Maximum speed** 185 km/h; **Cruising speed** 167 km/h; **Range** 500 km; **Engine type** Turbomeca Artouste 11C; **Engine power** 460 shp; **Fuel capacity** 578 litres; **All-up weight** 1,598 kg.

The Alouette AH Mark 2 is a French helicopter which was originally the Sud Aviation SE-3130 Alouette II. During the early 1960s development of the Scout series was becoming protracted so the French helicopter was procured in limited numbers to tide the AAC over until the fully developed Scout became available in appreciable quantities. The Alouette AH Mark 2 was intended only as a stop-gap, but once in service it proved to be a first-class helicopter and a pleasure to fly, so much so that it remained in service long after its original withdrawal date. Today only a handful remain, all of them based in Cyprus where they will remain for an appreciable period until their replacement by Scouts—once the Lynx re-equipment programme has been completed.

Beaver AL Mark 1

Crew 6 or 7; **Length (fuselage)** 9.27 m; **Height** 2.896 m; **Wing span** 14.63 m; **Maximum speed** 262 km/h; **Cruising speed** 202 km/h; **Range** 1,078 km; **Engine type** Pratt and Whitney Wasp R-985 Junior; **Engine power** 450 bhp; **Fuel capacity** 505 litres; **All-up weight** 2,450 kg.

The Beaver is the Army's only operational fixed-wing aircraft but as it has been in service for many years, few are now left, and by the time these words are read the last of them may well have been phased out of service. The Beaver prototype, a Canadian design, first flew in 1947. Ever since, this rugged and dependable aircraft has been used for a variety of purposes. With the British Army it serves as a general purpose liaison and communications machine, but it has been used as an airborne ambulance, for dropping supplies and small groups of paratroopers, and as an airborne photographic platform. It has even been fitted with loudspeakers for 'voice from the sky' missions. The last complete Beaver unit is the Beaver Flight based at Aldergrove in Northern Ireland, but other AAC units occasionally add a Beaver to their strength. One

example has even found its way back to its country of origin for it is on the strength of the BATUS unit at Suffield.

While the original Beavers were designed by de Havilland Aircraft of Canada Limited, the Beavers for the British Army were assembled by de Havilland at Hawarden, Chester, in the United Kingdom.

Chipmunk T Mark 10

Crew 2; **Length (fuselage)** 7.823 m; **Height** 2.16 m; **Wing span** 10.465 m; **Maximum speed** 222 km/h; **Cruising speed** 191 km/h; **Range** 483 km; **Engine type** de Havilland Gipsy Major 8; **Engine power** 145 hp; **Fuel capacity** 82 litres; **All-up weight** 908 kg.

Ever since the Army Air Corps took over the responsibility for training its own pilots in 1957, pilot training has been carried out in the initial stages using the Chipmunk T Mark 10. The Chipmunks were all taken over from the Royal Air Force who up till then carried out the training for the Army (all pilots have to learn to fly fixed-wing aircraft before they graduate to helicopters).

The Chipmunk is a Canadian design, the DHC1,

which was built by the de Havilland works at Chester between 1949 and 1953. Ever since then they have been used to train generations of pilots for all the British Services although they are now used by only the Army for flying training proper. All the Army's Chipmunks are based at the AAC centre at Middle Wallop. One of these has been given a camouflage colour scheme for use in air observation training and is known as the 'Spitmunk' (unofficially), but its lavish paint scheme has made it some 20 kg heavier than standard Chipmunks.

Water craft

Landing Craft Logistic

Crew 36 + 34; **Length** 73.1 m; **Displacement (standard)** 884,755 kg; **Displacement (loaded)** 143,695 kg; **Engines** 2 × diesels; **Engine power** 2 × 2,000 bhp; **Speed** 10.6 knots; **Range** 6,435 km.

HMAV *Ardennes* (L4001) and *Arakan* (L4003) were both ordered during 1974 from Brooke Marine Limited of Lowestoft. The first to be commissioned, during 1977, was the *Ardennes*, soon followed by the *Arakan* during 1978. Both ships are used for store, supply and equipment carrying, usually from Marchwood to the BAOR port at Antwerp, but both have been used to carry supplies and equipment among the various bases and ranges in the Scottish islands. Both ships have the distinction of being the single most expensive items ordered for the Army. They can each carry five Chieftain tanks apiece and have accommodation for 34 troops in addition to their 36-man crews. Both vessels are operated by 20 Maritime Regiment, RCT. A third vessel was ordered in late 1979.

Ramped Powered Lighters

These vessels are mainly used for short-haul stores-carrying over approaches to ports and beaches after being loaded from RFA Logistic Landing Ships. Not all are in use at any one time. All are powered by twin diesel engines.

RPL 01 *Avon*, RPL 02 *Bude*, RPL 03 *Clyde*, RPL 04 *Dart*, RPL 05 *Eden*, RPL 06 *Forth*, RPL 07 *Glen*, RPL 08 *Hamble*, RPL 09 *Itchin*, RPL 10 *Kennet*, RPL 11 *London*, RPL 12 *Medway*.

Landing Craft Marine

Length 25.7 m; **Displacement (light)** 76,272 kg; **Displacement (loaded)** 178,985 kg; **Engines** 2 × Paxman YHXAM diesels; **Engine power** 2 × 624 bhp; **Speed** 10 knots.

The LCMs are normally carried in the well of HMS *Intrepid*, but as this ship can only carry four of these large ramped landing craft, not all the vessels remain in use. They are used to carry lorries and other large vehicles from the ship to the shore, and each can carry up to 100 tonnes of vehicles, including tanks. They are numbered L700-711, L3507 and L3508.

Landing Craft Vehicles and Personnel

Length 41.5 m; **Displacement (light)** 8,644 kg; **Displacement (loaded)** 13,730 kg; **Engines** Foden diesel; **Engine power** 200 bhp; **Speed** 10 knots.

These ramped landing craft (LCVP142-149) were at one time operated by the Royal Navy before being handed over to the RCT. There are eight of them, carried between the Assault Ships HMS *Intrepid* and *Fearless*, and as a result of their use in the

Above *HMAV* Arakan (UKLF PR).

Above left *Chipmunk T Mark 10.*

Right *RPL12* Medway *at Marchwood Military Port* (MoD).

Below *LCMs depart at speed from HMS* Fearless *on their way to San Carlos in May 1982* (Popperfoto).

Above *The GSL WB 06* Perch. **Above right** *An Assault Boat Mark IV, with men of the Parachute Regiment, and* **below right** *a landing party springs ashore from a Dell Quay craft. Both were used extensively in the Falklands crisis* (MoD).

Falklands, the planned withdrawal from service of *Fearless* has been postponed. Each LCVP can carry up to 35 troops or two Land Rovers.

General Service Launches

These small craft are 14.3 metres long and intended for use in harbours and ports as general service vessels for a variety of purposes. They are used as light tugs, as harbour ferries, and even, as the illustration shows, as fire-fighting vessels. Not all the ensuing vessels are kept in use at any one time: WB 01 *Carp,* WB 02 *Chub,* WB 03 *Bream,* WB 04 *Barbel,* WB 05 *Roach,* WB 06 *Perch* and WB 07 *Pike.*

Command and Control Craft

With the withdrawal of the Army's amphibious role, not all the following craft still remain in use, but as their name implies they are intended as general control craft during a landing. Each one is 12.5 metres long, and in the past some have been used for target-towing. L 01 *Petrel,* L 02 *Tern,* L 03 *Fulmar,* L 04 *Skua,* L 05 *Shearwater* and L 06 *Shelduck.*

Assault Boat Mark IV

Weight 190 kg; **Length** 5.3 m; **Beam** 1.8 m; **Weight capacity** 1,130 kg; **Load area** 7 m².

The Mark IV Assault Boat was designed and developed by the Military Engineering Establishment at Christchurch, but production began in 1961 under the aegis of Laird (Anglesey) Limited. The boat was designed to carry a load of 1,130 kg or a crew of two plus 11 fully equipped soldiers. Construction is basically aluminium with some steel parts but the weight is kept low so that it can be easily manhandled over land. To increase the carrying capacity of the design, two boats can be secured together, stern to stern. For silent use each boat has stowage points for paddles but the more usual power source is an outboard motor.

Assault Boat Mark 5

Weight 181 kg; **Length** 4.88 m; **Beam** 1.68 m; **Weight capacity** 1,043 kg; **Depth (hull moulding)** 0.602 m; **Depth (under keels)** 0.641 m.

In 1979 it was announced that the MoD had placed a contract for 624 assault boats to replace the existing Assault Boat Mark IV. The new design was originally known as the Sea Jeep and was designed by A.E. Freezer and Company of Hayling Island, but the service designation will be Assault Boat Mark 5. The production run will be carried out by Fairey Allday Marine. The Mark 5 is constructed from aluminium alloy overall and has built-in buoyancy tanks which render the craft virtually unsinkable. The boat can carry up to 12 fully-armed men or 1,043 kg of supplies, and it can be carried overland by four men or dragged by two. Under the hull are three prominent keels which act as stabilisers in water and double as 'runners' when the boat is beached. Integral grab rails are provided all round the craft and the overall design is such that the boats can be stacked six high for storage or carriage.

Dell Quay Rigid Raiding Craft

Crew Up to 10; **Length** 5.2 m; **Beam** 2.2 m; **Height** 1.1 m; **Weight** 590 kg; **Engine type** See text; **Fuel capacity** Up to 113 litres; **Maximum operating speed** 35 knots.

The Dell Quay Rigid Raiding Craft is a militarised version of a well-known Dory 17 hull.

The original military models were used by the Royal Marines but now their use has spread to other arms of the Services, including the Ulster Defence Regiment where they are used for the patrolling of inland waterways. The hull is constructed from a sandwich of GRP and foam which renders the craft not only extremely strong but unsinkable, even when extensively damaged. The hull has accommodation for up to nine armed men plus a cox—the soldiers sit upon inflated rolls along each side. For propulsion outboard engines (one or more) are used but the usual 'military' fit is a single 140 hp Johnson.

The applications for the Dell Quay type of light craft are legion. They can be used as raiding craft, even through heavy surf, and in quieter waters can be used for the carriage of light supplies. In patrol situations their high speed is a valuable asset.

Combat Support Tug Mark 2

Length overall 8.15 m; **Length along waterline** 6.88 m; **Beam** 2.5 m; **Maximum draught** 0.52 m; **Weight (approx)** 3,860 kg; **Engine type** 2 × Sabre 210; **Engine power** 2 × 180 hp; **Fuel capacity** 252 litres; **Maximum speed** 24 knots.

Development of the Combat Support Tug began during 1975 and the first prototype was delivered by Allday Aluminium Limited of Gosport early in 1977. The prototype Mark 1 was given extensive trials both in the United Kingdom and on the River Rhine in Germany, as the result of which several modifications were incorporated into the pre-production model, the Mark 2. The first of the Mark 2s was delivered in May 1978 and a small pre-production batch continues to carry out various trials at the time of writing—a production order for 56 was given in early 1980.

The Army intends to use the Combat Support Tug as an aid to military bridge building and doubtless it will find myriad other uses involving Mexeflote and similar pontoons and rafts. The basis of the craft is the well-tried Allday 8-metre hull which has been converted and strengthened for the military role. The twin engines do not drive conventional propellers but instead power water jets which are not only more handy and manoeuvreable but also provide the craft with a very shallow draught for use in shallow waterways. The water jets enable the Combat Support Tug to manoeuvre precisely in confined areas and can even be directed so that it can be driven backwards.

Fitted as standard is a removable cabin top, while a mast/roll bar, davit and ladders for use by divers are optional extras. Apart from its use as a tug, the Combat Support Tug can also carry two NATO standard ammunition pallets. When not in the

water the tug can be carried on a special trailer produced by Crane-Fruehauf, but once the cabin and mast have been removed it can also be carried on the back of a suitable lorry.

Considerable overseas interest is being shown in the Combat Support Tug and export orders from other NATO states are understood to be in the pipeline, so this small craft may well become a widely used piece of NATO equipment.

Mexeflote

Mexeflote is a multi-purpose pontoon equipment that has been specifically designed for operation in salt-water maritime conditions. It can be made up into rafts, jetties, causeways and can even be used for rudimentary breakwaters. Despite the large number of possible applications and configurations possible, Mexeflote is constructed from only three basic components, namely the bow, centre and stern pontoons, which are all connected by special linkages. The dimensions of the three pontoon types are as follows: **Length** 7.92 m (bow)/ 6.1 m (centre)/ 6.1 m (stern); **Width** 2.44 m/2.44 m/2.44 m; **Depth** 1.45 m/1.45 m/1.45 m; **Weight** 59.09 kg/46.54 kg/ 44.18 kg.

Above *A Combat Support Tug Mark 2 on its special trailer.* **Below** *A laden Mexeflote awaiting the tide* (MoD).

For most applications, Mexeflote consists of the centre pontoons only, joined together by pontoon connectors, each of which weighs 73.94 kg. When rafts are needed, the bow and stern pontoons are added. The rafts concerned are powered by their own specialised power units in the shape of 5-cylinder Dorman 5LB diesel engines, derated to 75 bhp. The engine units have a capacity of 7.98 litres and the complete units weigh 3,162 kg. The larger the rafts, the more engine units will be required.

Mexeflote is widely used by the Army but as the accent is now being changed away from amphibious towards conventional land warfare, the Mexeflote units are more and more being employed for docking facilities. The RCT Logistic Carriers often carry ready-assembled jetties along their sides ready for launching once near a landing position, and Mexeflote jetties are still used during some NATO exercises.

Production of Mexeflote was originally carried out by the Gloster Railway Carriage and Waggon Company, but the licence for production is now held by Fairey Engineering.

Uniforms and insignia

The British Army may today be seen in any of the following uniforms: No 2 Dress (khaki service dress); No 6 Dress (lightweight, stone-coloured warm weather version of No 2 Dress); No 8 Dress (temperate combat dress with Disruptive Patterned Material; No 9 Dress (tropical DPM combat dress); No 12 Dress (Coveralls); No 13 Dress (Barrack Dress) and No 14 Dress (shirt-sleeve order). Apart from these uniforms, there are certain parts of the Army which are more exotically costumed. Officers and senior NCOs wear Mess Dress for their regular dinner nights; No 10 Dress being for temperate wear, No 11 being its tropical equivalent. No 1 Dress (Blues) is worn by the Household Division and certain officers as well as by many of the regimental bands, No 4 Dress (in white) being its tropical equivalent. Battle Dress (No 5 Dress) served the Army through the Second World War and into the 1960s but was then replaced by No 2 Dress which had also been the Army's daily costume prior to 1939.

Apart from this extensive wardrobe, the Household Division wear Full Dress with scarlet tunic (blue for the Blues and Royals) and nearly all regimental bands have been authorised to wear their full dress for ceremonial purposes.

The Household Cavalry, the King's Troop, Royal Horse Artillery and the mounted section of the Corps of Royal Military Police also wear 'mounted service dress' consisting of stiff khaki cap, SD jacket with shirt and tie, beige whipcord breeches and butcher boots.

Due to lack of space this book will deal mainly with Service Dress, Barrack Dress and Combat Dress. For the same reason, some of the myriad 'tribal items' of distinction which each British regiment wears (shoulder titles, collar badges, button design and regimental side hat) have had to be excluded. These may be found in Osprey's Men-At-Arms book *The British Army 1965-80*.

It should be understood that uniform is not a static item in the British or in any other army. It changes constantly in many ways and in Britain it is the Army Dress Committee which tries gallantly to regulate the flood of tiny amendments dear to the hearts of their patrons.

Officers' bages of rank
(Worn on the shoulder straps, usually gold but there are regimental exceptions.)

General Officers
Field Marshal: Crown over crossed batons within a wreath; scarlet gorget patches* with gold oakleaf embroidery and button; red hat band with cap badge of gold crowned lion over a crown over crossed batons within a laurel wreath; gold oakleaf embroidery to top and edge of black peak.

General: As for Field Marshal except shoulder badges are a crown over a four-pointed star ('pip') over a crossed baton and sabre.

Lieutenant General: As for General except that the shoulder badge is a crown over a crossed baton and sabre.

Major General: As for General except that the shoulder badge is a pip over a crossed baton and sabre; cap badge is a lion over a crown over a crossed baton and sabre within a laurel wreath.

Brigadier: Cap badge is a crowned lion over a crown, red hat band, gold oakleaves to edge of peak; shoulder badge is a crown over three pips in triangular formation (point up). Scarlet gorget patches with crimson lace and gold button.

Field Officers
Colonel: As for Brigadier except the shoulder badge is a crown over two pips all in line.

Lieutenant Colonel: Regimental cap; cap badge, collar badges and buttons; shoulder badge is a crown over a pip.

---

* Most General Officers wear scarlet gorget patches but some wear them in the colour of their corps. Examples are: RAMC—dull cherry, RAChD—purple, RAPC—primrose, RAVC-maroon, RAEC—Cambridge blue, RADC—emerald green, ACC—grebe grey and WRAC—beech brown.

Major: As for Lieutenant Colonel except that the shoulder badge is a crown.

Junior Officers

Captain: As for Major but three pips in line on the shoulder.

First Lieutenant: As above but only two pips.

Second Lieutenant: As above but only one pip.

Officer Cadets: White collar patches with white cord and a gold button.

Warrant Officers (WOs): There are many different regimental deviations from the rank titles shown here, particularly among the Guards, but brevity forces their exclusion. The badges are usually either white woven or brass, but there are several regimental exceptions.

Conductor (RAOC only): The Royal Coat of Arms worn on the forearm within a blue laurel wreath within a red ring.

Warrant Officer First Class (WOI): The plain Royal Coat of Arms (WO1s of technical corps have the coat of arms outlined in the regimental colour).

Warrant Officer Second Class (WOII): A crown on the forearm (certain technical appoinments have the crown within a laurel wreath).

NCOs

(Rank distinctions worn on the upper arm.)

Staff Sergeant: A crown over three chevrons, point down.

Sergeant: Three chevrons, point down.

Drum (Pipe/Bugle) Major: Four chevrons, point up, on the *forearm* and surmounted by a drum or bagpipe or bugle, except in the Foot Guards.

Corporal: Two chevrons, point down.

Lance Corporal: One chevron, point down.

No 2 Dress (Service Dress)

A variety of hats is worn with the uniform. Officers can wear a khaki peaked cap with brown leather chinstrap, two 'gold' buttons and the regimental cap badge; this is the No 2 Dress Cap. The next possibility, for more formal occasions, is the No 1 Dress Cap in regimental colours with black patent leather chinstrap and peak (the latter edged in gold braid for Field Officers, on top and bottom for Colonels). Some regiments (Royal Tank Regiment, Parachute Regiment, Special Air Service) do not wear either of the above hats but always wear their regimental berets which other corps only wear sometimes. The last possible headgear to be worn with No 2 Dress is the regimental side cap.

Left *Soldier of the 1st Battalion, the Royal Regiment of Wales, wearing temperate DPM combat dress and carrying a GPMG* (Major R.P. Smith, RRW).

Other ranks wear the No 1 Dress Cap, beret or side cap with No 2 Dress; the exceptions to this rule are the Guards and the Royal Military Police who have stiff-topped all-khaki peaked caps, 'gold' buttons and brown leather chinstraps with brass buckles.

The jacket—Officers: There are various minor regimental differences in style to this garment, the main ones being the 'Highland' pattern with its cutaway front skirts (to give access to the sporran) and two rear vents, the 'Lowland' style with slightly longer skirts and the 'English' pattern with single rear vent and full skirts. All varieties have four pockets with buttoned flaps of various regimental designs and four front button except for officers of the Foot Guards who wear buttons according to regiment (Grenadiers—singly; Coldstream—in pairs: Scots—in threes; Irish—in fours; Welsh—in fives). For most regiments the top pockets have a central pleat and the skirt pockets are of the patch type. The top pocket flaps are usually trident shaped, those on the skirt pockets square. The shoulder straps run up beneath the collar and the cuffs are usually pointed (Polish) with buttons to the rear according to regiment.

Most regiments wear collar badges—the Guards wear none—and certain regiments wear shoulder titles, eg, Other Ranks in the Guards.

The jacket—Other Ranks: Four-button front (three-button with cutaway skirts and two rear vents for Highland and Lowland regiments; slightly longer skirts for Lowland regiments); two breast pockets with buttoned flaps having a single point, inset skirt pockets, no buttons on the rectangular flaps. No decoration to cuffs; single rear vent for all except above-mentioned regiments. The shoulder straps do not reach the collar and have rounded top ends. For most regiments all the buttons are of one size.

The trousers: These are narrow in the leg (bottoms about 42.5 cm) and match the colour of the jacket except for the Royal Hussars who wear crimson trousers, the 5th Royal Inniskilling Dragoon Guards who wear dark green and the Royal Irish Rangers who wear piper green trousers. The Highland regiments wear kilts or trews, the Lowland regiments wear trews.

The shirt and tie: Both are khaki.

The shoes: Most officers wear brown; Light Infantry and Scottish regiments wear black brogues as do the Royal Irish Rangers. Other ranks wear black shoes, WOIs wear officer-pattern brown shoes.

The Sam Browne Belt: (Worn by officers and RSMs.) This anachronistic item is brown with brass fittings for most dismounted regiments and is always polished to a mirror-like finish. Officers of

A Sergeant Air Gunner of the AAC wearing the Corps' distinctive light blue beret and temperate DPM combat dress (PR HQ 1 Div).

Cavalry regiments frequently wear brown leather bandoliers with brown leather pouches instead of the Sam Browne.

Gloves: Brown leather for officers of most regiments and corps; black for Light Infantry and Highland regiments. Other ranks wear khaki, dark green or black woollen gloves according to regiment.

Canes: Another anachronism; most Infantry officers and those from dismounted corps carry a short cane in various regimental patterns. Officers of the Royal Tank Regiment carry 'Ashplant' walking sticks (a tradition dating from World War 1).

Senior NCOs and Warrant Officers wear red worsted sashes from right shoulder to left hip (under the shoulder strap) when on parade or on certain duties. The sash has long red tassels hanging at the left hip.

Regimental Distinctions worn in No 2 Dress and sometimes No 13 and No 14 Dress

(All berets dark blue initially, but now being replaced by khaki in Infantry, and all jerseys olive green unless otherwise stated.)

Collar badges, buttons, shoulder titles, No 1

Infantry on exercise on Salisbury Plain wearing the windproof and waterproof Olive Drab smock and overtrousers and the woollen gloves which are now being phased out (PR HQ UKLF).

Dress caps and side caps are not included due to lack of space. Each regiment or corps wears its own individual cap badge (officers of the Royal Hampshires wear a different badge from soldiers in the same regiment). Coveralls are olive green for all regiments except the Royal Tank Regiment which wears black. All service parade belts are white unless otherwise stated.

The Household Division

The Life Guards: Cap badge—gold cypher 'EIIR' within a crowned ring; red lanyard on right shoulder; stable belt red over blue; black polo-necked jersey sometimes worn under olive green coveralls.

The Blues and Royals: Cap badge—bronze 'EIIR' within a crowned ring; red lanyard on left shoulder; on upper left arm a gold Napoleonic eagle on black cloth backing; stable belt blue with a red central stripe.

Royal Horse Artillery: (See Royal Artillery.)

The Foot Guards: (All berets khaki; all stable belts blue with red central stripe.)

Grenadier Guards: Cap badge—a flaming brass grenade in various forms according to rank.

Coldstream Guards: Cap badge—a gold, eight-pointed Star of Order of Garter.

Scots Guards: Cap badge—a gold, four-pointed Star of Order of St Andrew.

Irish Guards: Cap badge—a gold, eight-pointed Star of Order of St Patrick.

Welsh Guards: Cap badge—a gold leek.

The Royal Armoured Corps

Where an item is marked with an asterisk (*) this indicates that it is only worn by part of the regiment, usually officers and senior NCOs.

1st The Queen's Dragoon Guards: Cap badge—'silver' Imperial Austrian double eagle; white lanyard on right shoulder; royal blue stable belt; brass crowned wreath enclosing 'GREYS' in Gothic script on blue cloth backing on upper left arm.

The Royal Scots Dragoon Guards (Carabiniers and Greys): Cap badge—'silver' Napoleonic eagle over crossed 'brass' carbines on a plinth inscribed 'WATERLOO'; Light grey beret; on the upper left arm is the silver Prince of Wales' plumes.

4th/7th Royal Dragoon Guards: Cap badge—brass, eight-pointed star on red patch; white lanyard on right shoulder; brown leather waist belt for Service Dress; stable belt dark red over dark blue with narrow central yellow stripe; on the upper left arm a black diamond bearing one gold over two maroon chevrons (dating from World War 1).

5th Royal Inniskilling Dragoon Guards: Cap badge—crowned, interlocked 'VDG' in silver on dark green cloth backing (shamrock shaped on beret); white lanyard on left shoulder; silver Hanoverian horse on dark green cloth backing on upper right arm; stable belt red over yellow with narrow dark green central stripe.

The Queen's Own Hussars: Cap badge—silver Hanoverian horse over brass scroll bearing regimental title; on lower left arm silver 'Maid of Warsaw' badge (a mermaid carrying a round shield and scimitar) on crimson cloth backing (World War 2); stable belt—equal stripes of blue-yellow-blue each with a narrow red central stripe; officers wear a lovat green, V-necked jersey with white 'QOH' on khaki epaulettes.

The Queen's Royal Irish Hussars: Cap badge—crowned lion over a crowned Irish harp within a brass ring resting on a scroll; the blue beret has a green headband; yellow lanyard on right shoulder; crowned, silver harp badge on upper arm* (Lance Corporals wear two chevrons without the badge); stable belt green with narrow central stripes yellow over dark blue; dark green, V-necked jersey.

9th/12th Royal Lancers (Prince of Wales's): Cap badge—crossed lances under the crowned Prince of Wales's plumes over a scroll bearing 'IX-XII'; red and yellow lanyard on left shoulder; red stable belt with two yellow stripes.

The Royal Hussars (Prince of Wales's Own): Cap badge—the Prince of Wales's silver plumes over a brass scroll bearing 'THE ROYAL HUSSARS'; reddish brown beret with round-topped crimson patch behind the badge; stable belt—three equal stripes yellow-red-yellow, each yellow stripe edged in narrow dark blue lines on the outer side only; officers wear dark green, V-necked jerseys with crimson epaulettes.

13th/18th Royal Hussars (Queen Mary's Own): Cap badge—silver, entwined 'QMO' under a crown and behind a 'Z' shaped scroll; white lanyard on right shoulder; silver entwined 'QMO' on upper sleeve for NCOs; on upper left arm a diamond halved vertically white and dark blue; stable belt dark blue-white-dark blue-white; officers wear dark green, V-necked jerseys.

14th/20th King's Hussars: Cap badge—officers—a gold Prussian eagle; senior NCOs wear a black Prussian eagle with gold crown, orb and sceptre on blue over yellow cloth backing*; junior NCOs and privates have the black eagle on a blue over yellow patch divided diagonally; on each upper sleeve small crossed kukris in silver (an honour dating from World War 2); stable belt—blue-lemon yellow-blue; officers wear dark green, V-necked jerseys with khaki epaulettes.

15th/19th The King's Royal Hussars: Cap badge—a crowned lion on a crown within a brass ring over 'XV.XIX' over a brass scroll; red cloth patch behind badge; silver lion over crown badge on right arm*; stable belt—dark blue with narrow central stripe yellow over red.

16th/5th The Queen's Royal Lancers: Cap badge—crowned gold crossed lances behind silver '16' over a gold scroll; stable belt—equal stripes red over yellow over blue.

Left *Soldiers of the 2nd Battalion, 2nd King Edward VII's Own Gurkhas, most of them wearing the Olive Green crewnecked woollen jersey, enjoy a campfire session at Suffield (PR HQ UKLF).* **Right** *A RMP in shirtsleeve order at Catterick (UKLF Mobile Team (York)).*

A Gurkha rifleman wearing the lightweight cotton DPM 'safari jacket' (PR HQ UKLF).

17th/21st Lancers: Cap badge—silver skull and crossbones with scroll bearing 'OR GLORY'; on upper right arm the cap badge*; stable belt dark blue with twin central white stripes.

1st Royal Tank Regiment: Cap badge—silver World War 1 tank within crowned laurel wreath over a scroll bearing 'FEAR NAUGHT'; black berets; white cloth World War 1 tank badge on upper right arm; stable belt equal stripes green over red over brown; officers and senior NCOs wear black, V-necked jerseys with black epaulettes; red lanyard.

2nd Royal Tank Regiment; As above except—yellow flash around base of shoulder straps with brown, red and green vertical central stripes; yellow lanyard.

3rd Royal Tank Regiment: As for 1 RTR except—green shoulder strap flash and green lanyard.

4th Royal Tank Regiment: as for 1 RTR except—blue shoulder strap flash and lanyard.

Royal Regiment of Artillery

Cap badge—a brass cannon under a crown and over a scroll; white lanyard on left shoulder*; red stable belt with dark blue central band having a central yellow stripe; officers wear dark blue jerseys with dark blue epaulettes having brass buttons and 'RA' shoulder titles; Royal Horse Artillery officers have a silver cap badge of the royal cypher ('EIIR') within a crowned oval garter over a scroll with 'ROYAL HORSE ARTILLERY'; stable belt light blue with narrow yellow central stripe.

Corps of Royal Engineers

Cap badge—'EIIR' within a gold, crowned ring within a silver laurel wreath over a gold scroll; blue lanyard on right shoulder; red stable belt with two narrow dark blue stripes.

Royal Corps of Signals

Cap badge—silver Mercury under a gold crown over a gold scroll bearing 'Certa Cito'; senior NCOs wear cap badge (minus crown) over rank chevrons; blue lanyard on right shoulder; black SD belt; stable belt light blue over dark green with narrow dark blue central stripe; dark blue jersey.

The Scottish Division

(All stable belts are made of a strip of that tartan of which the regimental trews are made.)

The Royal Scots (The Royal Regiment); 1st Foot: Cap badge—silver, four-pointed star with St Andrew's cross; as centrepiece St Andrew with his cross within a ring; no beret; dark blue glengarry with scarlet, green and white diced band and scarlet Toorie; trews in No 8 Hunting Stuart tartan.

The Royal Highland Fusiliers (Princess Margaret's Own Glasgow and Ayrshire Regiment); 21st, 71st and 74th Foot: Cap badge—a crowned, flaming grenade in gold with superimposed, entwined cypher 'HLI'; no beret, glengarry as above; trews in No 5A Mackenzie tartan (HLI sett).

The King's Own Scottish Borderers; 25th Foot: Cap badge—large silver thistle wreath enclosing a castle on a St Andrew's cross over a scroll, all under a crowned lion on a crown; glengarry as above; trews in No 7 Leslie tartan.

The Black Watch (Royal Highland Regiment); 42nd and 73rd Foot: Cap badge—a large, four-pointed star with a St Andrew's cross, in the centre a crowned oval enclosing St Andrew and his cross, around the oval a thistle wreath; khaki bonnet (blue for parades) with scarlet toorie and red hackle over badge (over left ear); kilt and trews in No 1 (42nd or Black Watch) tartan.

Queen's Own Highlanders (Seaforth and Camerons); 72nd, 78th and 79th Foot: Cap badge—a crowned thistle over a stag's head over a scroll; blue glengarry as above with blue cut-feather hackle behind badge; kilt in No 2, Mackenzie tartan (Seaforth sett); trews in No 4, Cameron of Errackt tartan.

The Gordon Highlanders (75th and 92nd Foot): Cap badge—a silver stag's head rising from a mural crown within a wreath and over a scroll; glengarry as above but with scarlet, blue and white dicing; kilt and trews in No 3 (Gordon) tartan.

The Argyll and Sutherland Highlanders (Princess Louise's); 91st and 93rd Foot: Cap badge—a large silver wreath enclosing the boar's head and wild cat separated by the reversed cypher 'L'; glengarry as above but with scarlet and white dicing; kilt and trews in No 1 (42nd) tartan; senior NCOs and officers wear grey shirts and grey V-necked jerseys.

The Queen's Division

The Queen's Regiment; 2nd, 3rd, 31st, 35th, 50th, 57th, 70th, 77th, 97th and 107th Foot: Cap badge—in silver the Prince of Wales's plumes over a winged dragon within a brass ring and over a scroll; lanyards* on left shoulder—1st and 2nd Battalion dark blue; 3rd Battalion royal Dutch orange; stable belt dark blue.

The Royal Regiment of Fusiliers; 5th, 6th, 7th and 20th Foot: Cap badge—a gold flaming grenade bearing St George and the dragon within a crowned ring; a white over red hackle is worn over the badge; stable belt—equal stripes of crimson-yellow-crimson.

The Royal Anglian Regiment; 9th, 10th, 12th, 16th, 17th, 44th, 48th, 56th and 58th Foot: Cap badge—a small, eight-pointed silver star bearing a gold castle over a scroll; khaki beret with oval-topped black patch behind the badge; lanyard*—1st Battalion yellow; 2nd Battalion black; 3rd Battalion purple; 4th Battalion grey-red-black stripes; stable belt—dark blue with red central band having narrow yellow central stripe; dark green jersey.

The King's Division

The King's Own Royal Border Regiment; 14th, 34th and 55th Foot: Cap badge—within a crowned gold laurel wreath a lion guardant worn on a red, diamond-shaped patch; stable belt blue with narrow central yellow stripe; at top of right arm a gold glider badge (World War 2).

The King's Regiment; 8th, 63rd and 96th Foot: Cap badge—a gold fleur-de-lys bearing a silver prancing horse over a scroll on a square scarlet cloth patch; officers wear grey shirts in shirt-sleeve order; lanyard*—dark green on left shoulder; dark green, V-necked jersey*; dark green stable belt with narrow central maroon stripe.

A Corporal of the 1st Battallion, the Royal Welch Fusiliers, on patrol in Belize. He wears the DPM cotton hat and carries an L2A3 (PR HQ UKLF).

The Prince of Wales's Own Regiment of Yorkshire; 14th and 15th Foot: Cap badge—a running silver horse over a scroll; maroon stable belt with narrow central yellow stripe and black edges; dark green jersey.

The Green Howards (Alexandra, Princess of Wales's Own Yorkshire Regiment): Cap badge—a crowned silver cross entwined with the cypher 'A' over a scroll, on a 5 cm square grass green patch; grass green lanyard on left shoulder; grass green stable belt with narrow central white stripe; dark green, V-necked jersey* with grass green epaulettes.

The Royal Irish Rangers; 27th (Inniskilling), 83rd and 87th Foot: Cap badge—crowned Irish harp and scroll on piper green bonnet with matching hackle behind the silver; piper green stable belt.

The Queen's Lancashire Regiment; 30th, 40th, 47th, 59th, 81st and 82nd Foot: Cap badge—a crowned rose within a gold oval and over

A close-up of the pilot model for the new GRP helmet, here being worn with respirator and ear defenders (Directorate of Clothing and Textiles).

a scroll, worn on a diamond-shaped primrose yellow patch; maroon lanyard* and stable belt.

The Duke of Wellington's Regiment (West Riding); 33rd and 76th Foot: Cap badge—a rampant lion rising from a mural crown and bearing a flag, all over two scrolls; worn on a scarlet patch; red lanyard*.

The Prince of Wales's Division

The Devonshire and Dorset Regiment; 11th, 39th and 54th Foot: Cap badge—a silver castle and key behind a sphinx with brass scrolls top and bottom; grass green lanyard*; grass green stable belt with orange central stripe; at the top of each sleeve a strip of 1914-1918 pattern French Croix de Guerre ribbon (World War 1).

The Cheshire Regiment; 22nd Foot: Cap badge—an eight-pointed silver star enclosing an oak apple sprig within a ring; red lanyard*; cerise stable belt with buff central stripe.

The Royal Welch Fusiliers; 23rd Foot: Cap badge—a gold, flaming grenade bearing in silver the Prince of Wales's plumes within a ring under a white feather hackle; maroon and dark blue stable belt; at rear of SD collar five black silk ribbons about 22.5 cm long by 5 cm wide, each with a swallow-tailed end.

The Royal Regiment of Wales; 24th/41st Foot: Cap badge—the silver Prince of Wales's plumes behind a mural crown with scroll on a grass green patch; grass green stable belt with wide white central stripe having narrow red edges; grass green jersey.

The Gloucestershire Regiment; 28th and 61st Foot: Cap badge—a large silver sphinx on laurel leaves over a scroll; dark blue stable belt with narrow red central stripe and narrower yellow stripes near outer edges; black jersey; on the back of all headdress is a small silver sphinx within a wreath (Battle of Alexandra, 1800); at the top of each sleeve is the gold edged, royal blue US Presidential citation ribbon (Korean War).

The Worcestershire and Sherwood Foresters Regiment; 29th, 36th, 45th and 95th Foot: Cap badge—an eight-pointed star enclosing an antelope within a ring, worn on Lincoln green patch; Lincoln green lanyard* on right shoulder; Lincoln green stable belt with narrow maroon central stripe.

The Royal Hampshire Regiment; 37th and 67th Foot: Cap badge—officers'—a crowned, eight-pointed silver star enclosing a red rose within a blue and gold ring and over a blue and gold scroll; Other Ranks'—within a crowned laurel wreath a tiger over a rose over a scroll; stable belt—black with stripes of yellow, red, green and mauve; black jersey.

The Staffordshire Regiment (The Prince of Wales's); 38th, 64th, 80th and 98th Foot: Cap badge—the Prince of Wales's plumes over the Staffordshire knot on a buff backing of 'Holland Cloth'; black lanyard* on left shoulder; black stable belt; gold glider at top of right arm (World War 2).

Duke of Edinburgh's Royal Regiment (Berkshire and Wiltshire); 49th, 62nd, 66th and 99th Foot: Cap badge—a small, gold Maltese cross bearing a dragon within a ring, worn on a square red cloth backing; blue lanyard*; blue stable belt with two narrow red stripes.

The Light Division

The Light Infantry; 13th, 32nd, 46th, 51st, 53rd, 68th, 85th, 105th and 106th Foot: Cap badge—a silver stringed bugle badge with red backing; rifle green beret and lanyard on left shoulder; rifle green stable belt.

The Royal Green Jackets; 43rd and 52nd Foot, The King's Royal Rifle Corps, Rifle Brigade: Cap badge—a silver Maltese cross within a crowned laurel wreath; rifle green beret; green and black lanyard*; rifle green stable belt.

Soldiers wearing full NBC kit 'guard' a Rapier site at RAF Gutersloh during an exercise. The paper and carbon suits are worn with the respirator and black rubber gloves (over white cotton inners) with 1958 pattern web equipment (Soldier Magazine).

The Parachute Regiment

Cap badge—a silver winged parachute under a crown under a lion; maroon beret and stable belt; light blue and white parachutists' badge at top of right sleeve; lanyard*—1st Battalion red; 2nd Battalion blue; 3rd Battalion green.

The Brigade of Gurkhas

All regiments wear the khaki Gurkha hat (really two sewn together) with flat brim and light khaki pagree, the badge being on the left side. Alternative parade headgear is the black Kilmarnock (pill box) with cap badge in front and toorie in the regimental colour; rifle green berets are worn on fatigues and for training.

2nd King Edward VII's Own Gurkha Rifles (The Sirmoor Rifles): Cap badge—Prince of Wales's plume, scroll and coronet (silver for officers, black for ORs) worn on red backing; black toorie and black and red diced band to Kilmarnock; black lanyard* on left shoulder; stable belt—rifle green central band edged in narrow red stripes; black outer edges.

6th Queen Elizabeth's Own Gurkha Rifles: Cap badge—two silver kukris in saltire (hilts and cutting edges down) over '6' all ensigned with the crown; scarlet toorie to Kilmarnock; rifle green and black lanyard; rifle green and black stable belt.

7th Duke of Edinburgh's Own Gurkha Rifles: Cap badge—two silver kukris in saltire, points and cutting edges up; between the points '7', between the hilts the reversed crowned cypher 'P'; black toorie to Kilmarnock; rifle green and black lanyard; rifle green and black stable belt.

10th Princess Mary's Own Gurkha Rifles: Cap badge—silver, a stringed bugle horn interlaced with a kukri fesswise, the blade to the sinister; above the kukri the cypher of HRH Princess Mary (The Princess Royal) and below it '10'; black toorie to Kilmarnock; black lanyard; rifle green and black stable belt.

Gurkha Engineers; Cap badge—two silver kukris in saltire, blades up, cutting edges out under a gold flaming grenade; over kukri hilts a gold scroll bearing 'UBIQUE'; yellow toorie and head band to Kilmarnock; lanyard and stable belt as for Royal Engineers.

Gurkha Signals: Cap badge—as for Royal Corps of Signals but with addition of two kukris in saltire, blades up, cutting edges in, behind the globe; dark blue toorie to Kilmarnock, lanyard and stable belt as for Royal Corps of Signals.

Gurkha Transport Regiment: Cap badge—as for Royal Corps of Transport but scroll bears 'GURKHA TRANSPORT REGIMENT' and the royal cypher is over two kukris in saltire (silver blades, gold hilts), hilts down, cutting edges out; black toorie to Kilmarnock.

Special Air Service Regiment

Cap badge—silver dagger with light blue wings and scroll bearing 'WHO DARES WINS' on dark blue patch; beige beret.

Army Air Corps

Cap badge—silver eagle within a crowned wreath on a square dark blue patch; light blue beret; senior NCOs wear a light blue eagle edged dark blue above their chevrons.

Royal Corps of Transport

Cap badge—brass, eight-pointed star under a crown and enclosing 'EIIR' within a scroll; dark blue lanyard (left); dark blue stable belt with twin

A soldier of the 1st Battallion the Royal Scots wearing white camouflage clothing over his parka during an exercise in Norway (PR HQ UKLF).

narrow central white lines, two narrow red stripes towards outer edges.

Royal Army Medical Corps

Cap badge—within a gold, crowned laurel wreath a silver snake and staff, below the wreath a gold scroll; dull cherry lanyard (left); stable belt in three equal stripes; crimson over dark blue over yellow.

Royal Army Ordnance Corps

Cap badge—silver shield bearing three antique cannon under three balls, all within the crowned, gold garter wreath over a scroll; red and dark blue lanyard on left shoulder; stable belt dark blue with three narrow red stripes.

Corps of Royal Electrical and Mechanical Engineers

Cap badge—under a gold crown and scroll a silver, prancing horse chained to a globe, all superimposed on a gold lightning flash; stable belt dark blue with two narrow stripes each red over yellow.

Corps of Royal Military Police

Cap badge—brass 'EIIR' within a crowned laurel wreath; below the wreath a scroll; red beret; red lanyard on left; red stable belt.

Royal Pioneer Corps

Cap badge—silver piled rifles, pick axe and shovel behind a wreath, all under a crown and over a scroll; red and green lanyard on left shoulder; dark blue stable belt with narrow central stripe red over green.

Intelligence Corps

Cap badge—a crowned rose between laurel leaves over a scroll; Cypress green beret.

Royal Army Veterinary Corps

Cap badge—within a gold crowned wreath a centaur; all over a scroll.

Royal Army Education Corps

Cap badge—gold crown over a scroll, all superimposed on a silver flaming torch; light blue and dark blue lanyard (left) and stable belt.

Army Catering Corps

Cap badge—on a gold crowned circular disc a silver flaming bowl all over a gold scroll; lanyard* grey and yellow (left); grey and yellow stable belt.

Women's Royal Army Corps

Cap badge—within a crowned gold wreath a rampant silver female lion; dark green beret with beech brown patch behind the badge; Lovat green, single-breasted four-buttoned jacket with dark green piping to shoulder straps; lovat green skirt; black gloves, shoes and handbag; white blouse, black 'tie'.

Queen Alexandra's Royal Army Nursing Corps

Cap badge—brass cross within a crowned laurel wreath over a scroll; grey beret; grey jacket and skirt, as for Women's Royal Army Corps with crimson piping to shoulder straps; white blouse; black 'tie', gloves, shoes and handbag.

Temperate Combat Dress

This consists of hat, jacket and trousers in DPM (olive drab, black, brown, green and buff). The jacket has four patch pockets with buttoned flaps, buttoned cuffs and is fitted with draw-strings at waist and hem. The front has a full length, double-ended zip and a buttoned fly flap. The collar is only about 3 cm high and can be buttoned up. Under this jacket can be worn an olive green, quilted liner in sleeveless jerkin style. The olive-green trousers have a double-ended fly zip and draw-strings at the ankles. Around the waist are loops to take the web belt. The lower ends of the trousers are enclosed in khaki puttees which replaced web gaiters in the period 1974-76. For normal wear black Direct Moulded Sole (DMS) boots are worn but for extreme cold special boots with thicker soles and thermal insoles are worn.

The heavy, olive green woollen jersey with crew neck may be worn under or instead of the combat jacket. Beneath this is worn the combat shirt ('Shirt Hairy Mary' to the soldiers) in flannel-like material. In 1976 black leather 'combat gloves' were introduced into Northern Ireland and they are now being issued to all soldiers to replace the unsatisfactory khaki knitted gloves.

Combat headdress is still the steel helmet of 1950s vintage but is is being replaced by a composition 'Combat Helmet' with increased ballistic and shock protection and a much firmer sit. This item has been troop-trialled in Northern Ireland. A variation of this item is the new parachutist's helmet.

Cold Weather Clothing

This consists of temperate combat clothing with the following additions: string vest; 'long johns' in olive green for the legs; a quilted, sleeved under-jacket; quilted under-trousers; a DPM parka reaching to the knees and special, thick-soled boots with thermic insoles. In snowy conditions this is worn under a windproof, white-hooded smock and trousers together with special sheepskin mittens and ski-boots. For non-skiing duties in deep snow

A Sergeant of the RMP in early riot gear for the Northern Ireland situation, including plastic visor on helmet, baton and plastic shield. His helmet is black with red band and front patch bearing 'MP' in white while his red armband carries the same legend in black on red. Under the US-pattern flak jacket can be seen the respirator and pistol lanyard (Directorate of Clothing and Textiles).

Canadian-pattern white Mukluks are worn over the cold weather boots.

Tropical Combat Wear

Special lightweight cotton DPM hat, 'safari jacket' and trousers, with or without shirt of same basic style as temperate combat dress; either DMS boots or special jungle boots of US Army Vietnam pattern (commercial hockey boots have also been used). For desert conditions suede boots of commercial pattern are very popular, as are plimsolls.

New equipment developments

Helmet: Until recently the British army wore a steel helmet with single chinstrap and curved bottom edge coming low over ears and neck. This was designed to give protection only against shell splinters; a helmet protecting against small arms projectiles at close range would have been far too heavy for a man to wear for more than a few minutes at a time.

This helmet had four main disadvantages: it was unstable and fell off easily; it provided minimal protection against blows to the head (rocks, clubs, etc): its shape over the eyes made it difficult for the wearer to operate some of the newer weapons without considerable inconvenience and contortions; and it was difficult to wear earphones with it.

In about 1975 a new 'Northern Ireland Combat Helmet' made of glass reinforced plastic was introduced. It weighed less than the steel model, fitted more closely to the head and had a chinstrap which was anchored at four points to the helmet and thus gave a much firmer fit. It also afforded 'bump' protection and had less pronounced front and rear peaks, thus permitting easier operation of many weapons in various positions. Facilities were included for the rapid fitting of a plastic visor for internal security duties. This helmet proved to be a great improvement on the old steel model and is now being introduced into general use. A variation of this basic pattern is the new parachutist's helmet.

The combat glove: Northern Ireland has proved to be a comprehensive testing ground for all items of Army combat clothing and it soon became obvious that the knitted khaki glove was totally inadequate. It was thus replaced with (initially) a commercial pattern, black leather ski glove which, with added padding strips along the knuckles, has become the new combat glove.

Windproof waterproof clothing: To protect soldiers from adverse weather in situations where they are exposed to the elements but must remain stationary for long periods, an olive drab smock and overtrouser suit was developed. It is completely proof against wind and rain and thus preserves body heat.

The disadvantage of such clothing is that if the wearer has to engage in strenuous exertion while wearing it, it becomes a very efficient sauna and the man is rapidly soaking in his own sweat. Subsequent inaction leads to considerable loss of body heat in most uncomfortable conditions. These garments are now being issued with the DPM camouflage print.

Tank crew clothing: Two items of interest have recently been developed; first is a waterproof, olive green, one-piece coverall to protect the crews of armoured fighting vehicles from inclement weather when carrying out maintenance in the field such as track changing. This garment has the inherent disadvantage of all waterproof clothing—it catches

fire relatively easily. As fire is a constant hazard in a tank in a combat situation, a fire-resistant coverall is also being developed.

As the Chieftain tank has no heating when in 'silent watch' mode, crew efficiency and comfort suffers considerably in winter in north-west Europe. Experiments were made with a coverall containing electrical heating wires all over the body and designed to be plugged into the tank's battery system. The device worked but the drain on the batteries was too great so it was rejected and instead development is proceeding on electrically heated insoles for the men's boots and electrically heated mittens which will plug into the tank battery system with quick-release snatch plugs.

NBC clothing: Since the German gas attacks of World War 1, the British Army has been careful about chemical warfare defence. The current S6 respirator, of black rubber with built-in filter, is the latest in a line of continuously developed items. It provides complete protection for the optical and respiratory systems against known Soviet NBC warfare agents.

To protect the rest of the body each soldier is issued with a two-piece NBC suit in olive drab, charcoal impregnated paper. This suit offers complete protection against NBC agents for several hours. It then has to be removed and replaced by a new suit. Three are given to each soldier.

No country has the complete answer to protection against the NBC threats. The grey rubber suit of the Warsaw Pact forces has the advantage of being more robust than the British paper model but it acts as a dreadfully efficient sauna bath and leads to rapid exhaustion of the wearer. It has to be decontaminated—an operation not required with the disposable British suit—and is not proof against certain NBC agents for more than a few hours.

The British NBC suit is worn with disposable rubber and paper-charcoal overboots and black disposable rubber gloves with white cotton inner gloves.

Web Equipment (WE): Even today, a large proportion of the British Army wears '1937 Pattern' WE (much hated because of the constant need to blanco it) but this is now being replaced by '1958 Mark II WE' with heavy shoulder yoke and with the ammunition pouches, water bottle, respirator and small pack being attached to the waist belt. The bayonet is held in its scabbard on the side of the left-hand ammunition pouch and the equipment is made of olive drab synthetic material which is resistant to both water and NBC agents. All metal fittings are in matt black finish. A folding entrenching tool is carried on the back.

For tropical wear a special type of WE was

Front and rear views of an AT RAOC demonstrating the Mark 2 EOD suit developed by SCRDE and Galt Glass Ltd. These pictures show how the GRP panels fit into their appropriate pouches and the intercom system on the back (connected to the helmet, with visor here raised).

developed during the war and called '1944 Pattern'. Its advantages were that it absorbed very little water in its olive green fabric and thus did not greatly increase the soldier's load in the 'rain forest' environment. It was usually worn with two water bottles. 1944 Pattern WE is characterised by broad shoulder straps with two narrower straps falling to the rear of each and crossing to attach to rear and sides of the belt.

Parachutist's smock: Since World War 2 the British airborne forces have worn the 'Denison Smock' with its peculiar camouflage pattern, ribbed woollen cuffs and crutch strap. It has become enshrined almost as a ceremonial item (particularly since Arnhem) and only with great reluctance could the Parachute Regiment be persuaded recently to accept the introduction of a new smock in standard DPM colours.

Barrack Dress trousers: These dark green, 100 per cent synthetic textile items were introduced in 1974-76. With their permanent creases they were designed to smarten up the soldiers' appearance at less cost than Service Dress would incur. The Scottish regiments were extremely reluctant to adopt them as they suspected the introduction of these items as the 'thin end of the wedge' of a plan to deprive them of their trews.

Many units prefer to wear the light olive drab 'Trousers Lightweight' for barrack wear as these contain a percentage of natural fibres and present more resistance to oils in the dirty job situation such as vehicle maintenance. Coveralls ought to be worn for this work but are unpopular, particularly in summer.

Special combat clothing: The terrorist war in Northern Ireland has led to the development of a range of protective clothing which at first glance may seem novel but on reflection is merely an updated selection of historic items of personal armour using modern materials instead of the more conventional wood, steel and leather.

In the early stages of the most recent 'Troubles' in 1969-70 the troops and police were frequently called upon to stand firm for hours under a hail of stones, bottles and molotov cocktails with no protective clothing at all. To give them at least a degree of protection they were issued with cricket pads and light metal shields. As the situation continued to deteriorate the Stores and Clothing Research and Development Establishment (SCRDE) began to develop special items. The 'Combat Helmet Northern Ireland', of glass reinforced plastic (GRP) with improved ballistic and bump protection, firmer sit and optional plastic visor, was one such item. GRP leg greaves and light, transparent plastic riot shields were others. When the threat of being picked off by an IRA terrorist with a rifle became greater, the British government authorised the purchase of a quantity of US pattern 'Flak Jackets' to protect the upper body. These were made of multiple layers of

'Kevlar'—a synthetic fibre much stronger than steel in certain respects and a substance tested in the US space programme. These Flak Jackets afford protection against normal projectiles from pistols and sub-machine-guns from close range (about 5 m) and from soft-cored rifle and machine-gun bullets from about 400 m (depending upon strike velocity and angle).

Of course, this armour, as in the Middle Ages, had the conventional disadvantage—its protection could only be bought at the high price of its weight. The wearer was very limited in his movements, tired much more easily when wearing it and moved much more slowly than if he had not worn it. Mobility itself is protection and the age-old tussle between mobility and armour continued its maddening spiral.

A British company (Bristol Composite Materials Engineering Ltd) has recently developed an armoured vest which is in use with the Royal Ulster Constabulary and with some British Army units in Northern Ireland. Kevlar has the disadvantage of suffering a great reduction in its ballistic protective properties if wet (it regains them when dried out again). In order to cut down the weight of a vest designed to protect against armour-piercing projectiles fired from a Kalashnikov assault carbine at close range to acceptable limits, this company has developed 'composite armour' plates (ceramic and GRP) which for any given level of ballistic protection are much lighter than armoured steel.

Vests of this type were used by the West German elite anti-terrorist group 'Grenz-Schutz-Gruppe 9' (GSG9) in their successful raid on the Lufthansa jet held by hijackers in Mogadishu in 1977. To give the GSG9 men greatest mobility within the close confines of the plane's cabin, they used the vests without the ceramic-GRP plates. One GSG9 man was shot from a range of about 3 m by a terrorist using a Makarov pistol, the bullet lodging in the side of the armoured vest, and the policeman reported that all he felt was a slight bump 'as if someone had poked me in the ribs with a finger'! He shot the terrorist.

The Explosive Ordnance Disposal (EOD) suit: Ammunition Technicians (ATs) and Ammunition Technical Officers (ATOs) of the Royal Army Ordnance Corps have the unenviable task of attempting to disarm IRA terrorist bombs. To give them some degree of protection in this hazardous job and EOD suit was developed at great speed and produced partly by SCRDE Colchester and partly by the British firm of Galt Glass. It consists of a helmet with massive plastic visor and built-in intercommunication facilities, a two-piece smock of Kevlar in an olive green cover and Kevlar leggings in olive green covers. The chest is protected by a GRP plate shaped to deflect shock waves from a bomb away from the head and the lower abdomen is protected by another such shield. On the back of the equipment is a small two-way radio with a range (under suitable conditions) of several hundred metres.

The suit is, of course, extremely heavy (over 30 kg) and severely limits the movements of the wearer. It is designed to be worn only for a few minutes at a time while the ATO carries out his initial examination of the bomb and so this disadvantage is of limited validity. As one ATO said to me 'at least it enables you to be buried in one piece'. Since the introduction of this suit (1974) various international firms have come up with improvements which are easier to don and to take off than the in-service EOD suit and which afford greater ballistic protection without increasing the limitations to the wearer's mobility.

Dress for the 1980s

The final winner in the contest to select a new uniform for the British army was a dark green Service Dress with matching cap and trousers. Troop trials were carried out in 1977-78 but the whole project has been shelved and a decision on its introduction or abandonment is not expected in the near future.

Specialist badges

The British army is traditionally extremely niggardly with the award of medals and badges of achievement and skill when compared to other armies and this was also the case in the Napoleonic era. Highly qualified soldiers of the British army, who have seen action in World War 2, Africa, Cyprus, Aden, Dhofar and Northern Ireland frequently wear far fewer medals and badges than their equivalents in other armies who have never heard a shot fired in anger or been involved in any more perilous situation than the Nijmegen marches. In the British army the purple and dark green 'General Service Medal' covers a span of campaigns which would fill many a chest in another army.

Badges for skill at arms or for technical skills are usually worn only by NCOs and privates. Exceptions (worn also by officers) are: pilots' badge—a crowned lion over a crown between light blue wings, all on a dark blue ground—worn on the left breast; fully trained parachutists' wings—a white parachute between light blue wings on khaki—on the upper right arm; parachutists' badge (known as the 'Edward Bear Badge' after the custom of the RMAS of always throwing a battered Teddy Bear (with a parachute) out of an airplane before the officer cadets follow it on their first jump). The 'Edward Bear Badge' is worn on the lower left arm.

'A' Class Tradesman: (Various corps.) An 'A' between laurel leaves, all in white, worn on the upper arm (privates and junior NCOs only).

Aircraft Technician, REME: Within a crowned, winged yellow ring the yellow letters 'AT'; around the yellow ring the black letters 'REME'.

Air Despatcher, RCT: Within a crowned, winged yellow ring the letters 'AD'.

Air Gunner: On a dark blue ground a yellow 'G' within a crowned ring with a single light blue wing to the left side, worn on the left breast.

Air Observer: As above but the 'G' is replaced by an 'O'.

Ammunition Technical Officer: Black, gold and yellow flaming bomb worn on the lower left sleeve.

Ammunition Technician: A larger version of the above in black, yellow and red worn above the rank chevrons or below the warrant badge.

Anti-Tank Gunner: 'AT' within a laurel wreath in regimental colours or brass.

Armament Artificer: Crossed hammer and pincers, but this badge also covers a number of other trades including blacksmith, fitter, etc.

Army Parachute Jumping Instructor: A small white parachute within light blue wings, below the parachute 'APJI' in yellow within a green laurel wreath.

Artificer, REME: (Staff Sergeants and Warrant Officers.) White crossed hammer and pincers on khaki worn over the chevrons or under the warrant badge.

Assault Pioneer: Crossed axes.

'B' Class Tradesman: (Various corps.) A 'B' between laurel leaves, all in white, worn on the upper arm (privates and junior NCOs only).

Bugler: A white cloth or brass bugle on the upper arm.

Bugler (Light Infantry.) As above but a stringed bugle horn.

Corps badges: (In regimental colours or in brass, worn by senior NCOs of the following corps above their chevrons.) *Royal Artillery:* a Napoleonic cannon side view; *Royal Engineers:* a white, flaming grenade; *Royal Corps of Signals:* the figure of Mercury on a globe.

Diver, Royal Engineers: An old-fashioned brass diver's helmet over the letters 'SW' (shallow water).

Driver: A five-pointed white star worn on the left upper arm (privates and junior NCOs only).

Drummer: Representation of a white cloth or brass drum worn on the upper arm (also over the

Lack of space forbids more than a cursory glance at ceremonial clothing but, plastic cups and sandwiches notwithstanding, this shot from Berlin encapsulates a great deal. It shows members of the King's Troop, Royal Horse Artillery, in both Full Dress and No 2s, in the courtyard of the Charlottenburg Palace. Black busby with white plume; red bag; yellow cords; dark blue dolman and breeches; red collar and trouser stripe; yellow cords and ball buttons (Army PR).

four chevrons of a Drum Major).

Farrier: A white horseshoe on khaki on the upper arm (privates and junior NCOs only).

Gun Layer: 'L' within a laurel wreath in regimental colours or brass.

Marksman (Light Machine-Gun): 'LMG' within a laurel wreath in regimental colours or brass.

Marksman (Rifle): Crossed rifles. (A similar badge is worn by WOs and senior NCOs of the Small Arms School Corps in white on khaki as a technical qualification.)

Mortarman: 'M' within a laurel wreath in regimental colours or brass.

Musician: A white cloth or brass lyre worn on the upper arm.

Physical Training Instructor: Crossed sabres, points up.

Pilot, AAC: A crowned lion standing on a crown between light blue wings, worn on the left breast.

Piper: White cloth on brass bagpipes worn on the upper arm.

Radar Technician, REME: 'R' between lightning flashes in white on khaki.

Royal Engineers Bomb Disposal: A yellow bomb under a blue cross on a red oval worn on the cuff.

Saddler and Harness Maker: A bit worn on right upper arm. Usually only worn by the King's Troop, Royal Horse Artillery, but may be worn by Household Cavalry.

Signaller: Crossed flags in white, yellow and dark blue worn on the lower arm (privates and Lance Corporals) or over the chevrons (Corporals).

Sniper: Crossed rifles under an 'S' in regimental colours or brass.

Special Air Service: A white parachute and wings on a dark blue ground worn on the upper right arm.

Telecommunications Technician, REME: 'T' between lightning flashes in white on khaki.

Trumpeter: White cloth or brass crossed trumpets worn on the upper arm.

Wheelwright: An old-fashioned cartwheel.

Instructor's Badges

Crossed gun barrels: Assistant Instructor in Gunnery (AIG), Royal Artillery.

'QI' in wreath: Qualified Instructor in Field Engineering, Royal Engineers.

Crossed rifles: Weapon training instructor. Worn on right arm, position depending on rank.

Crossed swords: Assistant Physical Training Instructor.

Crossed semaphore flags: Assistant Instructor of Signalling, Royal Signals.

A spur: Roughrider, or Equestrian Instructor. Worn on right arm with the position depending on rank.

Good conduct stripes

These are awarded for ascending periods of 'undetected crime' and are worn only by privates and Lance Corporals on the lower left sleeve. They take the form of chevrons in the regimental colour, point up. One chevron = two years' service; two chevrons = five years; three = eight years.

Variations in rank titles

Usual title	Foot Guards	Household Cavalry	Royal Artillery	Cavalry of the Line and other mounted corps
Regimental Sergeant Major (RSM)	RSM and Superintending Clerk	Regimental Corporal Major	RSM	RSM
Company Sergeant Major (CSM)		Squadron Corporal Major	Battery Sergeant Major	Squadron Sergeant Major
Regimental Quarter Master Sergeant (RQMS) (badge with wreath)	RQMS or Orderly Room QMS	Regimental Quarter Master Corporal *or* Farrier Quarter Master Corporal. Squadron Quarter Master Corporal *or* Staff Corporal of Horse (*NB* These NCOs wear a crown over 4 chevrons)	RQMS	RQMS
Staff Sergeant (SSgt) or Colour Sergeant (CSgt) or Company Quarter Master Sergeant (CQMS)	Sgt or CSgt or CQMS	Corporal of Horse	Battery QMS (BQMS)	Squadron QMS (SQMS)
Sergeant (Sgt)	Sgt	Lance Corporal of Horse	Sgt	Sgt
Corporal (Cpl)	Cpl	Cpl	Bombardier	Cpl
Lance Corporal (LCpl)	LCpl	LCpl	Lance Bombardier	LCpl

Index

The following index combines a glossary of abbreviations. Where an abbreviation is common, eg, AFV, it is not indexed as it would be of no value as a reference. Bold type denotes a main or major entry. Italics denote an illustration only.

1 (Br) Corps   17, 18, 21, 33, 39, 40, 42, 46, 52-53, 56, 65, 68, 72, 76, 83, 133-134, 168-169, 174, 198, 245
1 Armoured Division   17, 18, 34
1 Regiment RMP   76
2 Infantry Division   17-19
2 Infantry Brigade   19
2 Armoured Division   18, 34, 60
3 Armoured Division   17, 18, 34
3 Brigade   89
4 Armoured Division   17, 18, 34
4 Armoured Brigade   17, 18, 19
5th Field Force   17, 18
5 Infantry Brigade   19-20, 34
6 Armoured Brigade   17, 18
7 Armoured Brigade   17, 18
8 Brigade   89
11 Armoured Brigade   17, 18
12 Armoured Brigade   17, 18
15 Infantry Brigade   18
20 Armoured Brigade   17, 18
22 Armoured Brigade   17, 18
24 Infantry Brigade   18
33 Armoured Brigade   17, 18
39 Brigade   89
49 Infantry Brigade   18
51 Highland Brigade   19
52 Lowland Brigade   19
4th/7th Royal Dragoon Guards   20-21, 262

9th/12th Royal Lancers   20-21, 263
13th/18th Royal Hussars   20-21, 263
14th/20th King's Hussars   20-21, 263
15th/19th The King's Royal Hussars   20-21, 263
16th/5th The Queen's Royal Lancers   20-21, 263
17th/21st Lancers   20-21, 264

AAC See Army Air Corps
Abbot See FV433
ACC See Army Catering Corps
ACE See Allied Command Europe
Ace High   55
ADP Automated Data Processing   59
AEC See Army Education Corps
AEC Militant Mark 1 See FV11001-11041; Militant Mark 3 See FV11046-11047
AFCENT See Air Forces Central Europe
AFV Armoured Fighting Vehicle
Air Defence Regiment   33, 34, 136
Air Despatch Squadron   66
Air Forces Central Europe   53
Air Portable Bridge Class 16 247
Allied Command Europe   18; Allied Command Europe Mobile Force (Land)   18, 24, 35, 53, 66
Alligator M2 Back endpaper, 42, 243-245
Alouette   46, 252-253
AMF(L) See Allied Command

Europe Mobile Force (Land)
AMETS See Artillery Meteorological System
Amphibious Engineer Regiment   40, 42, 245
Anti-tank Mine Mark 7   40, 146
APC Armoured Personnel Carrier
APTC See Army Physical Training Corps
APDS Armour Piercing Discarding Sabot
APFSDS Armour Piercing Fin Stabilised Discarding Sabot
APSE Armour Piercing Secondary Effects
APTC See Army Physical Training Corps
APU Auxiliary Power Unit (FH70)
Arakan See HMAV
Ardennes See HMAV
Argyll and Sutherland Highlanders   27-28, 265
ARK Armoured Bridgelayer
Armoured Division (organisation table)   22
Armoured Division Engineer Regiment   40, 42
Armoured Engineer Regiment   40, 42, 203
Armoured Reconnaissance Regiment   23-25, 82, 168, 174
Armoured Recovery Vehicle M578   205, 206
Armoured Regiment   21-23
Army Air Corps   19, 46, 49, 69, 138, 268
Army Catering Corps   24, 49, 70, 268
Army Education Corps   50, 71, 268
Army Physical Training

Corps   24, 50, 74-75
Army strengths   20
Artillery Division   18, 33
Artillery Meteorological System   37
Artillery Weapon Data Transmission System   37, 39
ARV Armoured Recovery Vehicle
Assault Boat Mark 4   256; Mark 5   257
AT Ammunition Technician
ATAF Allied Tactical Air Force   92
ATGW Anti-tank Guided Weapon
ATO Ammunition Technical Officer
Autoject   91
Aveling-Barford Motor Grader   43
AVLB Armoured Vehicle Launched Bridge
AVRE Assault Vehicle Royal Engineers
AWDATS See Artillery Weapon Data Transmission System

BAC British Aircraft Corporation
BAOR See British Army of the Rhine
Bar Mine/Layer   40, 144, 183
BARV Beach Armoured Recovery Vehicle
Base Workshops   64
BAT Battalion Anti-tank Gun
BATES See Battlefield Artillery Target Engagement System
Baton rounds   109
Battlefield Artillery Target Engagement System   35, 38-39, 52, 58, 60
Battle Group   15, 18

BATUS *See* British Army Training Unit Suffield
Beaver 47, **253**
Bedford MK *47*, **217**, 219; RL **215-217**; TK *45*, **221**; TM **222-224**
Beeswing 137
BEF *See* British Expeditionary Force
Belize 19, 26, 45, 64, 76, 265
Bell 47G 47
Berlin 19, 26, 30, 47, 215
Berlin Brigade 19, 21, 76, 181, 213
BFPO British Forces Post Office
BL Breech Loading
Black Watch 27-28, 264
Bloodhound 92
Blowpipe 34, **133**, 134, 138, 171; trailer/launcher **134**
Blues and Royals 20-21, 262
Borneo 15, 110
BOXER (code name for Army telephone network) 53
BQMS Battery Quarter Master Sergeant
British Army of the Rhine 13, 16, **17**, 19-20, 26, 40, 52, 63-64, 68, 141
British Army Training Unit Suffield 26, 47, 76, 253
British Expeditionary Force 10
Bruin 52, 56, 59
Brunei 15, 19
Buccaneer 91-92
Bv 202 37, *39*, 147, **207**

Calibres
5.56 mm IW **100**; LSW **101**
5.56 mm Rifle M16 **99**
7.62 mm Rifle L1A1 30, 78, 87, **96**; L39A1 **98**; L42A1 **98**
General Purpose Machine-Gun L7A2 30, 32, 87, **103**, 162, 172, 173, 177, 181, 185, 186; L8A1 **103**, 153, 175; L20A1 **103**, 248, 251; L37A1 **103**, 153, 161, 169, 170, 174, 180; L41A1 **103**; L43A1 **104**, 166; L46A1 **104**
Machine-Gun L4A4 78, 87, **101**, 181, 183, 184, 185, 186, 194, 195, 200, 207
.30 Machine-Gun L3A3 **104**, 165, 189, 190; L3A4 **104**, 189, 194, 205
7.65 mm Pistol Automatic

Walther Type PP XL47E1 78, **94**
9 mm Pistol Automatic L9A1 87, **94**
Sub-machine-Gun L2A3 78, 87, **95**, *265*; L34A1 **95**
.50 Machine-Gun L40A1 **104**, 113
30 mm Rarden **115**, 174, 175, 181
40 mm Grenade Launcher M79 **105**
51 mm Light Mortar 30, **109**
66 mm Rocket L1A1 **110**
76 mm Gun L5A1 117, 189; L23A1 **116-117**, 166
81 mm Mortar 30, 83, **112**, 180, 209, 214
84 mm Gun 'Carl Gustav' 30, 32, **113**, 180
105 mm Gun L5 Pack Howitzer 79, **118**, 121, 209; Field L13A1 (Abbot) **119**, 184; Field L118 Light Gun **121**, 214; L119 122
120 mm Wombat 30, 83, **111**, 180, 209, 211; Tank L11A5 **122**, 153; Modern Technology **124**
155 mm Howitzer L121 (FH70) 35, **125** 197; M185 **129**, 195; SP70(80) 128, 129, **193**
165 mm Demolition Gun 201
175 mm Gun M113 **128**, 198
8-in Howitzer M2A1E1 **129**, 200
Cannon 30 mm Rarden L21 **115**, 174-175, 181; 155 mm Howitzer M185 **129**, 195; 175 mm Gun M113 **128**, 198; 8-in Howitzer M201 129
Carl Gustav **113**
Cavalry 20-25, 274
CB 300 Container Bodies 221; CB 01 217
Central European Operating Agency 68
Central European Pipeline System 68
Centurion *See* FV4002, 4003, 4006, 4016, 4017 and 4018
CEOA *See* Central European Operating Agency
CEPS *See* Central European Pipeline System

Cervantes 151
CET *See* Combat Engineering Tractor
Chain Gun 159
Challenger 157 (*See* FV4030)
Cheshire Regiment 28, 30, 266
Chieftain *See* FV4201, 4202, 4204 and 4205
Chinook 92, 248
Chipmunk 47, **253**
Chobham armour 159
Clansman 52, **58**, 83, 157
Claribel *See* Radar
Class 16 Bridge **247**
Classic **143**
Claymore mine **143**
CN Tear Gas (alpha-choroaceto-phenone) 108
Coles Crane *67*; Hydra-Husky *41*
Combat Engineering Tractor 42, **199**, 236
Combat Support Tug **257**
Combat Team 18
Combat Vehicle Reconnaissance (Tracked) 164 (*See* also Scorpion)
Combat Vehicle Reconnaissance (Wheeled) 171 (*See* also Fox)
Command and Control Craft **256**
Commander **235**
Commando Regiment 35, 43
Communication Project Agency 52
Condor engine 159, 235
CONRATES (term used for full-time members of UDR, *qv*) 78
Conscription 14
Copperhead 35
CPA *See* Communications Project Agency
CPV Command Post Vehicle
CQMS Company Quarter Master Sergeant
CRA Commander Royal Artillery
Crawler Tractors *42*
Crusader **235**
Crusader/EKA **241-243**
CRYP (Series name for range of cryptological coding and decoding equipment developed by Marconi) 61
Cryptography 61
CS Gas (ortho-chlorobenzal-malono-nitrile) 87-88, 108-109

CSgt Colour Sergeant
CSM Company Sergeant Major
CSWS Crew Served Weapon Sight 143-144
CVR(T) *See* Combat Vehicle Reconnaissance (Tracked)
CVR(W) *See* Combat Vehicle Reconnaissance (Wheeled)
Cymbeline *See* Radar
Cyprus 12, 19, 24, 45-46, 64, 72, 76, 189, 253

Dell Quay Launch 78, **256-257**
Deuce-and-a-half 215
Devon and Dorsetshire Regiment 28, 30, 266
Districts, Military 20, 83
Divers 45, 207
Divisions: Guards 27, 31; King's 27, 32; Light 30-32, 266; Prince of Wales's 30, 31; Queen's 27, 31; Scottish 27, 31
DMS Direct Moulded Sole
DPM Disruptive Patterned Material
DS/T Discarding Sabot/ Training
Duke of Edinburgh's Royal Regiment 29-30, 266
Duke of Edinburgh's Own Gurkha Rifles 29-30, 267
Duke of Wellington's Regiment 28, 30, 266
Dummy Axles **243**

Eager Beaver 71, 145, **236-237**
Electronic Warfare 52, 55
EOD *See* Explosive Ordnance Disposal
Equipment Designation System 93
ESR Electro-Slag Refined (steel)
Explosive Ordnance Disposal 44, 45, *68*, 69, 87, 272
EW *See* Electronic Warfare

FAC *See* Forward Air Controller
FACE *See* Field Artillery Computer Equipment
Falklands 16, 26, 32, **89**, 122, 135, 170, 171, 254, 255
FDC Fire Direction Centre
Ferret *See* FV701, 703 and 704

FFV Förenade Fabrikswerken 113
FH Field Howitzer
FH70 35, **125**, 197, 226
Field Artillery Computer Equipment **36-37**, 181, 209, 213
Field Cash Office 80
Field Engineer Regiment 40
Field Regiments—Artillery 34-35, 184
Fighting Vehicle System 131, 183
Foden 6 × 4 Tanker **232**; 8 × 4 Tanker **231**; Tipper **232**; Truck **231**; FH70 Limber **226**; FH70 Tractor 128, **226**
FOO Forward Observation Officer 36-37
Forward Air Controller 92
Forward Repair Group 64
Fox *See* FV721
FRG *See* Forward Repair Group
FSAPDS Fin Stabilised Armour Piercing Discarding Sabot (*qv* APFSDS)
FV Field Vehicle
FV101 Scorpion 24, 92, **163**
102 Striker 137, **165**
103 Spartan 24, 36, 42, 92, 134, 151, **166**, 174
104 Samaritan 72, **167**
105 Sultan **168**
106 Samson **169**
107 Scimitar 23, 24, 116, **170**, 176
180 Combat Engineering Tractor 42, **199**, 236
400 MCV-80 prototype 179
420 FV432 prototype 173
431 Load Carrier 173
432 APC 30, 31, 32, 36, 37, 42, 59, 72, 113, 114, 145, 147, 151, **173**, 183, 188, 190; Variants **174-179**
433 Abbot 34, **180**, 198
434 Repair *62*, **181-182**
438 Swingfire 137, 138, **182**
439 Signals **183**
601(C) Saladin 24, 105, 165, **185**, 190
603 Saracen 24, 87, 105, 165, **186**
604 Command 186
610 Artillery Command 186

611 Ambulance 186
622 Stalwart 145, 147, **221**
623 Stalwart 222
624 REME 222
652 Salamander 221
701 Ferret **189**
703 Vigilant Ferret **191**
704 Ferret 87, **189-191**
711 Big Wheel Ferret **190**
712 Swingfire Ferret 136, **191**
721 Fox 24, 116, **171**
722 Vixen 172
1119 Recovery **241**
1601 Truck 184
1611 Pig 87, **183**, 187
1612 Radio 183
1613 Ambulance 183
2361 Land Rover Trailer 211
2380 Land Rover Trailer 211
2381 Land Rover Trailer 211
2412 Rapier Trailer 136
2420 Bridge Trailer 248
2425 Cymbeline Trailer 151
2501 Bedford RL Trailer 217
2505 Bedford RL Trailer 217
2508 Bedford RL Trailer 217
2692 Dummy Axle **243**
2721 AVRE Trailer 203
2842 Trailer (MGB) 147, 247
3221 Recovery Trailer 241
3561 Dummy Axle **243**
3601 Tank Transporter Trailer 235
3705 Giant Viper Trailer 147
4002 Centurion AVLB 161
4003 Centurion AVRE **201**
4006 Centurion ARV **203**
4016 Centurion ARK 161
4018 Centurion BARV **203-205**
4030 Challenger **157-159**
4201 Chieftain 123, **152**, 159
4202 Chieftain prototype 153

4204 Chieftain ARV **159**, 203
4205 Chieftain AVLB 42, **160-163**
4211 Shir Iran 158, 159
4333 Stormer 167
11001-11041 Militant Mark 1 125, **224**
11044 Medium Recovery 238
11046-47 Militant Mark 3 **223**
11301 Scammell 6 × 6 238
12001-4 Antar **232-235**
13001-13197 Bedford RL variants **217**
13115 Bedford Recovery **238**
13801-4 Bedford MK **219**
18061 Shorland 78, 105, **187**
18067 Land Rover Ambulance 72, **212**
30011 Tank Transporter Trailer 235
FVS *See* Fighting Vehicle System

Gazelle 45-47, **251**
General Police Duties Branch 75
General Purpose Machine-Gun *See* Calibres, L7A2, etc
General Service Corps 49, **79**
General Service Launch **256**
General Support Rocket System *See* Multiple Launch Rocket System
Giant Viper 40, **146-147**, 183, 202, 204
Gibraltar 19, 26, 64, 76, 118
Gibraltar Regiment 50, 79
Giraffe 342 **237**
Gloucestershire Regiment 29-30, 266
Gordon Highlanders 27-28, 265
GPD *See* General Police Duties (Branch)
GPMG *See* General Purpose Machine-Gun
Greenfinches 78
Green Howards 28, 30, 265
Grenade Dischargers: L1A1 **106**; Launcher M79 **105**; CS **108**; HE **106-107**; Irritant **108**; Smoke **107**
GRP Glass-Reinforced Plastic
GS General Service

GSRS *See* General Support Rocket System
Guards, Coldstream 27-28, 262; Division 15, 27, 31, 274; Grenadier 27-28, 262; Irish 27-28, 99, 262; Scots 27-28, 262; Welsh 27-28, 262
Gurkha, Brigade 19, 30-31, 267; Engineers 31, 40, 45, 49, 267; Signals 31, 49, 51, 268; Transport Regiment 31, 49, 65, 268 (*See* also individual regiments)
Gun *See* under respective Calibre

HAC *See* Honorable Artillery Company
Harrier 43, 52, 91-92
HASE Head Angulation Sighting Equipment 36
Hawkswing 138, 251
HE High Explosive
HEAT High Explosive Anti-tank
Heli-Telly 88, **141**
Hercules 31, 121, 168, 176, 203
HESH High Explosive Squash Head
HE/T High Explosive/Tracer
HMAV Her Majesty's Army Vessel; *Ardennes, Arakan* 66, **254**
HMG Heavy Machine-Gun
HMS *Fearless* 254, 255
HMS *Intrepid* 66, 254
Hong Hong 19, 26, 45, 47, 64, 72, 76
Honorable Artillery Company 84, 118
Horizontal Action Anti-tank Mine 40, **145**
HOT (Haut Subsonique Optiquement Teleguide Tire d'un Tube) 139
Hospitals, Military 72
Household Cavalry 20, 74, 259, 274
Howitzers *See* under respective Calibre
HQ Head Quarters

IFCS *See* Improved Fire Control System
IFF Identification Friend or Foe
II Image Intensifiers 144
India 12
Indian Army 11

Individual Weapon *See* under Calibres
Infantry 27-32, 82
Intelligence Corps 49, **66-67**, 268
Intrepid See HMS
IR Infra-Red (devices) 144
Ireland, Northern *See* Northern Ireland
IS Internal Security
IW *See* Individual Weapon
IWS Individual Weapon Sight

Jaguar **91-92**
JHQ Joint Head Quarters
Junior Leaders 35, 45, 55, **81**

Kenya 13, 19
King's Division 27, 32, 265
King Edward VII's Own Gurkha Rifles 29-30, 267
King's Own Royal Border Regiment 27-28, 265
King's Own Scottish Borderers 27-28, 264
King's Regiment 27-28, 265
King's Troop, RHA 35, 74, *273*
Korea 13, 16

L60 engine 154, *157*
LAD *See* Light Aid Detachment
Lance 33-34, *132*
Landing Craft, Logistics 66, **254**; Marine **254**; Vehicles and Personnel **254**
Land Rover, ½-ton **208**; ¾-ton **209**; 1-ton **211**; Ambulance **212**; *See* also FV section
Larkspur 52, 83
LAW *See* Light Anti-armour Weapon
LCL *See* Landing Craft, Logistics
LCM *See* Landing Craft, Marine
LCVP *See* Landing Craft, Vehicles and Personnel
LED Light Emitting Device
LHD Left-Hand Drive
Life Guards 20-21, 262
Light Aid Detachment 63
Light Anti-armour Weapon 32, **110**
Light Division 30-32, 266
Light Gun *See* Calibres
Light Infantry 27, 29-32, 266

Light Mobile Digger *43*
Light Support Weapon *See* Calibres
LMG Light Machine-Gun
Loader-Transporter M688 132
Low Mobility Range (vehicles) 231-232
LRATGW Long Range Anti-Tank Guided Weapon
LRF Laser Range Finder 36
LSL Landing Ship Logistics
LSW *See* Light Support Weapon
LT *See* Loader-Transporter
LTM Laser Target Marker 36
Lynx 46-48, 138, 142, **248**

M2 *See* Alligator
M107, M109, M110 *See* under respective Calibres
Machine-Guns *See* Calibres
MAG *See* Maintenance Advisory Group
Main Repair Group 64
Maintenance Advisory Group 65
Malaya 8, 10, 13, 190
Marauder 87, 149
Marchwood 66, *255*
Maritime Regiments 66, 254
MBT Main Battle Tank
MBT 80 157, 159
MCV Mobile Combat Vehicle
MCV 80 32, **179**
Medium Girder Bridge 148, 219, **245-247**
Medium Mobility Range (vehicles) 226-230
MEXE Military Engineering Experimental Establishment 199
Mexeflote **258**
Mexeshelter 90
MGB *See* Medium Girder Bridge
MGRA Major General Royal Artillery 33
MIACAH (Mine Anti-Char à Action Horizontale) 40, 145
Midge 34, **139**
Milan (Missile d'Infanterie Leger Anti-char) 30, 51, 114, **137**, 181
Military hospitals 72
Military Provost Staff Corps 50, *75*, 76

Military Port, Marchwood 66, *255*
Militant, Marks 1 and 3 *See* AEC
Mine Detector No. 4C **147**
MLRS *See* Multiple Launch Rocket System
MLT Medium Level Tripod
Modular Distribution Systems 65
MORCOS Mortar Data Computing System 113
Mortars *See* under Calibres
MOULD (code name for signals network) 53
Mounted Troop, RMP 74, 76
MPSC *See* Military Provost Staff Corps
MRG *See* Main Repair Group
MUKRCS (code name for signals network) 56
Multiple Launch Rocket System 35, **129-131**, 183 200
Muzzle Reference System 156
MVEE Military Vehicles Experimental Establishment 163, 167, 175, 200

NAIAD (chemical warfare detector) 91
NATO *See* North Atlantic Treaty Organisation
NBC Nuclear, Bacteriological and Chemical 89-91, 270
NBC Suit 90, 267, 270
NCO Non-Commissioned Officer
Nepal 31, 72
Nerve gas *See* NBC
NICS (NATO-wide Communications System) 55
Night Observation Devices 36, **141-143**
Nitesun **143**
NOD *See* Night Observation Devices
'Noddy Suit' 90
NORTHAG NATO Northern Army Group 17, 53
North Atlantic Treaty Organisation (signing of) 12; (communications) 55
Northern Ireland 19, 26, 45, 51, 53, 64, 74, **85-89**, 105, 142, 149, 176, 188, 190, 192-193, 237, 253, 270-271

NRA National Rifle Association
NSDAP National Sozialiste Deutsche Arbeiter Partei 10

Observation Post 36, 47
Oliphant Patrol Radar 152
OP *See* Observation Post
Operation Banner 86-87, 89; Bracelet 87, 188; Kremlin 191
OPRA Observation Post Royal Artillery (*qv* Centurion)
Ordnance Company 68
Ordnance, QF, 25 pr **117**, 122
OTU Officers' Training Unit

PACER (equipment used to measure muzzle velocity of artillery pieces) 36
PADS *See* Position and Azimuth Determining System
Parachute Regiment 15, 29-31, 79, 83-84, 89, 267
Pembroke 92
Phantom 92
Pig *See* FV1611
Pistols *See* under respective Calibres
PIRA Provisional IRA
POL (Petrol, Oil, Lubricants) 69
Port, Marchwood Military 72
Position and Azimuth Determining System 36, **38**
Postal and Courier Communications 44
PPI Planned Position Indicator
Princess Mary's Own Gurkha Rifles 29-30, 267
Prince of Wales' Division 30, 266
Prince of Wales' Own Regiment of Yorkshire 27-28, 265
Prowler *See* Radar
Provost Companies 75
Provost Marshal 77
PSI Person of Special Importance (previously VIP)
Ptarmigan 52, **56**, 59
Puma 66, 92, 121, 210

QARANC Queen Alexandra's Royal Army

Nursing Corps 50, **71,** 269

Queen's Division 27, 265

Queen's Dragoon Guards 20-21, 262

Queen Elizabeth's Own Gurkha Rifles 29-30, 267

Queen's Gurkha Engineers 31, 40, 45, 49, 267

Queen's Lancashire Regiment 28, 30, 265

Queen's Own Highlanders 27-28, 264

Queen's Own Hussars 20-21, 263

Queen's Own Yeomanry 20, 176

Queen's Regiment 27-28, 265

Queen's Royal Irish Hussars 20-21, 263

RA *See* Royal Artillery

RAC *See* Royal Armoured Corps

RAChD *See* Royal Army Chaplain's Department

Radar GS No 14 (ZB298) 24, **149,** 171, 181, 195; FA No 15 (Cymbeline) 34-35, **150,** 181, 213; No 17 Mark 1 **151;** GS No 18 (Prowler) **152;** GS No 20 (Claribel) **152**

RADC *See* Royal Army Dental Corps

RAF *See* Royal Air Force

Railways 66

RAMC *See* Royal Army Medical Corps

Ramped Powered Lighters **255**

Ranger 40, **144,** 147, 183

RAOC *See* Royal Army Ordnance Corps

RAPC *See* Royal Army Pay Corps

Rapier 34, 92, **134,** 213-214

RARDE *See* Royal Armament Research and Development Establishment 116

RA(V) Royal Artillery (Volunteer)

RAVC *See* Royal Army Veterinary Corps

RCT *See* Royal Corps of Transport

Recovery Vehicle Light **238;** Medium **238;** Heavy **241;** *See* also Crusader/EKA

RE. *See* Royal Engineers

REME *See* Royal Electrical and Mechanical Engineers

RFA *See* Royal Fleet Auxiliary

RHA *See* Royal Horse Artillery

Rifle *See* Calibres

RINT Regimental Intelligence

RMAS *See* Royal Military Academy Sandhurst

RMP *See* Royal Military Policy

RN *See* Royal Navy

Rocket 66 mm HEAT L1A1 **110**

Rolls-Royce Condor 159, 235

Royal Air Force 44, 52, 69, 71, **91,** 222, 238; Germany 92; Regiment 92, 135

Royal Armament Research and Development Establishment

Royal Anglian Regiment 27-28, 265

Royal Armoured Corps 20, 24, 175, 262

Royal Army Chaplains' Department 50, **79**

Royal Army Dental Corps 50, **71**

Royal Army Medical Corps 24, 50, 66, **70-71,** 268

Royal Army Ordnance Corps 47, 49, **67,** 71, 268

Royal Army Pay Corps 21, 50, **80**

Royal Army Veterinary Corps 50, 71, **73,** 268

Royal Artillery **32,** 49, 69, 82, 165, 184, 274

Royal Corps of Transport 47, 49, **65,** 82, 165, 184, 274

Royal Dragoon Guards 20-21, 262

Royal Electrical and Mechanical Engineers 47, 49, **62,** 69, 186, 268

Royal Engineers **40,** 49, 69, 71, 92, 264

Royal Fleet Auxiliary 66

Royal Green Jackets 29-30, 266

Royal Hampshire Regiment 29-30, 266

Royal Highland Fusiliers 27-28, 264

Royal Highland Regiment 27-28, 264

Royal Horse Artillery **32,** 49, 125, 259

Royal Hussars 20-21, 263

Royal Inniskilling Dragoon Guards 20-21, 262

Royal Irish Rangers 28, 30, 265

Royal Lancers 20-21, 263

Royal Military Academy Sandhurst 50, **81**

Royal Military School of Music 50, 82

Royal Military Policy 30, **75,** 259, 268

Royal Navy 44, 69, 71, 248

Royal Pioneer Corps 50, **70-71,** 268

Royal Regiment of Artillery **32,** 49, 69, 82, 165, 184, 264, 274

Royal Regiment of Fusiliers 27-28, 265

Royal Regiment of Wales 29-30, 266

Royal Signals and Radar Establishment

Royal School of Artillery 35

Royal School of Military Engineering 45

Royal Scots 27-28, 264

Royal Scots Dragoon Guards 20-21, 262

Royal Signals 49, **51,** 264

Royal Tank Regiment 20-21, 264

Royal Ulster Constabulary 77, 85, 87-88, 192, 193

Royal Welch Fusiliers 28, 30, 266

Royal Yeomanry 20, 172

RPC *See* Royal Pioneer Corps

RPH Remotely Piloted Helicopter

RPL *See* Ramped Powered Lighter

RQMS Regimental Quarter Master Sergeant

RSM Regimental Sergeant Major

RSME *See* Royal School of Military Engineering

RSRE *See* Royal Signals and Radar Establishment

RUC *See* Royal Ulster Constabulary

S6 Respirator 90, **266**

SAS *See* Special Air Service

SASC *See* Small Arms School Corps

SACEUR *See* Strategic Reserve of the Supreme Allied Commander Europe

Saladin *See* FV601

Samaritan *See* FV104

Samson *See* FV106

Saracen *See* FV603

SATCOM (NATO *(qv)* Satellite Communications) 55

Scammell Commander **235;** Crusader **235;** dumptruck 44

School of Catering 70; Electronics 64; Electrical and Mechanical Engineering 64; Infantry 30, 51; Signals 55, 57

Scimitar *See* FV107

Scorpion *See* FV101

Scottish Division 27, 264

Scout 46-48, 73, 138, 142-143, 248, **251-253**

SCRDE *See* Stores and Clothing Research and Development Establishment

Self-Propelled Launcher M752 132

Sennelager 6, 74, 118, 155, 178, 186, 200, 243

SHAPE *See* Supreme Headquarters Allied Powers Europe

Shir Iran *See* FV4211

Shorland *See* FV18061

Short SB 301 78, **188-189;** SB 303 189

SH/Prac Squash Head/Practice

SIB *See* Special Investigation Branch, RMP *(qv)*

Signal Brigades 54; Regiments 52-53; Training 55

SIMFICS Simulator for IFCS *(qv)* on Chieftain *(qv)*

SIMLAN Simulator for Milan *(qv)* missile system

Skyshout 88, 251

Small Arms School Corps 49, **51**

SMG (Sub-Machine-Gun) *See* Calibres

SP Self-Propelled

SP70 (80) **193-194**

Spartan *See* FV103

Special Air Service 19, **48-49,** 83, 89, 213, 268

Special Investigation Branch, RMP *(qv)* 76

Special Water Dispenser 191

SPG Self-Propelled Gun

SPL *See* Self-Propelled Launcher M752

SS11 47, **137,** 251

SSR SACEUR *(qv)* Strategic Reserve 19
Staffordshire Regiment 29-30, 266
STARRNET Static Radio Relay Network 52, 56, **61**
Stores and Clothing Research and Development Establishment 91, 259-273
Strategic Reserve of the Supreme Allied Commander Europe 19, 49
Striker *See* FV102
Sub-Machine-Gun *See* Calibres
Suez 14
Suffield 19, 64, 84, 147, 178, 185, 197, 217, 253
SUIT Sight Unit Infantry Trilux 87
Sultan *See* FV105
Sundance 157
Supreme Headquarters Allied Powers Europe 18
Survey, Royal Artillery **36**
SWD *See* Special Water Dispenser

Sweep 149
Sweep 148
Swingfire 33-34, **136**, 169, 186

TA 18, 19, 45, 73, **83**; Units **84**
TACIPRINT 42
Tank Bridge No. 8 161; No. 9 161
Task Force 18
Tear Gas *See* CN
TEREX Motor Scraper *41*
Tornado 92
TOS Tactical Operations System
TOW (Tube-launched Optically-tracked Wire-guided) 47, **137**, 248
Tracked Rapier **197**
Transport Regiment 65
Triffid 57
Truck, Cargo, 2½-ton **145**, 215
Twiggy 87, 144
Type A Regiments, Armoured 21, 22, 23; Reconnaissance 23, 24, 25

Type B Regiments, Armoured 21, 22, 23; Reconnaissance 23, 24, 25

UDR *See* Ulster Defence Regiment
UIAT Universal Industries d'Armes de Terre
UK, Defence 19, 20
UKLF (United Kingdom Land Forces) 20
UKMF (A) (UK Mobile Force (AIR)) 92
UKMF(L) (UK Mobile Force (Land)) 18, 19
Ulster Defence Regiment 50, **77**, 86, 89, 192, 257
Ulster *See* Northern Ireland
ULSTERNET Code name for Signals network used in Northern Ireland
UNFICYP United Nations Forces In Cyprus
Uniforms 259 onwards
Unimog (Universal Motor Gerät) **213**

Value Engineered Abbot 181
VDU Visual Display Unit
VP Vital/Vulnerable Point

Wavell 35, 52, 58, **59**, 179
WE Webbing Equipment
Wessex 66, 92, 121, 210
Wheelbarrow *Front endpaper,* 87, **147**
Wheeled Tractors, armoured *43-44*
White Helmets 55
WO Warrant Officer
Wombat 30, 83, **113**, 180, 209, 211
Worcestershire and Sherwood Foresters Regiment 29-30, 266
Womens Royal Army Corps 48, 50, 68, 70, 74, 76, **80**, 83, 268
WRAC *See* above

XM-2 179; XM-3 131, 179

ZB298 *See* Radar